BIRTH CONTROL
and the Christian

A Protestant Symposium
on
The Control of Human Reproduction

BIRTH CONTROL
and the Christian

A Protestant Symposium
on
The Control of Human Reproduction

Edited by
Walter O. Spitzer and Carlyle L. Saylor

Tyndale House Publishers
Wheaton, Illinois

Coverdale House Publishers Ltd.
London, England

Distributed in Canada by
Home Evangel Books, Toronto, Ontario

Dedicated
to the
medical missionaries
whose
thoughtful inquiries
from
many lands
were
the principal stimulus
for
the publication
of this
book
and to the
members and friends
of the
Christian Medical Society
whose support
made it
possible

FOREWORD

So enamored is contemporary man of the adventure of scientific breakthrough at the frontiers of human existence, and so gripped is he by the secular orientation of daily life, that those who would speak frankly of God and of sex in the same sentence may seem an odd company. Yet the stress and strain of the modern outlook, loosed as it is from moral and spiritual certainties, has left its sorry stamp upon modern life in wide evidences of cultural breakdown and in a multitude of individuals carrying psychic burdens. Not since the Apostle Paul wrote his letters to the Corinthians has reflection on sex and its implications from the Christian point of view been as urgently needed as today.

Modern men may smile at the dead gods worshipped by the ancient Greeks, but for multitudes today *eros* has come alive again. In the closing third of the 20th Century man is shaping new notions of the "good life" shaped by sexual attitudes holding promise of dimensions of pleasure or satisfaction that invite the verdict that fulness of life is to be found in an infinity of sex experience. These attitudes easily become more of an obstacle to an open hearing of Christian proclamation than the intellectual problems which biblical faith is thought to pose for a secular mentality. In his recent book Cambridge Professor Donald MacKinnon remarks that "the most deep-seated unwillingness to take seriously the claim of the Christian religion may have its roots" in our time not in "the unintelligibility of such fundamental concepts as that of a creator God, an immaterial soul" and other theistic beliefs, but in a suspicion that the Christian image of the good life seems "seriously to deflect men and women from securing and even enjoying the richness of experience with which the future may even now furnish themselves and their descendants." [1]

How is the evangelical community to gain a hearing for sound biblical perspectives today? Not, surely, by the repetition of clichés or by an uncritical reasserting of Victorian traditions in the name of the Gospel of Christ and the Law of God. Needless defense of Victorian attitudes may provoke unmerited sympathy for the "new morality" because, as Jesus warned the Pharisees, tradition too can make the Word of God void. But by reviewing its own past and present pronouncements critically in the light of God's Word, and testing its own mood as well as the contemporary mood by the scriptural standard, evangelical Christianity may be able to exhibit its cutting edge at the frontiers of ethical discussion.

The British commentator Malcolm Muggeridge has asserted that many church leaders and clergy today needlessly defer to imaginative restatements of Christianity that virtually make the abundant life to consist in carnal-mindedness. "Anyone who suggests that the pursuit of happiness, the contemporary cult of eroticism, underpinned by the birth pill, and fortified by the greatest outpouring of por-

---

[1] *Borderlands of Theology*, London, Lutterworth Press, 1968, pp. 51 ff.

nography yet known, runs directly counter to the Christian way of life, is sure to be condemned as a life hater." [2]

The papers presented to the Symposium on the Control of Human Reproduction and printed in this volume, represent an effort by evangelical leaders to stay abreast of current developments and to appraise them from an authentically biblical point of view. Evangelical pronouncements on birth control, on divorce, on the whole range of problems associated with human life and reproduction, need to be canvassed in the searching light of biblical principles. Nobody will contend that in these essays the last word has been achieved in evangelical perspective on these important concerns. But none can gloss over the significance of the fact that this conference, jointly sponsored by the Christian Medical Society and *Christianity Today* brought together theologians, physicians, lawyers and sociologists, for a sustained discussion of crucial issues. Former Supreme Court Justice Tom Clark served the symposium as Honorary President, and presented one of the essays as well. It is good that the papers are now available for wider reading, for they constitute a worthwhile contribution to the Christian discussion of sexual morality.

Carl F. H. Henry
Editor-at-Large
Christianity Today

---

[2] *Anglican World*, 1968, Issue 36, Volume 8, Issue 1, p. 49.

PREFACE

When an undertaking depends for its success on the effective teamwork of many individuals, it is difficult to acknowledge fairly the contribution of each one and easy to overlook the vital work which others may have done in the background. The Symposium on the Control of Human Reproduction and the publication of *Birth Control and the Christian* are examples.

As co-sponsors of the Symposium, the staff members of the Christian Medical Society are especially grateful to Dr. Carl F. H. Henry, Editor Emeritus of *Christianity Today*, for his extremely valuable assistance in the choice of participants from the non-medical disciplines. His suggestions concerning the curriculum proved to be wise and helped to ensure the thorough coverage of primary topics. Dr. Henry's successor at *Christianity Today*, Dr. Harold Lindsell, had a key role in the formulation of the Affirmation, and as co-chairman of the Consultation itself, he helped guide the discussions to a fruitful outcome. Dr. Harold J. Ockenga, pastor of Park Street Church in Boston and

Chairman of the Board of *Christianity Today,* served as president of the Symposium. In this capacity he was responsible more than anyone for the fact that what had been thought unlikely of accomplishment was in fact achieved in slightly less than four days. Dr. Ockenga's knowledge and appreciation of the relative importance of the issues being discussed and his ability to guide the discussions firmly and kindly were deeply appreciated.

Members of the Christian Medical Society staff who gave time, effort and counsel beyond the call of duty were Lewis P. Bird, Dr. Haddon W. Robinson and Sidney S. Macaulay. As is often the case, the least conspicuous made some of the greatest contributions: Mrs. Rachel Buick, Administrative Secretary, invested hours of effort in preparing for the Symposium and the publication of this book. Her careful attention to detail avoided many costly errors that would have prejudiced the effectiveness of every other person involved.

The text of *Humanae Vitae* (Appendix 2) appears by courtesy of the Catholic News Service. Dr. Montgomery's article on Birth Control is printed by permission of *Christianity Today,* where it first appeared. The position statements of the various denominations were kindly supplied by the respective bodies. Of such kindnesses are books like this developed.

As the book goes to press, the position represented in the Affirmation is being presented to a State legislative committee charged with studying and proposing changes in the abortion laws of that State and recommend possible revisions. Such use, whether by a committee of the legislature, a family physician, or a married couple seeking to act in love for each other and in obedience to God, will determine the validity of these efforts.

The Editors

February, 1969   *Oak Park, Illinois*

LIST OF CONTRIBUTORS

—V. Elving Anderson, Ph.D., Professor of Genetics, University of Minnesota Medical School

—Donald Bouma, M.A., Ph.D., Professor of Sociology, Western Michigan University, Kalamazoo

—David F. Busby, M.D., Psychiatrist, Professor of Pastoral Psychology and Counselling, Trinity Evangelical Divinity School, Deerfield, Illinois

—Tom C. Clark, Associate Justice (Retired) U.S. Supreme Court, Washington, D.C., Director of the Federal Judicial Center

—Ozzie Edwards, Ph.D., Associate Professor of Sociology, University of Illinois, Chicago Campus

—Sarah C. Finley, M.D., Pediatrician, Assistant Professor in Pediatrics—Laboratory of Medical Genetics, Medical College of Alabama, Birmingham, Alabama

—Wayne C. Finley, Ph.D., M.D., Director—Laboratory of Medical Genetics, University of Alabama Medical Center, Birmingham, Alabama

—Harold W. Hermann, M.D., Associate Director, Medical Research Department, Mead Johnson Research Center, Evansville, Indiana

—Philip Edgecumbe Hughes, M.A., Th.D., Professor of Historical Theology and Chairman, Department of Theology, Conwell School of Theology, Philadelphia, Pennsylvania

—Paul K. Jewett, Th.M., Ph.D., Professor of Systematic Theology, Fuller Theological Seminary, Pasadena, California

—Lloyd A. Kalland, Th.D., Professor, Philosophy of Religion, Gordon Divinity School, Wenham, Massachusetts

—Kenneth Kantzer, Ph.D., Professor of Systematic Theology, Trinity Evangelical Divinity School, Deerfield, Illinois

—William B. Kiesewetter, M.D., Surgeon-in-Chief, Children's Hospital, Pittsburgh, Pennsylvania

—Thomas F. Lambert, Jr., M.A., B.C.L. (Oxford), Editor, Journal of the American Trial Lawyers Association

—Eugene B. Linton, M.D., Associate Professor of Obstetrics and Gynecology, Bowman Gray School of Medicine, Winston-Salem, North Carolina

—Robert P. Meye, Th.M., D.Théol., Professor of New Testament, Northern Baptist Seminary, Oak Brook, Illinois

—John Warwick Montgomery, Ph.D., D.Théol., Chairman, Division of Church History and History of Christian Thought, Trinity Evangelical Divinity School, Deerfield, Illinois

—Christopher T. Reilly, Jr., M.D., Private Practice, Ridgewood, New Jersey

—John H. Scanzoni, Ph.D., Associate Professor, Department of Sociology, Indiana University, Bloomington, Indiana

—C. Gordon Scorer, M.D., F.R.C.S., Consultant Surgeon and Urologist, Hillingdon Hospital, Middlesex, England

—Oliver J. Steiner, M.D., Clinical Instructor, University of Buffalo School of Medicine, Private Practice in Obstetrics & Gynecology

—Duncan W. Vere, M.D., F.R.C.P., Senior Lecturer in Medicine, London Hospital, England

—Merville O. Vincent, M.D., F.R.C.P.(C), Psychiatrist, Assistant Medical Superintendent, Homewood Sanitarium, Guelph, Ontario

—Orville S. Walters, Ph.D., M.D., F.A.C.P., Professor of Health Science and Lecturer in Psychiatry, University of Illinois, Urbana, Illinois

—Bruce K. Waltke, Ph.D., Th.D., Professor of Semitic Languages and Old Testament Exegesis, Dallas Theological Seminary, Dallas, Texas

—Ross L. Willows, M.D., F.R.C.S.(C), Gynecologist, Associate Professor of Obstetrics and Gynecology, University of Manitoba, Winnipeg, Canada

TABLE OF CONTENTS

INTRODUCTION

A PROTESTANT SYMPOSIUM
ON THE CONTROL
OF HUMAN REPRODUCTION

For a number of years, leaders of the Christian Medical Society have seen the need to examine carefully the moral issues underlying the decision to perform an abortion, a sterilization, or to recommend the practice of contraception. Discussions in many local meetings of physicians and clergymen made it apparent that there were few commonly accepted Christian ethical guidelines in this area. Although the Bible has a great deal to say about sexual morality, it is virtually silent on the specific issues in this book. The editors of *Christianity Today* also felt that interdisciplinary study and discussion might produce material helpful to those for whom a biblical ethic is normative.

The combined pressures of the world population explosion and a shifting morality (expressed, for example, by situation ethics) are felt alike by physicians and pastors, by parents and teen-agers, by government leaders and hungry or unwanted children. These pressures are augmented by the technological revolution which has produced a wide variety of safe, simple and inexpensive means of limiting human fertility. The awesome possibility of modifying the genetic code and thereby affecting human personality and physiology may be at hand. The social, psychological, moral, economic and spiritual implications of these developments are incalculable.

Yet it is an axiom of human behavior that what man *can* do simply and cheaply, with little or no harmful result, he *will* do. The Christian church has at times appeared to oppose changes in human behavior, simply out of a resistance to change, often with little or no solid biblical reason for doing so. When technology touches so closely upon sexual morality and family structure, Christians must relate biblical principles to present reality. Tradition can neither be discarded out of hand nor allowed to impose "burdens too heavy to be borne."

Accordingly, in 1966, a curriculum was drawn up, participants were appointed and the study of the issues began in systematic fashion. It was decided that the Consultation be called late in August, 1968, in New Hampshire. The purpose of the meeting was established as follows: "To study the medical, theological, and legal principles bearing on the problems of contraception, sterilization and induced abortion with a multidisciplinary approach. To seek to establish moral guidelines for decision which will be medically sound, rooted in a biblical ethic and which will be of pragmatic value to the practicing physician and minister." The result of the Protestant Symposium on the Control of Human Reproduction is presented in this book.

Although a wide range of subjects was included in the curriculum and a number of disciplines were represented among the participants, it was not expected that the Consultation could be either exhaustive or final. Disciplines such as anthropology, social work, biochemistry, physiology and many others might profitably have contributed to the discussions. However, practical considerations made it necessary to limit the number of participants and the variety of subjects considered.

The Book

Birth Control and the Christian is much more than a mere compilation of the papers presented at the Symposium. It is noteworthy that some of the opinions held by participants prior to the Consultation were significantly changed during the discussions. Such changes are reflected in the final text presented here. The editors have attempted to organize the material so that it can be useful alike to the concerned layman, the physician, the minister and to other professionals in the course of helping their clients to make valid decisions. The student of any of the disciplines contributing to this book will find the appendices useful as research tools.

The editors again commend the many responsible scholars for being willing to undertake this difficult and controversial task. We anticipate that some controversy will be aroused by this book, but honest controversy frequently results in needed clarification and charitable relationships. The attempt to discover reliable guidelines for ethical decision frequently brings us to the shores of mystery; yet despite our uncertainty, a decision must be made. Even the refusal to decide in some of these issues constitutes a decision. And, in the contemporary situation, that refusal may be a most cold and unchristian decision indeed. We commend this volume to all who must make decisions governing human reproduction, either for themselves or for others, with the hope that they may be guided to decisions that are both compassionate and just. "For this is the love of God, that we keep his commandments. And his commandments are not burdensome" (I John 5:3).

The Affirmation

The document entitled, "A Protestant Affirmation on the Control of Human Reproduction" (Part III in the text), emerged as a written consensus of the scholars participating in the Consultation. Twenty-five authorities in theology, medicine, genetics, law and sociology deliberated together during most of the four-day session. Further, unidisciplinary committees in theology and medicine drafted sections of the Affirmation for submission to the plenary sessions. The theological committee is mainly responsible for Section I of the Affirmations, and the medical committee for Sections II and III. These sections were then discussed and modified somewhat in plenary sessions before formal adoption. Considerations from genetics, sociology and law were incorporated in the final version. A development worthy of mention is the remarkable agreement between Section I and Section II, when each section was prepared independently by one of the major disciplines represented at the Symposium.

A further chronological note is in order. The papers constituting the major part of this volume were completed by June 20, 1968, nearly a month before the release of *Humanae Vitae*. The papal encyclical, which has produced controversy both within and without the Roman Catholic church, was thus not in view prior to the actual meeting of the Symposium. By late August, of course, the papal letter was familiar to the participants. While not intended to constitute a Protestant reaction to the encyclical, the Affirmation naturally deals with many of the same issues from the perspective of evangelical Protestantism.

There is considerable diversity in denominational background and professional discipline among the participants in the Symposium, and certainly between them and any persons involved in the preparation of *Humanae Vitae*. Yet they share a common concern to establish a solid basis for ethical decision. Beyond that point, Protestants and Catholics take different paths on the question of authority. Protestants are committed to Scripture as a dependable and unchanging rule. Roman Catholics have given equal weight to the authority of the Church and to tradition for the criteria from which contemporary standards are to be derived.

Many issues relating to the control of human reproduction are decided by the Roman Catholic Church on the basis of Natural Law. The concept of Natural Law was most fully formulated by Thomas Aquinas, although it is rooted in a much earlier period of church history. Natural Law is derived primarily from pre-Christian Greek philosophy, especially from Aristotle. The concept is thus extra-biblical in its main development; although work, the family, conscience, and certain other human characteristics are termed "creation ordinances." That is, they are such a constituent part of man's nature that they are recognized even apart from knowledge of biblical law (cf. Romans 2). The main difference between Protestant and Roman Catholic thought in this area has to do with the validity of a law which would bind the conscience with regulations neither expressed nor implied in Scripture. The definition of a precept as *law* presupposes a prescriptive code and brands breaches of it as sins. If Natural Law is accepted as a universally binding code, then the definitions of *Humanae Vitae* are clear, unambiguous and consistent. It is the opinion of the editors that the encyclical errs in elevating a venerable tradition of Western culture to the status of divine revelation.

It should be emphasized that the Affirmation does not purport to be *"The* Protestant View" of the subject. The participants represent the evangelical or conservative theological viewpoint within Protestantism. Because there is very little biblical teaching dealing directly with the issues in question, the participants had primary recourse to principles derived from Scripture. Substantial but secondary use was made of reason, tradition and experience in seeking to establish guidelines. Thus, the Affirmation is to be considered as a contribution to a continuing conversation, not as the final word.

by Walter O. Spitzer, M.D.
and Carlyle L. Saylor, B.D.

A PROTESTANT AFFIRMATION ON THE CONTROL OF HUMAN REPRODUCTION

I. THEOLOGICAL BASIS

Prologue

We affirm that ultimate values come from God through biblical revelation rather than from the human situation alone. For some questions the Scriptures provide specific answers. For example, the Bible affirms that marriage is sacred and prohibits sexual intercourse outside that relationship. On other issues the Bible speaks primarily through principles such as the sacredness and value of human life, and the need to act in love for God and man. Where specific answers are lacking Christians acting under the authority of Scripture may differ from one another in the conclusions they reach because different weight may be given to different principles.

The Christian is obligated to understand as fully as possible the problems that confront him and to enunciate clearly the biblical principles underlying his efforts to resolve them. He recognizes that the will of God may become known to him more fully through discussion and interaction with men of like faith. Therefore, while a symposium can provide information and direction it cannot speak with binding authority in any instance. Each man is ultimately responsible before God for his own actions, and he cannot relinquish this responsibility to others no matter how qualified they may appear to be.

The Character of Sexual Intercourse as a Means of Procreation and as an Expression of Fellowship in Married Love

Sexual intercourse is a gift of God and is to be expressed and experienced only within the marriage relationship. In this act husband and wife become one flesh. Marriage is ennobled by God and is likened in Scripture to the union between Christ and His Church. Coitus includes the purposes of companionship and fulfillment, as well as procreation. Any marriage which does not seek to fulfill all of these sexual functions constitutes an incomplete relationship. The Bible teaches that procreation is one purpose of marriage and considers children to be an evidence of God's blessing. The Biblical norm is productivity for all of nature, including man. It gives the sense not of a static balance but of a dynamic and abundant creation.

Procreation, however, is not the sole purpose of the sexual relationship even as coitus is not the sole component of the marriage relationship.

God intended sexual intercourse to be continued and to be enjoyed even if procreation is impossible. Therefore, procreation need not be the immediate intent of husband and wife in the sex act. Coitus may be simply the expression of love and a mutual fulfillment of normal desires.

The Prevention of Conception

Because of the Christian's high view of the sexual relationship, contraception often presents complicated ethical questions. This is true whether the individual employs so-called natural means (*coitus interruptus* and rhythm), or methods made possible by medical science.

The Bible does not expressly prohibit contraception but it does set forth certain abiding principles such as the sanctity of life, the command to multiply, and the mutual obligation of husband and wife to satisfy each other's sexual needs.

The prevention of conception is not in itself forbidden or sinful providing the reasons for it are in harmony with the total revelation of God for married life. Disease, psychological debility, the number of children already in the family, and financial capability are among the factors determining whether pregnancy should be prevented. The method of preventing pregnancy is not so much a religious as a scientific and medical question to be determined in consultation with the family physician. Of all the methods of contraception, sterilization presents the most difficult decision because it impairs the creative activity God has given to man and is usually irreversible. Yet there may be times when a Christian may allow himself (or herself) to be sterilized for compelling reasons which outweigh these factors.

Induced Abortion, the Fetus and Human Responsibility [1]

Abortion confronts the Christian with the most perplexing question of all: Is induced abortion permissible and if so, under what conditions? If it is permissible in some instances is the act of intervention still sinful? Can abortion then be justified by the principle of tragic moral choice in which a lesser evil is chosen to avoid a greater one? As to whether or not the performance of an induced abortion is always sinful we are not agreed, but about the necessity and permissibility for it under certain circumstances we are in accord.

Good

The Christian physician who is asked to perform an abortion will seek to discover the will of God in this as in every other area of his life. He needs divine guidance for himself in his practice and for counselling his patients. The physician in making a decision regarding abortion should take into account the following principles:

1) The human fetus is not merely a mass of cells or an organic growth. At the most, it is an actual human life or

---

[1] *Unless otherwise specified, when the word "abortion" without qualification is used in the text, induced abortion and not spontaneous abortion is intended. In addition, unless otherwise specified, the word fetus is used in reference to the developing life from the time of conception until birth.*

at the least, a potential and developing human life. For this reason the physician with a regard for the value and sacredness of human life will exercise great caution in advising an abortion.

2) The Christian physician will advise induced abortion only to safeguard greater values sanctioned by Scripture. These values should include individual health, family welfare, and social responsibility.

3) From the moment of birth, the infant is a human being with all the rights which Scripture accords to all human beings; therefore infanticide under any circumstances must be condemned.

Christian Conscience, Natural Law and Legal Authority

The Scriptures inform us that all men are bound by God's moral law. To this fact, the universal phenomenon of conscience bears witness. Because of sin, men are severely limited in their ability to perceive the content of this law. Apart from the guidance of Scripture and the Holy Spirit, men tend to equate it with the mores of their particular culture. Nor do we believe that ethical judgments can be based on the situation alone. While the individual must consider the circumstances present in each situation, his ethical decision should be controlled by biblical principles.

The fallenness of human nature requires the guidance of laws. Such laws are for the benefit of society and should be administered in recognition of the authority of God as the Supreme law giver. Harmful pressures easily result from the codification of law in a way that is either too authoritarian or too permissive. The Christian maintains that in avoiding legalism on the one hand and license on the other, the prescriptions of legal codes should not be permitted to usurp the authority of the Christian conscience informed by Scripture.

II. PRINCIPLES OF THE CHRISTIAN PHYSICIAN IN THE CONTROL OF HUMAN REPRODUCTION

The rendering of guidance is basic to a physician's concern and effective work. This *may* well result in the confession to the patient or colleagues of his view of life as a Christian. In the realm of the control of human reproduction, his view of Christian life is reflected in the following Biblical principles:

Sanctity of Family Life

1) The sanctity of marriage as a God-given institution. It is lifelong and secure in love. Husband and wife live for each other and in God's service.

2) Children are God's gift, born into the love and security of the family for nurture and training.

Responsibility, Fulfillment, Self-discipline and Divine Grace in Sexual Relationship

1) The sexual relationship is a good gift from God to mankind, but this, as all of God's good gifts, has been marred by the effects of sin on human thought, will and action. The forgiveness and the grace of God are a constant human need.

2) Sexual intercourse is rightly confined to marriage. Therefore, fornication, adultery and prostitution with or without contraception are not Christian options.

3) Sexual intercourse is to be undertaken with understanding and consideration of one marriage partner for the other.

Preservation of God-Given Life

1) It is the duty of physicians to preserve human life and the integrity of the human body.

2) Physicians are called upon to maintain and restore the health of the whole man.

Mitigation of the Effects of Evil

1) We live in a world pervaded by evil. Human relationships become distorted; unwanted children are born into the world; genetic defects are not uncommon and harmful social conditions abound. Therefore, it is the duty of Christians to be compassionate to individuals and to seek responsibly to mitigate the effects of evil when possible, in accordance with the above principles.

2) When principles conflict, the preservation of fetal life or the integrity of the human body may have to be abandoned in order to maintain full and secure family life.

III. GUIDELINES FOR PROFESSIONAL PRACTICE [1]

The Prevention of Conception

The Symposium on the Control of Human Reproduction affirms the role of the physician in the support of the integrity of the family. The partners in marriage should have the privilege of determining the number of children they wish to have in their family. The physician should cooperate by providing counselling, taking into consideration both medical and moral factors. It is recognized that at times permanent sterilization, either male or female, may be indicated.

If contraception is indicated, the physician should assist in selecting the best available method for *this* purpose. Although better and simpler contraceptive techniques are expected to be developed in the foreseeable future; in some countries, the intrauterine device (I.U.D.) is expected to be the contraceptive method of choice for some time.

The single person seeking contraceptive advice requires concerned counselling *by the physician*. If he provides contraceptive agents, he participates in the intent of their use.

Induced (Therapeutic) Abortion

The sanctity of life must be considered when the question of abortion is raised. At whatever stage of gestation one considers the developing embryo or fetus to be human, even at birth, the potential great value of the developing intrauterine life cannot be denied. There may, however, be compelling reasons why abortion must be considered under certain circumstances. Each case should be considered individually, taking into account the various factors involved and using Christian principles of ethics. Suitable cases for abortion would fall within the scope of the American College

---

[1] *The physician must always be the captain of the health-care team. Therefore, specific reference is made to him in this section. Nevertheless, these guidelines apply in general to other members of the team. The underlying principles also apply to practitioners of other professions who assist families in making decisions.*

of Obstetricians and Gynecologists Statement on Therapeutic Abortion. However, we believe that sociological pressures that justify abortion rarely occur in isolation. We do not construe the A.C.O.G. Statement as an endorsement of abortion for convenience only or on demand.

The American College of Obstetricians and Gynecologists Statement on Therapeutic Abortion

Termination of pregnancy by therapeutic abortion is a medical procedure. It must be performed only in a hospital accredited by the Joint Commission on Accreditation of Hospitals and by a licensed physician qualified to perform such operations.

Therapeutic abortion is permitted only with the informed consent of the patient and her husband, or herself if unmarried, or of her nearest relative if she is under the age of consent. No patient should be compelled to undergo, or a physician to perform, a therapeutic abortion if either has ethical, religious or any other objections to it.

A consultative opinion must be obtained from at least two licensed physicians other than the one who is to perform the procedure. This opinion should state that the procedure is medically indicated. The consultants may act separately or as a special committee. One consultant should be a qualified obstetrician-gynecologist and one should have special competence in the medical area in which the medical indications for the procedure reside.

Therapeutic abortion may be performed for the following established medical indications:

1. When continuation of the pregnancy may threaten the life of the woman or seriously impair her health. In determining whether or not there is such risk to health, account may be taken of the patient's total environment, actual or reasonably foreseeable.
2. When pregnancy has resulted from rape or incest: in

this case the same medical criteria should be employed
in evaluation of the patient.

3. When continuation of the pregnancy is likely to result in
   the birth of a child with grave physical deformities or
   mental retardation.

Approved by the Executive Board May 9, 1968

Changes in the state laws on therapeutic abortion that
will permit honesty in the application of established criteria
and the principles enunciated in this statement should be
encouraged. Provisions should be included to protect the
physician from legal action or medical liability should he
refuse to perform the operation because he finds a particular
abortion to be against his moral standards.

Fetal Indications for Prevention of Conception and For Therapeutic Abortion with Specific Reference to Genetic Considerations

Much human suffering can be alleviated by preventing
the birth of children where there is a predictable high risk
of genetic disease or abnormality. This appears to be a
proper Christian objective.

An accurate diagnosis of genetic defect and statement
of risk for subsequent pregnancies can often be based on
examination of a single affected child. (Multiple abnormalities in a family are not essential to establish indications for
intervention.) In some conditions a significant risk can be
determined prior to the production of any children, through
evaluation of the family history and laboratory tests. The
assistance of a consultant who is a specialist in human genetics is required.

When a genetic problem is encountered the physician
should point out the implications for subsequent pregnancies. The parents should be helped to understand the medical, emotional, and financial problems involved in rearing a
child with a congenital disease. The long-term consequences
of contraception and sterilization should be explored. The
family may wish to consider other factors, and the decision
concerning additional pregnancies should be left to the parents. If contraception is attempted but fails, the risk of

severe defect in the child might constitute a fetal indication for abortion. The couple may prefer voluntary sterilization for husband or wife (the choice depending on the specific case). We find the principles of care for the individual and society on which we have agreed to be in accord with generally accepted precepts of sound clinical genetics.

When an affected individual is not mentally competent to make decisions for himself, the genetic problems should be made clear to the guardian or guardians. In such circumstances, involuntary sterilization could be considered upon the request and express permission of the guardians.

The Christian in an Over-Populated World

The control of human reproduction demands the attention of Christians from the standpoint of the desperate needs not only of individuals and families but also of nations and peoples. This Affirmation acknowledges the need for discriminating involvement of the people in programs of population control at home and abroad, so that the services or counsel rendered may conform both professionally and ethically with the principles embodied in this Affirmation. It is emphasized, however, that participation in programs of population control should be in response to requests for help from the states or communities involved.

SYMPOSIUM
ON THE
CONTROL
OF
HUMAN
REPRODUCTION

SECTION 1

BIBLICAL DATA
AND A
THEOLOGICAL BASIS

Chapter 1
OLD TESTAMENT TEXTS BEARING ON THE ISSUES

SUMMARY

Bruce K. Waltke, Professor of Old Testament at Dallas Seminary, presents a discussion of the applicability of Old Testament legislation to contemporary problems which had only tangential relevance to people in the ancient world. Old Testament teaching is evaluated on five methods of limiting fertility: Continence (in marriage), infanticide and sterilization (i.e., castration) are all condemned. Abortion and contraception by *coitus interruptus,* on the other hand are not explicitly forbidden.

Extensive consideration is given to two passages. Genesis 38:8–10, the famous "Onan passage," is interpreted as dealing with the irresponsible use of sex rather than prohibiting contraception as such. Exodus 21:22 ff. is seen not to apply the *lex talionis* to abortion. Although abortion is not thus totally forbidden, a decision to abort must give consideration to texts indicating a high value for the fetus.

In similar fashion contraception is not forbidden as such, but the Old Testament emphasis is on the blessings of marriage and the family, including children.

BRUCE K. WALTKE, A.B., Th.M., Th.D., Ph.D. *Professor Waltke has served on the teaching staff of Dallas Theological Seminary since 1958. He was appointed Professor of Semitics and Old Testament in 1967. His educational qualifications include: B.A.,* Magna Cum Laude, *from Houghton College, Th.M. and Th.D. from Dallas Theological Seminary, Ph.D. from Harvard University. An ordained minister in addition to his academic responsibilities, Dr. Waltke speaks and writes frequently for religious and scholarly publications.*

OLD TESTAMENT TEXTS BEARING ON THE PROBLEM OF THE CONTROL OF HUMAN REPRODUCTION

by Bruce K. Waltke

INTRODUCTION

Before turning to the passages in the Old Testament pertaining to the problem of the control of human reproduction, it is first necessary to resolve some of the tensions that a Christian normally experiences when seeking to apply the Old Testament to his life.

First, we must resolve the theological tension concerning the applicability of instructions in the Old Testament today. One rightfully asks: "In what sense is the Old Testament authoritative for the church?" This same tension can be felt within the New Testament itself. On the one hand the Apostle Paul says, "We are discharged from the law" (Rom. 7:6), but on the other hand he writes: "All Scripture is inspired by God and profitable for teaching, for reproof, for correction, and for training in righteousness, that the man of God may be complete, equipped for every good work" (2 Tim. 3:16, 17). A valid working hypothesis to relieve this tension is suggested by John Bright: Old Testament passages must be referred to the New for its verdict, whether it be ratification, modification or abrogation.[1]

Second, we face a sociological tension. In contrast to our society a man living in the Old Testament world valued a large family because it provided both economic and national security. Survival demanded growth and expansion. Fagley says: "Underpopulation, rather than overpopulation was the dominant reality." [2] In addition, men in the ancient society differed from Christians today in that they sought "social immortality"; i.e., preservation of their memory upon earth through their offspring. Christians, on the other hand, seek "individual immortality"; i.e., the hope of life after death. In a word, Old Testament saints living in the structure of a rural society were much more favorably disposed toward large families than many Christian couples today living in overcrowded cities. For us, children tend to be a financial hindrance rather than help. In the light of these changed conditions we must raise the question: "How relevant is the obviously favorable attitude toward large families in the Old Testament for us?" In order to relieve this second tension, we must select only those texts that indicate the eternal purposes and attitudes of the Creator.

A third tension is a logical one growing out of the apparently recent technology for the prevention and control of life. Were the authors of the Old Testament conscious of techniques for such things as birth control and abortion? If not, we may be asking the Old Testament writers questions that they had never faced and thus be in danger of inferring

---

[1] John Bright, *The Authority of the Old Testament* (New York: Abingdon Press, 1967), p. 200.

[2] Richard Martin Fagley, *The Population Explosion and Christian Responsibility* (New York: Oxford University Press, 1960), p. 110.

wrong answers from the Scriptures. In the course of this paper, therefore, we will attempt to determine whether they were aware of such means by studying the Old Testament itself and the extra-Biblical literature of the Ancient Near East.

Let us now consider texts pertaining to the means of limiting human reproduction. In each case we will seek to determine whether or not God prohibits it. After this, we will look at the texts which advance reasons for the institution of marriage, in order to determine the ends which any non-prohibited method of birth control should serve.

TEXTS BEARING ON THE MEANS OF LIMITING HUMAN REPRODUCTION

A married man and woman in the world of the Old Testament had five means by which they could limit their reproductive capacity: abortion, sterilization, infanticide, continence, and contraception by withdrawal (often referred to as *coitus interruptus* in the older literature). We shall consider these respectively.

Texts bearing on Abortion

Under this heading we will advance from the Scriptures two arguments which allow procured abortion and then three arguments which protect the fetus.

The first argument in favor of permitting induced abortion is the absence of any biblical text forbidding such an act. Here we must appeal to the literature of the Ancient Near East to weigh this negative evidence. In this case the silence of the Bible is significant because an Assyrian law dated between 1450 B.C. and 1250 B.C. prescribed death by torture in cases of induced abortion. The text reads: "If a woman by her own deed has cast that which is within her womb, and a charge has been brought and proved against her, they shall impale her and not bury her. If she dies from casting that which is in her womb, they shall impale her and not bury her." [3] Against this background the silence of the Old Testament appears to be both deliberate and instructive. The failure of God to set forth a similar law becomes even more profound when one realizes that the Mosaic Code is normally more extensive and more severe than these other Codes in sexual matters.[4] Kaufman says: "The sexual prohibitions of the Torah are more comprehensive and their violations more severely punished [than in these other codes]." [5] From this negative evidence we may infer that God does not invariably prohibit abortion.

A second argument in favor of permitting induced abortion is that God does not regard the fetus as a soul [Hebrew *nephesh*], no matter how far gestation has progressed. Therefore, the fetus does not come under the protection of the fifth commandment. That He does not so regard the fetus can be demonstrated by noting that God does not impose a death penalty for the destruction of a fetus. A basic feature of the Mosaic Code is the *lex talionis,* or principle of "an eye for an eye, life for life" (*e.g.* Lev. 24:18). The law plainly exacts: "If a man kills any human life [Hebrew *nephesh adam*] he will be put to death." But according to

---

[3] H. W. F. Saggs, *The Greatness That Was Babylon* (New York: Hawthorn Books, 1962), p. 215.

[4] It should be noted in this connection that abortion was known in antiquity. The classical Greek philosophers advised abortion under certain circumstances. Plato (*Republic,* V, 460ff.) recommended that when parents have passed the age assigned for procreation the child should not be allowed to be born. Aristotle (*Politics,* VII, 16, 1335) objected to the birth of imperfect or deformed children and recommended abortion in certain circumstances. In Rome abortion was practiced for reasons of poverty, sensuality or luxury (Seneca, *Digesta,* 25, 3, 4). In the light of this evidence Neufeld concludes: "Foeticide, throughout the course of history, has never become a recognized social practice, but has been, in the main sporadic" (E. Neufeld, *Ancient Hebrew Marriage Laws* (New York: Longmans, Green and Co., 1944), p. 252, n. 3.

[5] Yehezkel Kaufman, *The Religion of Israel,* translated and abridged by Moshe Greenberg (Chicago: The University of Chicago Press, 1960), p. 318.

Exodus 21:22ff. the destruction of a fetus is not a capital
offense. The divine law reads: "When men struggle together
and one of them pushes a pregnant woman and she suffers
a miscarriage but no other harm happens, he shall be fined
according as the woman's husband may exact from him. . . .
But if harm does ensue, then you shall impose soul [*nephesh*]
for soul [*nephesh*] . . ." (Ex. 21:22–24). Clearly, then, in
contrast to the mother, the fetus is not reckoned as a soul
[*nephesh*]. The money compensation does not seem to have
been imposed in order to protect the fetus but to indemnify
the father for his loss. Mace concludes: ". . . but the fixing
of the indemnity is left to the husband, on the principle that
he has suffered the loss of a potential child." [6]

With respect to an accidental miscarriage the contrast
between the Mosaic law and the Assyrian law is once again
instructive. In a similar context the Assyrian law reads:
"[If a seignior] struck a (nother) seignior's [wife] and
caused her to have [a miscarriage], they shall treat [the
wife of the seignior], who caused the (other) seignior's
wife to [have a miscarriage], as he treated her; he shall
compensate for her fetus with a life. However, if that
woman died, they shall put the seignior to death; he shall
compensate for her fetus with a life. But when that woman's
husband has no son, if someone struck her so that she had
a miscarriage, they shall put the striker to death; even if
her fetus is a girl he shall compensate with a life." [7] We
should note this contrast between the Assyrian Law and
the Mosaic Law: the Old Testament, in contrast to the Assyrian Code, never reckons the fetus as equivalent to a life.

As indicated we will now advance three arguments which

[6] David R. Mace, *Hebrew Marriage: A Sociological Study* (London:
The Epworth Press, 1953), p. 207.

[7] James B. Pritchard, *Ancient Near Eastern Texts Relating To
The Old Testament* (Princeton, New Jersey: Princeton University
Press, 1950), p. 184. Hereafter *ANET*.

protect the fetus. In the first place, in contrast to the Assyrian Code quoted above, the Old Testament never exacts "a fetus for a fetus," apparently protecting the fetus.

Second, the conception is a gift of God. Mace observes: "It is an essential feature of the Hebrew belief about children that they are not simply the result of a sexual union, but a direct gift from God. . . . The Bible does not contest the fact that there is a causal connection between sexual intercourse and conception, but it denies that the effect is inevitable, or that parents possess the power to ensure it." [8] Eve at the birth of Cain declares that she has received him from the Lord (Gen. 4:1). Sarah believes that the Lord has restrained her from bearing (16:2), which is confirmed when Abraham later receives the divine assurance that she will now have a son (17:19). Taking pity on Leah, the Lord "opened her womb" (29:31), as He did also afterwards in the case of Rachel (30:22). Of Ruth it is recorded that "the Lord gave her conception" (Ruth 4:13). Babbage succinctly states: "God permits man to share in the joyous task of creation." [9] The Christian will, therefore, seek to protect the fetus because he ought not to destroy what God has put together.

Third, God is actively involved in the process of fashioning the fetus. Of himself David said: "You created my kidneys; you skillfully wove me in my mother's womb. . . . My skeleton was not hidden from you when I was carefully formed in the darkness; when I was embroidered with variegated colors in the innermost part of the earth" (Psalm 139:13–18).[10]

We conclude, therefore, that while the Old Testament does not equate the fetus with a living person, it places great

---

[8] Mace, *Hebrew Marriage*, p. 202.
[9] Stuart Barton Babbage, *Christianity and Sex* (Chicago: Inter-Varsity Press, 1963), p. 15.
[10] Translation my own.

value upon it. The Talmud appears to reflect the biblical balance by allowing abortion when the life of the mother was in danger (*Mishna, Oholot,* 7:6).

Texts bearing on sterilization

Apparently the early Hebrews realized that the male as well as the female could be the cause of a childless union. We read in Deut. 7:4 "There shall not be a barren male or female among you." In practice, however, only the male could be made sterile artificially.[11] We may assume that principles derived from texts pertaining to the sterilization of the man are also applicable to the woman.

The point to be made here is that God rejected the common Near Eastern practice of sterilizing males. According to Deut. 23:1 [2], a eunuch was excluded from the communal life in Israel. The law reads: "He whose testicles are crushed or whose penis is cut off may not enter the congregation of the Lord." This law is peculiar to the Mosaic Code. Neufeld says: "The restrictions imposed on a eunuch under the biblical law are isolated and outstanding and no parallel can be traced to some other Semitic legislations." [12]

In addition sterilization was also unique with respect to other types of mutilation of the body. While deformities of the body such as blindness, lameness, *et cetera* restricted Aaron's descendants from serving as priests, only this mutilation—whether congenital, accidental or self-willed—excommunicated a male from the covenant community. What then is the reason for this unique piece of legislation? We might tentatively suggest that God excommunicated eunuchs

---

[11] B. Landsberger, "Zu den Frauenklassen des Kodex Hammurabi," *Zeitschrift für Assyriologie,* 30 (1916–17), p. 71, assumed that women of the Ancient Near East could be artificially made sterile. Such an operation, however, was beyond the scope of ancient surgery according to G. R. Driver and Sir John C. Miles, "The SAL.ZIKRUM 'Woman-Man' in Old Babylonian Texts," *Iraq,* 6 (1939), p. 67. So also Saggs, p. 350.

[12] Neufeld, p. 223.

because they no longer mirrored His generative power. Delitzsch reasons: "The reason for the exclusion of emasculated persons from the congregation of Jehovah . . . is to be found in the mutilation of the nature of man as created by God." [13]

The least we can conclude from this text is that God looks with disfavor upon sterilization as a means of limiting human reproduction.

As stated in the introduction, however, this conclusion must be evaluated in the light of the teaching of our Lord with respect to eunuchs (Matt. 19:12).

Texts bearing on infanticide

Although infanticide in the Ancient Near East was normally practiced for religious reasons, it was also used to rid the parent of an unwanted child. For example, the mother of Sargon of Agade, by tradition a high-priestess expected to live in chastity, disposed of her unwanted child by exposure.[14] The fact that infanticide by exposure was known in Israel can be gathered from a reference in Ezekiel, where Jerusalem is described as though she "were cast out on the open field, for [she] was abhored, on the day [she] was born" (Ezek. 16:5). Moreover, it is well known that the Arabs practiced female infanticide.[15]

Godly Hebrews never engaged in infanticide. The Old Testament forbade the common practice of child sacrifice for it "profaned the name of God" (Lev. 18:21). Those that did practice it were to be stoned to death (Lev. 20:2). Undoubtedly, the life of the child also came under the protection of the fifth commandment.

---

[13] F. Delitzsch, *Biblical Commentary on the Old Testament,* Vol. III: *The Pentateuch* (Grand Rapids, Michigan: Wm. B. Eerdmans Publishing Co., 1951), p. 413.

[14] For text see *ANET,* p. 119.

[15] For female infanticide among the Arabs see Robertson Smith, *Kinship and Marriage* (London, 1903), pp. 291–96.

Texts bearing on continence

We may infer that continence was also practiced as a means of limiting children, from a Sumerian proverb which mentions a proud husband boasting that his wife had borne him eight sons and was still ready to lie down to accept his nuptual embrace.[16] Evidently, some wives would not. However, there is no evidence that periodic continence was known in Israel, for the spacing or limitation of pregnancies. In fact the Mosaic law indicates that continence has no place in marriage. A salient text leading to this conclusion reads: "If [the owner] marries another woman, he must not diminish from [the female slave] her food, her clothing or her conjugal rights" (Exod. 21:10). Mielziner notes: "The Mosaic law contains no express provision concerning marital rights and duties, except the injunction made in a certain case: 'Her food, her raiment, and her conjugal rights shall he not diminish.'"[17] In addition, as Charles Ryder Smith points out: "The Old Testament has no sanction for celibacy; its priests married, and even its typical ascetic, the Nazarite, was commanded other abstinences than this" (Num. 6).[18]

Sexual intercourse was only to be forgone by women during their ritual uncleanness occasioned by menstruation (Lev. 15:19–28; 18:19; 20:18) and childbirth (Lev. 12: 1–8), and by men for religious reasons (Exod. 19:15; 1 Sam. 21:4–5). Some have contended on the basis of the passages in Leviticus that continence should be practiced for birth control.[19] But this is not legitimate, for instead of limiting birth these restrictions tend to increase fertility.

---

[16] Saggs, p. 186.

[17] M. Mielziner, *The Jewish Law of Marriage and Divorce in Ancient and Modern Times* (Cincinnati: The Block Publishing and Printing Co., 1884), p. 99.

[18] Ryder Smith, *Bible Doctrine of Womanhood*.

[19] For example, Keith L. Brooks, *What Does the Bible Teach About Birth Control?* (Los Angeles: American Prophetic League), pp. 13ff.

Herman Wouk says: "The main practical result of this [abstinence after the menses] is that they rejoin at the time when the wife is most likely to conceive. It is the exact opposite of the rhythm system of birth control." [20]

The conjugal regulations in the Talmud accurately reflect the teaching of the Old Testament. Mielziner says: "The duty of conjugal cohabitation is legally, as well as ritually and ethically regulated in the Rabbinical Code. A continual refusal, on either side, regarding this duty, if not excused by sickness and circumstances, offers a ground for divorce." [21]

The apostle Paul in the New Testament likewise enjoins intercourse as a mutual duty owed by each to the other, to be withheld only during limited periods of special religious observance (1 Cor. 7:5).

Texts bearing on contraception

Three lines of evidence support the common assumption that withdrawal was undoubtedly the most universal and commonly practiced method of averting conception in Biblical times: 1) the terms for various kinds of temple prostitutes in Assyria and Babylonia; 2) references in the Talmud; 3) the incident of Onan recorded in Genesis 38:8–10.

The terminology applied to the female temple personnel in the Code of Hammurapi and other Babylonian documents indicates that these priestesses were sexually active, but in some way they prevented conception. No women consecrated to gods were allowed to bear children, even in marriage. Since sterilization of women and contraceptives were unknown and technically unfeasible in antiquity,[22] a priestess,

---

[20] Herman Wouk, *This Is My God* (Garden City, New York: Doubleday and Co., 1959), p. 156.

[21] Mielziner, p. 101.

[22] Concerning sacral prostitution and contraception in the Old Testament world see, Michael C. Astour, "Tamar the Hierodule," *Journal of Biblical Literature*, 85 (1966), pp. 185–96.

or hierodule, could avoid impregnation only by using abnormal methods of intercourse. One text prescribed the extreme precaution against impregnation by intercourse per
anum: "The high priestess will permit intercourse per anum
in order to avoid pregnancy." [23] However, this extreme measure of precaution does not seem to have been practiced by
other classes of female cult personnel. The titles and expressions used to denote these other priestesses may point
to the avoidance of pregnancy by *coitus interruptus*. Astour
concludes: "The expression *Kulmašītu ša qerebša ma'd[a]*
'a *kulmašītu* [24] whose womb is "many" (who has intercourse
with many men) points to a more normal way of intercourse, and if the term *kulmašītu (m)* [means 'pure (of)
semen'] . . . , it would hint to *coitus interruptus*, as in
Genesis 38:9."

The Talmud also indicates that withdrawal was practiced
to avoid pregnancy. According to the *Yebamot* section of
the Talmud (34b), during the twenty-four months in which
a child is nursed, "a man must thresh inside and winnow
outside," a euphemism for withdrawal.[25]

The case of Onan (Gen. 38:8–10) provides the one clear
example of withdrawal with contraceptive intent in the Old
Testament. Our text reads: "Then Judah said to Onan: 'Go
in to your brother's wife and perform the duty of a brother-
in-law to her, and raise up off-spring for your brother.' But
Onan knew that the offspring would not be his; so when he
went in to his brother's wife, he spilled [the semen] upon
the ground, lest he should give offspring to his brother.

---

[23] *The Assyrian Dictionary of the Oriental Institute of the University of Chicago*, edited by I. G. Gelb, T. Jacobsen, B. Landsberger,
and A. L. Oppenheim (Chicago: Published by the Oriental Institute),
IV, 1958, p. 325.

[24] Possibly from Sumerian NU.BAR "to separate sexual organs."

[25] A. van Selms, *Marriage and Family Life in Ugaritic Literature*
(London: Luzac & Co., 1954), p. 24, notes: "Comparisons between
sexual intercourse and the cultivation of a field abound in ancient
literature."

And what he did was evil in the sight of the Lord, and he slew him also."

The context clearly indicates that Onan's sin lay in his selfish unwillingness to honor his levirate duty.[26] Roman Catholic exegetes reject this explanation, however, and insist that God killed Onan for practicing birth control. They argue that Onan paid for his deed with his life, whereas the penalty for refusing the responsibilities of the levirate marriage was far milder in the normally severe Mosaic Code. Such a man, they point out, merely had his sandals removed and was spat upon the face before all the elders of the village. Ruth did not even insist upon this punishment when her nearest kinsman refused to honor his duty.

The texts can be harmonized by recognizing that the Mosaic Law pertains to a man who refuses to marry his brother's widow, whereas the case of Onan pertains to a man who was willing to marry his brother's widow but then perverted the institution. The Lawgiver had the bereaved couple at heart; but Onan used levirate marriage for his personal gratification. In a word, he used his brother's wife with no respect for her personality and dignity, and without brotherly concern. We conclude, then, that this passage instructs us concerning the responsible use of sex; it does not forbid contraception *per se*.

In the light of the fact that contraception was practiced by withdrawal, one would expect to find an express prohibition of the practice somewhere in the Bible if God considered it to be a sinful act in itself. But we do not find any such prohibition.

Two passages occur where one might ordinarily expect

---

[26] The institution of levirate [from Lat. *levir* = "brother"] marriage had a wide usage in the Ancient Near East. Similar, though not identical provisions, can be found in the Assyrian laws, the Hittite Code, and the Nuzi Tablets. According to this institution, a man was responsible to provide for his brother's widow, and to preserve the name of his deceased, childless brother (Deut. 25:5–10).

to find such prohibition. The first reads: "And if a man has an emission of semen, he shall bathe his whole body in water and be unclean until the evening. And every garment and every skin on which the semen comes shall be washed with water, and be unclean until the evening. If a man lies with a woman and has an emission of semen they shall bathe with water and be unclean until the evening" (Lev. 15:16–18). The cogent point is that the emission of semen apart from coitus is not regarded as a sinful act. Because no sacrifice is demanded, Barclay says: "No moral fault is implied in connection with these impurities. So the laws are ceremonial." [27]

The second passage is Lev. 20:10–21. Here the Bible lists sexual crimes punishable by death. All of these involve intercourse with a person apart from the marriage relationship. Once again we find no reference to withdrawal as a sexual abuse.

We conclude, therefore, that the Old Testament prohibits infanticide, sterilization and continence as means of avoiding pregnancy, but that it does not prohibit contraception.

Because God has not prohibited contraception, we must now turn to passages bearing on the purposes of marriage in order to determine what use may be made of this means.

TEXTS BEARING ON THE USE OF CONTRACEPTION: THE PURPOSE OF MARRIAGE

Van Selms says concerning the purpose of marriage in Ugarit: "As in most ancient societies the real purpose of marriage is the procreation of lawful sons." [28] This statement, however, would be a gross overgeneralization if applied to the Bible. Undoubtedly, some males in the Old Covenant regarded sex merely as a means for the procrea-

---

[27] R. A. Barclay, *The Law Givers* (New York: Abingdon Press, 1964), p. 39.

[28] A. van Selms, p. 13.

tion of children or as a source of sensual pleasure, but this understanding of marriage does not exhaust the divine purpose of marriage. God's reasons for giving marriage to His people are manifold:

For companionship

God instituted marriage that man might have company: "And the Lord God said: 'It is not good that the man should be alone; I will make a helper fit for him'" (Gen. 22:18). Likewise the psalmist says: "God gives the desolate a home to dwell in" (Ps. 68:6 [7]).

For completeness

It is within the framework of marriage that man achieves his unity; apart from marriage he is broken, incomplete. "Therefore a man leaves his father and mother and cleaves to his wife and they become one flesh." The joy of the reuniting of man and woman and the sadness of their parting are celebrated in an incomparable way in the Song of Songs.

For enjoyment

God instituted marriage in order to give pleasure—not merely sensual pleasure—to both the man and the woman. To the woman He said ". . . your desire shall be for your husband." To men the inspired sage advises: "Enjoy life with the wife whom you love . . ." (Eccl. 9:9). Other texts that belong under this heading are: Prov. 12:4; 18:22; 19:14; 31:31; Gen. 29:20; 1 Sam. 1:8; 2 Sam. 11:11.

For procreation

The Old Testament assumes procreation as a purpose of marriage and considers children as an evidence of God's blessing: "And God blessed them and said to them: 'Be fruitful and multiply and fill the earth and have dominion over the fish of the sea and over the fowl in the heavens and over every living thing that moves upon the earth' " (Gen. 1:28). The injunction is repeated again to Noah after the fall (Gen. 9:1, 7). When the text declares, "God blessed them," it means in part that He made them virile. On this basis He gives the command to reproduce. The Psalmist says: "Lo, sons are a heritage from the Lord, the fruit of the womb a reward. Like arrows in the hand of a warrior are the sons of one's youth. Happy is the man who has his quiver full of them!" (Ps. 127:3–5). By contrast a marriage without offspring is considered cursed: "But if you will not obey the voice of the Lord your God or be careful to do all His commandments and His statutes which I command you this day . . . cursed shall be the fruit of your body and the fruit of your ground, the increase of your cattle, and the young of your flock" (Deut. 28:15–18). The divine norm is for all of nature to be fertile. Predicting the golden age to come, Jeremiah says: "Behold the days are coming, says the Lord, when I will sow the house of Israel and the house of Judah with the seed of man and the seed of beast" (Jer. 31: 27; cf. also Gen. 1:22; 8:17; 49:22 and Ps. 128:3). Fagley correctly appraises norm as follows: "It is not a static balance, however, that is sought. Rather it is one that is dynamic, rapidly expanding. The dream might be called the abundant society. . . ." [29] Clearly, in the Old Testament, God does not regard children with contempt or treat the bearing of children as a common thing.

We must leave it to the moral theologian, however, to evaluate the applicability of this ideal to our present situation where, to use Thielecke's terminology, the order of creation and history are in tension.[30]

---

[29] Fagley, p. 112.
[30] Helmut Thielecke *The Ethics of Sex* (New York: Harper and Row, Pub., 1964), p. 202.

It should be noted that with the blessed promise of off-spring there is also the injunction to subdue the earth. Babbage says: "His dignity lies in 'subduing' it. . . . He has it in his hands to shape and transform it; this is his duty and responsibility." [31] This text may apply to cases of over-population where the balance with nature cannot be maintained. Perhaps in such cases God enjoins man to use his technological achievements to maintain a balance for the good life.

To produce a godly seed

God instituted monogamy, says Malachi, "to seek a godly seed" (Mal. 2:15). Innumerable Old Testament passages instructing His people on raising a godly seed belong here; for example, Deut. 6:4ff. We may infer from these that His people are expected to be co-laborers with God in producing a godly seed to bless the earth.

To illustrate His love for Israel

Finally, God used marriage to illustrate His love for Israel. The analogy of the love of a husband for his wife is repeatedly used by the prophets to illuminate God's persistent love for Israel. The analogy, however, can only be used by implication in the problem at hand.

In conclusion God intended marriage to serve all of these purposes: enjoyment, companionship, unity, procreation, to produce a godly seed, and to illustrate His love for Israel. Protestant theologians frequently justify birth control by separating these purposes from each other. While they may have legitimate grounds for doing so, such separation is against the ethos of the Old Testament. According to the Old Testament the Creator instituted marriage to serve all

---

[31] Babbage, p. 36.

these ends together. Montgomery's judgment harmonizes with this prudence derived from the Old Testament: "The burden of proof rests, then, on the couple who wish to restrict the size of their family." [32]

---

[32] John Warwick Montgomery, "How to Decide the Birth-Control Question," *Christianity Today*, March 4, 1966, p. 10 [554].

NOTE: Professor Montgomery does well in calling attention to an alternative interpretation of Ex. 21:22–24 (p. 87f). He errs, however, by asserting that I follow David Mace, an English sociologist, "against virtually all serious exegetes." On the contrary, measured by the weight of scholarly opinion Montgomery's view has little support. The view advanced in this chapter follows the traditional, normative interpretation of the passage as the following evidence confirms:

1) The translation presented in this chapter has the support of the following ancient translations: LXX, Peshitta, Vulgate, Onkelos, and Targum Jonathan. Of the English translations it consulted it agrees with AV, RV (ASV), Rotherham, JPS, Moffatt, American, Basic English, RSV, Jerusalem, Berkeley, Torah (1962), Confraternity, and Amplified. To my knowledge the only translations that disagree are the Improved (1912) and Young's Literal (a non-interpretative translation).

2) Commentators with whom I concur are: Philo, Jarchi, Aben Ezra, Rashi, Maimonides, Lange (with translation of Charles M. Mead), Murphy, S. R. Driver, A. H. McNeile, Dummelow, Philip C. Johnson, J. Edgar Park (in *IB*). Most recently John E. Huesman (*The Jerome Bible Commentary*, 1968) supports this view.

In addition, Montgomery is mistaken when he says: "The equality of mother and unborn child in Exodus 21 is upheld . . . by a classic Old Testament scholar such as the nineteenth-century Protestant Delitzsch." In reality, Keil (not Delitzsch) is making a different point; namely, the child in question is not a fetus but a fully developed human being. Lange calls this interpretation "strange." Obviously, Keil's interpretation has nothing to do with Montgomery's conclusion.

Chapter 2

NEW TESTAMENT TEXTS
BEARING ON THE ISSUES

SUMMARY

Robert P. Meye, Professor of Biblical Theology at
Northern Baptist Seminary, surveys the historical environment of the New Testament, the Judaic heritage of the
early church, and outlines the assumptions on which teaching concerning sex, marriage and family life are based.
Specific passages dealing with the nature of the marriage
relationship are considered and conclusions are drawn.

Because the control of human reproduction was not a
concern of the New Testament writers, the difficulty of
making unequivocal assertions on contraception, sterilization or abortion is emphasized. The author develops principles implicit and explicit in the New Testament which
need to be applied by those who must make ethical decisions
having to do with sex and reproduction. Dr. Meye stresses
the possibility of and need for forgiveness in view of the
ambiguity of many situations faced in family life.

ROBERT P. MEYE, B.A., B.D., Th.M., D.Theol. *Robert Meye is professor of Biblical Theology at Northern Baptist Seminary, Oak Brook, Illinois. He has served in this capacity since 1962. His undergraduate work was done at Stanford University, and seminary training was received at Fuller Theological Seminary. The University of Basle awarded him the degree of Doctor of Theology, following study under Barth, Eichrodt and Cullmann. In addition to his academic duties, Dr. Meye is Vice-Chairman of the Council on Theological Education of the American Baptist Convention. His publications include the book,* Those About Him: Discipleship and Revelation in Mark's Gospel.

NEW TESTAMENT TEXTS BEARING ON THE PROBLEM OF THE CONTROL OF HUMAN REPRODUCTION

by Robert P. Meye

A PROBLEMATIC ENDEAVOR

The task of laying bare the New Testament teaching bearing on the human control of human reproduction is a *dangerous* enterprise. If the history of New Testament study in the past is any guide at all, then there is a danger of hearing those parts of it which are welcome and excluding those parts which are unwelcome. Albert Schweitzer's famous comments regarding studies of the life of Jesus also have a special point for us; he observed that in the study of the central object of faith (Jesus) a scholar's own soul was bared.[1] By the same token, here in another area of study which also touches deeps of human conviction and experience, it is no less likely that we, as much as the

---

[1] Albert Schweitzer, *The Quest of the Historical Jesus* (trans. W. Montgomery; London: Adam and Charles Black, 1911), p. 4.

New Testament teaching, are apt to be that which is laid bare. That is not all loss; nevertheless, we must be clear when it is the New Testament, and when it is our attitude, which is exposed.

The burden is as frustrating as it is dangerous. It is hardly a surprise to most of us to be informed in advance that there is nothing said directly in the New Testament regarding birth control practices. For this reason, there is practically nothing available for our immediate assistance in New Testament commentaries and New Testament monographs. Neither have systematic studies seeking to develop the Biblical teaching uncovered any "text" which clearly and unambiguously speaks to our issues. In light of this, and in view of the seeming urgency of our current task of instructing the Church (at least) regarding birth control practices, the present project is frustrating. Danger and frustration, however, must not be allowed to thwart our proper quest of uncovering whatever implications the New Testament teaching may hold for our concerns. Beyond the danger and the frustration of the study, the various practices of birth control touch a complex web of human relationships and human science: the question of life itself and its meaning at its various stages of development; the psychological and spiritual meaning of physical actions; the extent to which Christian standards may or should be directed to a non-Christian world; the relation of the human endeavor to the divine will; and many other concerns. In other words, we must be alert to the broad significance of birth control practices. At this point, partially, though by no means fully warned, we may turn to the immediate concern of this paper, the New Testament teaching bearing on birth control practices.

PRIMITIVE CHRISTIANITY IN ITS HISTORICAL CONTEXT

As we have already indicated, it is important that we

observe the current "contexts" in which our discussion is carried on. We must also reckon with the world in which the Christian message was first believed and taught. In the absence of clear teaching in the New Testament, we are perforce heavily reliant upon our knowledge of the social context of Judaism and Hellenism in which Christianity existed, and we are above all bound to understand that the Old Testament was the Bible of the early Church, and a primary locus for its own understanding of its necessary obedience, after the words of Jesus and the apostles. We may operate with the following principle of interpretation: Wherever Christian faith did not stand in tension with these other norms, we may assume that it maintained the same practices as were in evidence in them.

It is not the task of this paper to present the Old Testament teaching which bears on the problems of birth control. However, something needs to be said here regarding the relationship of New Testament practice to the Old Testament community and practice. There are two observations of particular importance for the present study. The first is that the New Testament, whether in the teaching of Jesus or of Paul, as well as in other loci, maintains the stringency of the Old Testament over against the looseness of sexual morality so prevalent in the surrounding world. Just as the New Testament extends the Old Testament revelation of God, so does it also extend Old Testament concern for sexual purity. This would cause us to make full use of the Old Testament to fill in those sectors where the New Testament is silent.

There is a second factor regarding the New Testament teaching and practice which tends to modify the first—but not in the direction of relaxing that stringency. That factor is the pressure of the imminence of the Kingdom of God as it impinges upon the sexual life of the people of God. Both Jesus and Paul have always been a problem for the Church because their teaching and practice have seemed to militate

against the Old Testament mandate to be fruitful and
multiply. On the positive side, there would seem to be fruitful material there for any affirmation of the congruence
of some sort of birth control practice with the New Testament teaching. We will return to this factor at a later point
in the study, noting only that here as at many other points
there is a dialectical relationship between the Old and the
New Testaments which is at the best difficult to define. In
the face of difficulties, the Church as a matter of faith, has
assigned precedence to the New Testament revelation—and
it is to this part of the scriptural revelation of the will of
God that we are here bound to give special attention. With
this as our general approach, we may turn our attention to
a second "context" of the New Testament.

As far as Judaism is concerned,[2] the Old Testament marriage laws and practices were still in force, with strong
emphasis upon the family and procreation within marriage.
Irregular conduct was rigorously punished; fruitfulness of
the womb was the sign of great blessings. Judaism generally
frowned upon birth control and certainly upon sterilization and abortion. General famine was seen as a legitimate
reason for limiting reproductive efforts, and medical
grounds led to the allowance of contraceptive devices. The
very existence of the exceptions noted points to the general
pressure against birth control practices. Not all rabbis were
permissive; there was a basic abhorrence of any "waste of
nature." The Gentile world held a theoretical view which
resembled that of Judaism, but in practice it followed a
lower standard.[3] Although the declared purpose of marriage

---

[2] For studies in this area, see Louis Epstein, *Marriage Laws in
the Bible and the Talmud* (Cambridge: Harvard University Press,
1942) and *Sex Laws and Customs in Judaism* (New York: Bloch
Publishing Co., 1948). The author presents a comprehensive bibliography.

[3] For a brief survey and literature see D. S. Bailey, *The Man-
Woman Relation in Christian Thought* (London: Longmans, 1959),
pp. 3–18.

was procreation, contraception and abortion were widely used. Still, it must be noted that a large number of pagan writers speak of the practice of abortion as an evil practice.[4] It is not at all surprising, in view of these facts, to find that very early Christianity, as represented in the Didache and other writings separated from the New Testament by only a brief time-span, also viewed abortion as unlawful.[5]

As one turns to the New Testament representation of the faith of primitive Christianity, he begins with the presupposition that primitive Christianity maintained the reserve of Judaism with regard to birth control practices and paralleled both Judaism and Hellenism (at its best) in the disavowal of abortion. We must hasten to observe that this does not at all mean that such practices are eternally contradictory to the heart of the New Testament faith and practice. We must uncover the *foundation* in early Christianity of the (probable) maintenance of reserve or even rejection. Does the foundation admit of the practices under changed conditions? This, of course, is our question.

THE NEW TESTAMENT CONTEXT

There remains one crucial contextual question: What is the *New Testament* context for a valid discussion of the practices of contraception, sterilization and abortion? The New Testament obviously differs from our present world in one respect, viz., the fact that recent biological and genetic advances now confront us with a new, though not imminent, possibility: the creation and therefore the control of life by scientific and impersonal means. For our purposes it is better to abide with the more immediate and existential situation. Therefore, we remain in the first context of New

---

[4] The most careful study of this sector of ancient life may be found under the pertinent entries in the Pauly-Wissowa Real Encyclopäedie.

[5] Bailey, *op. cit.*, p. 24, esp. n.7.

Testament thinking about reproduction—the sphere of human sexual relationship. The single exception to this is found in the narratives in Matthew and Luke of the virgin birth of Christ. This is not only an exception, but it is an exception on the divine side, and cannot easily be applied to the present discussion.[6]

A second New Testament context for the discussion of human reproduction, formerly self-evident, has also been challenged in recent times, although from another quarter. In the not-too-distant past, it could have been affirmed as self-evident that the New Testament always limited legitimate sexual relationship and human reproduction to the marital bond. Now this view is widely challenged, or abandoned *within the church*.[7] The obvious significance of this "contextual" question is that the emphasis will be different if we discuss contraception, sterilization and abortion within the context of marriage than in a non-marital context. Moreover, the New Testament teaching is specifically concerned with *Christian* marriage, and attaches special meaning to such union. (As we proceed, we must, of course, be clear that entrance into the marital bond may have a different shape in the New Testament than in the Christian community today.) [8]

The teaching of the New Testament is stringent and

---

[6] It is notable that even Karl Barth, who has emphatically espoused the centrality of the virgin birth in Christian thought, and who has a way of extracting more theology from a text than any of his peers makes no use of the virgin birth in the lengthy section on the married life and procreation in his *Church Dogmatics*, Vol. III, Part Four, *The Doctrine of Creation* (Edinburgh: T. & T. Clark, 1961), sections 54 & 55.

[7] For a leading American spokesman, see Joseph Fletcher, *Situation Ethics: The New Morality* (Philadelphia: The Westminster Press, 1966). For a critique of this ethic with a counter-response by Professor Fletcher, cf. *Storm Over Ethics*, John C. Bennett *et al.* (Philadelphia: The United Church Press, 1967).

[8] Otto Piper, *The Christian Interpretation of Sex* (New York: Charles Scribner's Sons, 1951), pp. 153–172, "Marriage," analyzes marriage from a Biblical theological perspective and suggests some reservations regarding the traditional "law" of uniting the sexual relationship and marriage. (see pp. 167ff.)

clear in its rejection of adultery and fornication. There are
direct words against such illegitimate sexual relationships
(Matthew 5:32ff.; Mark 10:11 par.; 19ff. par.; 1 Corinthians 6:13ff.). They are placed in the context of that which
is gross evil (Mark 7:21; Romans 1:29; 1 Corinthians
6:9ff.). Idolatry, the gross sin against God, is described as
fornication and adultery (Revelation 14:8; 17:1ff.). Jesus
uses the expression "adulterous" pejoratively of the individual or of the nation which rejects him (Mark 8:38;
Matthew 12:39; 16:4). Speaking positively, marriage is
identified as that instrument by which God intends to create
"one flesh" (Mark 10:6ff. par.; 1 Corinthians 6:16ff.;
Ephesians 5:31.). The Church, the holy community, is holy
precisely in that it is united with, and is one with its Lord
(1 Corinthians 6:17). From whatever perspective one views
the New Testament, it is clear that the normative sexual
relationship belongs to the marriage bond.

At this point, we cannot help but observe that the
New Testament shows a balance which is congruent with
its realism regarding the vitality of sex in human relationship. Even though departures from the norm are met with
swift and sure judgment, they are also met with a grace
that is equally direct and strong.[9] The well-known story of
Jesus and the adulterous woman (John 8:3–11) is a prime
illustration of the grace of God manifest in Christ operative
in this area. The primitive Church surely followed in this
way, even though belief no doubt outran practice then as
now.

The foundation of the New Testament stringency collides
head-on with the general tone of the so-called "new
morality." Whereas the new morality wishes to take love
seriously,[10] the New Testament does as much, but surpasses

---

[9] Piper, *ibid.*, pp. 194–200, has an excellent chapter on "The
Gospel of Forgiveness."

[10] Cf. Fletcher, *op. cit.*, pp. 33, 57, 69.

that point of view by *assigning the sexual relationship an equally serious and ultimate value.*

> For this reason a man shall leave his father and mother and be joined to his wife, and the two shall become one. So they are no longer two but one. What therefore God has joined together, let no man put asunder. (Mark 10:7–9) Do you not know that he who joins himself to a prostitute becomes one body with her? For, as it is written, 'The two shall become one.' (1 Corinthians 6:16)

The expression "one flesh" is remarkable. A crucial mark of entrance into the marital bond is the new sexual relationship which not only symbolizes but actualizes an enduring oneness.[11] The New Testament, like the Old Testament, views sexuality with an unmistakable seriousness, so that one wonders how ascetic deviations could have ever gained a foothold in the Christian community. The New Testament emphasis upon the "one flesh" or "one body" underlines a point already present in the Old Testament so that we can see certain unity in the two testaments at this point, a basing of sex morality upon the *one body* (cf. Leviticus 20:11, 20, 21). The fact of the matter is that neither the Old Testament nor the New Testament speaks of procreation as the end of sexual union. The end is the one flesh which is the generally indispensable presupposition of the marital union. One must suppose that the New Testament simply takes over the Old Testament teaching in which fruitfulness is a divine blessing added to the one flesh. This, at least, does not close the door on some birth control practice.

There are two Pauline texts of particular value as we seek for some foothold from which to make an initial statement regarding the bearing of the New Testament teaching upon birth control. These are 1 Corinthians 7:1ff. and 1

---

[11] Cf. Piper, *op. cit.*, pp. 44ff.

Thessalonians 4:3ff. The two texts differ somewhat in their development—so some discussion is in order. In the former, Paul moves out from the affirmation that temptation to immorality comes to each man and each woman and that therefore sexual intercourse is the normal practice within the marital relationship (vv. 3ff.). Since these passions are not confined to husbands and wives, those who are unmarried are advised to marry in order not to live in the flame of passion which is temptation (7:9, 36). He then goes on to observe that there is sanctifying virtue in the married estate—an unbelieving mate is consecrated (sanctified) through the partner. Readers of this text should note that the basis upon which Paul can make this affirmation can only be the foundational Biblical teaching of the *one flesh*.

Although the meaning of 1 Thessalonians 4:4 is disputed, it is our contention that it offers a clear parallel to the teaching of 1 Corinthians 7, especially in its assignment of sanctifying value to the sexual relationship *within marriage*. In the Thessalonian letter, Paul's point of departure is the sanctification of the believer, which is the will of God (4:3). Paul goes on to develop this with a negative and a positive statement. Sanctification involves abstention from immorality (v. 3b) as it is manifested in the lust of the pagan who moves in a passion of lust, and transgresses even against his brother (vv. 5–6). Positively, each man is exhorted "to take a wife for himself in holiness and honour" (v. 4). We have demonstrated in a paper read elsewhere [12] that the reading of the Revised Standard Version given here is much to be preferred to the New English Bible and the Jerusalem Bible which perpetuate a view of the eminent

---

[12] "Skeuos in 1 Thessalonians 4:4. Its Translation and Interpretation," presented to a joint meeting of the Middle West Branch of the American Oriental Society and the Mid-West Section of the Society of Biblical Literature at their joint meeting, April 7–8, 1967.

Bishop Lightfoot [13] and the Roman Catholic Church respectively, which falls short of the realism of the Pauline view of marriage.

The sanctification of the Christian occurs in the honorable and holy, i.e., responsible, enjoyment of the sexual relationship, rather than the lustful "breaking into the marriage relationship of a brother" (v. 6). Marriage is instrumental in confining the natural disposition to sexual union. This, contrary to an opinion often expressed, is not a low view of marriage at all. When one takes seriously the one flesh which is the Biblical foundation of marriage, then it is a high view of marriage. It fulfils God's highest purposes for us, even our sanctification. That is to say, the sexual relationship within marriage is assigned a redemptive significance—for one can never think of sanctification without giving attention to the justification which makes it possible and which makes possible our ultimate redemption.[14] To utilize a more contemporary language, the New Testament attaches to the sexual relationship holifying and healthful meaning. The sexual relationship within the right context (marriage) and for the right purpose (wholesome regard first for one's partner) is good. There are, to be sure, exceptions to the rule of one flesh and marriage—but they are *exceptions*. And we are reminded quite forcibly in the New Testament that the sexual relationship is by no means free from demonic misdirection—Romans 1 is clear proof of that, as well as the stringent sayings of Jesus in the fifth chapter of Matthew.

Does all of this open a door to the practice of contraception? Rather, we should perhaps ask whether it opens a door to a practice (contraception) already engaged in by many Christians who have seldom reckoned seriously with

---

[13] Cf. J. B. Lightfoot, *Notes on the Epistles of St. Paul* (Grand Rapids: Zondervan Publishing House, 1895), pp. 52–59.

[14] Cf. Piper, *op. cit.*, pp. 13, 89ff., 93, 94f., 97.

the bearing of the Biblical teaching upon that practice? One is impressed by three factors—(1) the decisive teaching regarding one flesh, (2) the absence of any connection at all between discussion of the sexual relationship within marriage and the bearing of children, (3) the affirmation by Paul of the sanctifying value of marriage. (So far as the Old Testament is concerned, the ordinance of one flesh within a good creation, as in Genesis 2:24, points in the same direction.) Although it must be granted that these occur in the context of a general disposition against birth control practice and in knowledge of the fact that children result from the sexual union, on balance they do not seem to forbid some birth control practices and would seem at least to leave the door open for its responsible employment. To demand too much of the New Testament in the presence of its obviously limited teaching could paralyze Christian existence; we will turn later to principles by which one moves into the present from the New Testament teaching.

STERILIZATION AND ABORTION IN THE NEW TESTAMENT

We have already observed that some type of birth control would seem to be on the non-prohibited side of the New Testament teaching. There are two New Testament texts in which sterilization and abortion actually are mentioned, and we must now determine whether or not they give direction to our present quest. Suffice it to say in advance that we have inherited a very long tradition which denies either of them any real relevance.

Sterilization

There are eunuchs in the Bible; the eunuch of Acts 8 is well known to those familiar with the New Testament. The statement of Jesus given in Matthew 19:10–12 is not so familiar:

The disciples said to him, 'If such is the case of a man with his wife, it is not expedient to marry.' But he said to them, 'Not all men can receive this precept, but only those to whom it is given. For there are eunuchs who have been so from birth, and there are eunuchs who have been made eunuchs by men, and there are eunuchs who have made themselves eunuchs for the sake of the kingdom of heaven. He who is able to receive this, let him receive it.'

There are four observations crucial to the correct handling of this text:

(1) It is a historical fact that castration was forbidden in the Old Testament and was fundamentally alien to the Greek mind. However, it did enter into Greek life particularly in the cults of Asia Minor (Cybele, Attis, Artemis).[15]

(2) There is the saying of Jesus in Matthew 5:29f. which speaks of plucking out the eye or cutting off the hand for the sake of the kingdom righteousness. On the basis of 5:28 and such sayings as Mark 7:20ff., literal meaning is rightly denied to Matthew 5:29f.

(3) There is a complete absence of any data showing that either Jesus or any of his chosen disciples actually subjected themselves to this practice. The maintenance of this teaching and practice by Jesus and the primitive Church would have brought them into violent conflict with Judaism, not to mention the Hellenistic society; one would certainly expect to encounter traces of this conflict either in Christian or in Jewish literature. He does not.

(4) On occasion Jesus could move from a physical to a figurative meaning (Luke 9:60).

One may weigh against these considerations the fact that the first two classes of men described in the text are physical eunuchs. However as (4) indicates, this is not enough to require such an interpretation of the third member of the saying. The very fact that the Matthean community preserved this saying in the absence of the practice

---

[15] On this see Johannes Schneider's article "εὐνοῦχος" in the *Theological Dictionary of the New Testament*, vol. II, p. 765.

is additional evidence of its figurative meaning; in addition, the nearly unanimous figurative interpretation of the Christian community for two millennia has to be given some preference by the Christian interpreter of Scripture.

What does the text mean? It is important to note that in such sayings of Jesus the climactic member is the key element of the saying, and often embodies a wholly surprising turn in the direction of thought. The Roman Catholic exegete Josef Blinzler [16] has pointed to the likeness of the thought in this text with that in other teaching of Jesus regarding the kingdom of heaven in which it is a magnificent find or gift which claims all that a man has for its sake. There are those who are so grasped by the kingdom of God that they are not fit for marriage. The cause of the sacrifice in the three classes of men is the important thread binding them together; in the last case the cause is the kingdom itself. The result is that he, like those who are physically unfit for marriage, is also unfit for marriage. This reminds us of the words of Jesus which affirm that discipleship in the kingdom leads to the abandonment of even the marital relationship (Mark 10:28 par.). And this again is wholly parallel to the sayings of Paul in the seventh chapter of 1 Corinthians.

What is important for us is the simple observation that physical sterilization is not in question here. It is not so much a question of physical birth control as of being controlled by the gift of the kingdom! In conclusion, it may be speculated that Jesus' use of the word "eunuch" perhaps reflects an historical situation in which his opponents took issue with his own non-married life.[17] In Judaism, it was demanded that a rabbi should be a married man, and Jesus, who functioned as a rabbi, did not meet this stipulation.

---

[16] Josef Blinzler, "Εἰσὶν εὐνοῦχοι," ZNW 48 (1957), 254–270, pp. 262ff. Blinzler presents a careful discussion and surveys an extensive body of literature dealing with this text.

[17] Blinzler, *op. cit.*, pp. 268ff.

Those who called him a glutton and a winebibber may equally well have named him "eunuch" because of this. The antipathy reflected in this term would have been increased by the stringent demands of the kingdom of God which he placed upon his followers. But all this takes us beyond the scope of this paper and we may move on to a specific consideration of abortion in the New Testament, with the notation that the New Testament offers no ground at this point for the practice of sterilization.

Abortion

The term *ektroma*, meaning "abortion, abortive birth, untimely birth," appears but once in the New Testament, and is a term used by the apostle Paul to describe his own position among the apostles. It is entirely possible that the historical circumstances for Paul's use of *ektroma* may have paralleled Jesus' use of *eunochos*: It has been suggested that Paul's opponents used this term of him derogatively, and that Paul now takes it up in a positive presentation of his apostolate.[18] The text of 1 Corinthians 15:8 reads as follows:

> Last of all, as to one untimely born, he appeared also to me. For I am the least of the apostles, unfit to be called an apostle, because I persecuted the church of God.

It is possible that Paul may have been nicknamed *ektroma*, because of his small stature. The Latin equivalent of *ektroma, abortivus*, was used of grown men, because it was believed that dwarfs were the result of a premature birth.

---

[18] Cf. Thorlief Boman. *"Paulus abortivus*. (I Kor. 15,8),"* in *Studia Theologica* 18 (1964), pp. 46–50, where see also a critique of other significant studies of this aspect of 1 Corinthians 15:8.

Cf. also Johannes Schneider's article *"ἔκτρωμα"* in the Theological Dictionary of the New Testament Vol. II, pp. 465–467; and Johannes Munck, *Paulus Tanquam Abortivus* (1 Cor. 15:8), in *New Testament Essays: Studies in Memory of Thomas Walter Manson* (ed. A.J.B. Higgins; Manchester: Manchester University Press, 1959), pp. 180–193.

It could also be used of an immature or childish person. In any case the use of the term here hardly allows any inferences for current practice to be based upon the New Testament.

Texts Bearing on the Status of the Fetus

The practice of abortion inevitably raises questions regarding the status of the fetus—defining that term here in the broad sense of the conceptus from conception to childbirth. It is worthwhile to note those texts commonly used in support of the belief that the fetus is fully human, and must be accorded the same rights as are given to all human beings from birth onwards. Suffice it to say at the outset that there are no unequivocal proof texts in support of that position; what of the texts which do appear in the New Testament?

A favorite passage is Luke 1:41ff., where Elizabeth, in conversation with Mary, affirms that Mary's salutation caused the unborn babe in the womb of Elizabeth to leap for joy. It is thought that this text at least attaches the same values to the unborn life as one assigns to that life after birth. But can this be understood as a scientific statement? Can it really be more than a "manner of speaking"? That it must not be understood as anything but a manner of speaking would seem to be indicated by such texts as Hebrews 7:9–10 where we read that "Levi himself paid tithes through Abraham, for he was still in the loins of his ancestor when Melchizedek met him." The very specificity of these texts tends to remove them as evidence for the present discussion.

Neither are we provided with ultimate and specific help by the New Testament anthropology in which man is constantly viewed in terms of his wholeness as a person. There is no reason at all to relate this teaching to the unborn fetus.

THE DEVELOPMENT OF A SYSTEMATIC
APPROACH TO BIRTH CONTROL

We were warned at the outset regarding the risky and frustrating matter of investigating the New Testament teaching relevant to the practices of birth control. We have mostly experienced the frustrating aspect of this quest; the risk sets in at that point where one seeks to set forth the general disposition of the New Testament as it assists one, looking into the more or less unknown, to form an opinion and a practice. The risk is compounded by the complex way in which human relationships may be affected by these practices. Because we are called upon to deal justly with all men, we must exercise caution that justice shall be done on all sides of any relationship involving birth control practices. The following sections are merely sketchy proposals, all in need of further development, setting forth the New Testament teaching of particular importance in our quest.

Testing

The New Testament, as we know and have seen, does not clearly direct our way in every relationship of life. Faith is a prime characteristic of the Christian life, and its corollary in practice is that we do not walk by *sight*. Therefore, a central category of New Testament ethics is *testing* (i.e., proving). Such texts as Romans 12:1ff., Philippians 1:9 and 1 Thessalonians 5:19, call upon the Christian to continually apply his renewed mind to the formulation of correct Christian ethical judgment.[19] The Christian is also called upon to become a man approved of God (1 Thessalonians 2:3,4). The central measure is always the revelation in and through Christ, although there are other measures which will be noted in succeeding sections. What is important is the existence of the principle. Testing is a call to

---

[19] Oscar Cullmann, *Christ and Time* (trans. Floyd F. Filson; London: SCM Ltd., 1962), p. 228.

freedom in the area of Christian ethics; it means that the Christian is not bound by a legal code, but is free to walk through the world in the Spirit and to measure all practices by the norm which is in Christ, and the revealed norm of sacred scripture. If the Church of Christ really practiced this, it would be a "conservative" community in terms of conserving the good. However, it would not continue the practice of adopting as its own the norms of secular society one generation after that secular society has moved on to different standards. As new medical discoveries occur they may call for new freedom in practice.

So far as contraception is concerned, the layman is uncertain whether today's standard method (the pill) is safe. In the face of conflicting medical opinion, he wonders whether the practice is good, and he looks to the medical professions to tell him the truth, a truth based upon testing, albeit scientific testing. Is not even *such* testing a part of our Christian vocation?

Restraint

A corollary of the New Testament dependence upon the sovereignty of the true God who reveals Himself to us is a dependence upon him which manifests itself as awe in relation to him, and which manifests itself in concrete human relations as restraint evidenced in testing. The creator God has created my neighbor and has decreed that I am to love him as myself. The God who is sovereign has decreed that it is right to so love him as not to offend him or to become a stone of stumbling to his faith. Paul's example and teaching in Romans 14:1ff. comes to mind here. He did not always do that which he knew himself free to do, because he would not weaken the faith (and practice!) of his brother. The time when the regular practice of contraception would offend my brother is generally past; but this is not the case with abortion, a practice concerning which many have deep, even religious, convictions. However, we also must reckon with the fact that there are those within the Christian community who can see no final offense in abortion when it is entered into responsibly by a woman who is in consultation with a physician.

One could find in Jesus a precedent for their boldness in recommendation, and even in practice; Jesus did many things which cut right across the norms of Jewish practice, and he did them where men had to eat, to live, to be relieved of physical distress and anguish of soul. Perhaps the Christian doctor may recognize that a woman or a family is truly in distress because of a new pregnancy and feel himself called to go against even the religious norms of his immediate society. In this case, caution *may* be seen as the doctor's disposition to accept suffering himself rather than to allow the patient to suffer.

The great problem here is the nature of the fetus, which is on the one hand judged to have the status of a human being,[20] and on the other to be only a rather vital piece of human tissue which has no "human claim" upon anyone as yet. It seems to me that the policy of most physicians at this point is not based on caution, but certainty. Some are certain that the fetus is a human life, and would not destroy it; others are certain that it is not a human life, and have no qualms in aborting it. In view of our uncertainty regarding the status of the fetus, there is need for great restraint in the practice of abortion. Some would view the expression "restraint" as far too weak here. However, they must be reminded that one who permits abortion for some reasons has at least opened the door *to abortion for any reason.*

I stand as one perplexed, who at one time spoke out in public for a liberal abortion policy because it seemed to me that there was no *final* verdict possible. It still seems that

---

[20] Helmut Thielicke, *The Ethics of Sex* (trans. John W. Doberstein; New York: Harper and Row, Publishers, 1964), p. 228.

way to me. However, whereas I then was satisfied to let
the mother set her own course in the face of this uncertainty, I now see the necessity of greater responsibility in
instructing her. As I do so, I would rather err on the side of
restraint, even though I firmly believe that God remains the
forgiving one even at this point.

Man as Unity

The New Testament looks at man as a whole man, and
this is nowhere more graphic than in the case of its interpretation of the sexual relationship. A number of the texts
already referred to above assign the sexual relationship an
amazingly central role both within and outside the marriage
bond. But observe that it is central in terms of its effects.
Unless we are prepared to ascribe some sacramental value
to the sexual relationship, then the New Testament perspective must be seen as residing, at least in part, in the
manner in which it affects the whole man in all of his
relationships for better or for worse. We established above
that the sexual relationship is not secondary to the reality
of procreation, but precedes it. However, it is not unrelated
to the reality of procreation, and the Christian lives his
life in the grateful recognition that the gift of life comes
through the joy of sexual union. Is that joy complete in the
absence of a due regard for the disposition of the Creator?
To choose an extreme example, can one *continually* frustrate
the God-given possibility of procreation and suffer no harm
to the inner person? Or an even more extreme example:
Do only *physical* consequences follow from the aborting of
that which is unwantingly conceived? Since man finds fulfilment by participating in the creation process, it is hard
to imagine that he will not suffer loss if he wills not to
participate in it in a specific relationship. And, if he wills
to thwart that process once it is underway, will he not
suffer greater loss? Thus, caution for the whole person leads

to a reserve in the practice of abortion, and our ignorance of the status of the fetus simply increases that reserve.

Sin

Sin shatters the God-created wholeness of man; because of this, our present comments could well be included as part of the preceding section. However, we place it here to single out the New Testament picture in which sins in the sexual sphere are located at the heart of man, and are seen as affecting his whole person. We have no reason to suppose that the human attitude to practices which control the resultant reproductive process is free from this sinful disposition.

Here as much as anywhere, man can deceive himself. I am reminded of a comment of a doctor whose main practice for fourteen years has been obstetrics. He observed that all through that period of time there have been many mothers in his office who affirmed that they simply could not "go through with this pregnancy." Wise counsel and care led all of them through their pregnancies. It is easy to deceive ourselves regarding our own limits, whether mental or physical. We can equally well deceive ourselves regarding the rightness or the wrongness of a given practice in a concrete situation. This factor too should create a disposition to caution where the issues are more or less unresolved.

Community

Man exists in community; Christian man exists in a special community. All the categories thus far examined have their own special relation to this reality. The New Testament concept of *koinonia* which stands behind our term "community" designates participation in a common lot. If we are true to the New Testament teaching, we cannot stress this fact too much.[21]

---

[21] Cf. Otto Piper, *op. cit.*, pp. 94–107: "A Blessed Burden."

Is it not a tragedy then that until recently most individual reflection upon the practice of abortion has been a wholly private matter? The entire community has not been able to discuss this matter freely; this removes the ethical locus from the community and places it solely with the more or less isolated individual, and that in the face of one of the most problematic decisions that he has to make in life. It is true that the doctor is there, or a pastor, or a friend. But these are generally encountered as isolated individuals in this case—the full force of the communal vitality is not available. Where the full resources of the Christian community are made available in an anticipatory way, many calls for abortion will be eliminated. If that community ever comes to take seriously its unity with every member of the body, others in distress will not be treated as outcasts—cast out from the community's love and care just when it is needed most.

CONCLUSIONS

It must not be thought strange that the scriptures offer such scant and principal guidance for those who are rather seeking specific instruction regarding the control of human reproduction. Here, as everywhere, the man who seeks to be obedient to the whole counsel of God is called upon and privileged to give himself the more wholly to seeking God's good guidance of his children by every means of grace. The Christian will always remember that Jesus Christ is the Mediator of a New Covenant, and that the God of Israel, and the God and Father of the Lord Jesus Christ, our God, is always working a new thing in the world. We must be open to that leadership of the Spirit who ever leads the people of God into new paths of obedience. In the midst of all our endeavor, we are called upon to test every practice in order that we may ourselves become a people approved by God.

Chapter 3

THE RELATIONSHIP OF
THE SOUL TO THE FETUS

SUMMARY

Paul K. Jewett, Professor of Theology at Fuller Seminary, evaluates the biblical, theological, historical and biological evidence for the origin-point of individual human life. The author is careful to note that final statements as to the origin and nature of the soul are impossible. The scant quantity of biblical data and the conflicting theological opinions based on it are discussed. Biblical information on the value and divine origin of human life is emphasized. The value of the fetus is due to the fact that it is a primordial person and as such bears the divine image in some sense. Dr. Jewett considers the conflicting personal and societal values to be weighed in making a decision on abortion, and stresses that such decisions are ethically ambiguous.

PAUL K. JEWETT, B.A., Th.M., Th.D., Ph.D. *has served as Professor of Systematic Theology at Fuller Theological Seminary since 1955, before which he was Professor of the Philosophy of Religion at Gordon Divinity School for five years.*

He holds the B.A. degree from Wheaton College, Th.M. and Th.D. from Westminster Theological Seminary and the Ph.D. from Harvard University. His field of doctoral study was the theology of Emil Brunner, involving work at the Universities of Berne, Zurich and Basle in Switzerland, and at the Catholic Institute and University of Paris. Dr. Jewett is the author of two books on the thought of Emil Brunner and numerous articles in religious publications.

THE RELATIONSHIP OF
THE SOUL TO THE FETUS

by Paul K. Jewett

The removal of a small glob of living tissue from a human organism requires a surgeon who knows how, what, when and where to cut, and the consent of the patient to whom the tissue in question belongs. As technique, this cutting may be rather sophisticated, and the result will hopefully prolong the life of the patient, which makes the cutting significant as well as sophisticated. Yet sophistication requires only a skilled practitioner; and significance, a patient in need of help. When it comes to the removal of a small glob of living tissue called a "human fetus," however, the situation changes dramatically. This particular bit of surgery is no longer considered mere cutting with expertise (which requires a surgeon) for the purpose of inducing health (which requires a patient). Suddenly the circle is enlarged to include not only the surgeon and patient, but many others beside. Why this difference? Why is the surgeon's skill, and patient's consent, not enough to settle the issue in this case, as in the case of an appendectomy or tonsillectomy? What is it about fetal tissue that has drawn doctors, lawyers, legislators, sociologists, psychiatrists, and even philosophers and theologians into the discussion?

In answer to this question it may be observed that fetal tissue is unique. Of all the tissues in the body, it alone differs from the parent organism in that it has a fixed genetic makeup other than the mother's tissue, in whose body it is lodged. A woman, therefore, cannot say of fetal tissue, this is mine. She may give a kidney to someone else, and then it becomes someone else's kidney tissue. But such a choice is not hers, so far as fetal tissue is concerned. It never was hers to give or not to give. She must surrender it in birth—or die. She cannot keep it, any more than she can give it to someone else.

But we can hardly say the physical fact of genetic uniqueness is the basis of all the anxious inquiry among specialists concerning the fetus, for the same situation prevails, in this respect, in the animal world as in the world of mankind. Fetal tissue is fetal tissue, whether it be that of man or mouse. The issue is rather that human fetal tissue, if we leave it unmolested, will develop into a human being, and most people are convinced there is something unique about a human being which demands an attitude of reverential respect for his life and concern for his well-being. This is why the scruples become more articulate and the laws of society more explicit as the fetal tissue develops in the direction of individual humanity, from fertilized egg, to blastocyst, to embryo, to fetus (in the specialized sense), to premature, to infant.

To take the life of a child deliberately is considered to be murder. However, deliberately to prevent the implantation of a fertilized egg in the lining of the uterus is considered by many to be mere contraception, and it is anticipated that we will soon have a "morning-after pill." [1] In between these two extremes are many halfway houses of opinion. Early American law, for example, following the tradition of common law, forbade abortion after quickening, that is, about the 16th week of pregnancy, when fetal motion is felt. Today, in Norway abortions may not be performed after three months, in Denmark after four months, in Sweden after five months. Even where the laws are most permissive, abortions are not allowed, except to save a mother's life, after viability, that is, after about six months, when the fetus is able to survive the womb. This is the position taken by the American Law Institute, and endorsed by the American Medical Association at its June, 1967 meeting. Underlying such an approach is the assumption that the farther a fetus has developed toward full humanity, the more it participates in the unique values belonging to human life.

The same tendency to make the fully developed person the measure of all things is illustrated when factors other than the development of the fetus are considered as grounds for abortion. These factors almost invariably concern the mother, whose humanity cannot be doubted, rather than the fetus, whose humanity cannot be demonstrated. Thus laws allow abortion when there has been forcible or statutory rape, on the ground that pregnancy would impair the physical or mental health of the mother. Even when it is a matter of preventing a deformed or mentally retarded birth, it is the effect of such a birth on the mother and other

---

[1] The tendency to regard abortion as a phase of contraception is not uncommon. The two are so joined together in ancient ecclesiastical law in a common condemnation, (See Lloyd Kalland, "The Control of Human Reproduction," chapter 21) and in modern Japanese law in a common approbation. (See John Scanzoni, "A Sociological Perspective on Abortion and Sterilization," chapter 16).

members of the family, which weighs largely in the decision. How often we read a plea for abortion on the score that living with children in utter poverty creates a pattern of futility in life; that living with a deformed or mentally retarded child, bearing an illegitimate child or a child by rape, is a life situation with which many pregnant women cannot cope.

Although some geneticists insist that in every pregnancy there are always two patients, the mother and the unborn child, many of our laws do not reflect this fact. For example, a fetus aborted before 20 weeks of pregnancy does not require legal interment; it is treated as a mere pathological specimen. But is it a mere pathological specimen? That is the question. Since the potential for future development is already present in the fertilized egg as well as in the newborn child, should we permit intervention with an individual life at an earlier stage but not at a later one? And if so can we draw any line?

In order to frame an answer to these questions, one needs to know whether a fetus is a human being or not; and before one can decide this question, he must answer the more ultimate question—What is a human being? And such a basic question involves philosophy and theology; it demands that one try to become an expert in humanity.

In our religiously pluralistic society, we shall hardly achieve unanimity in such a quest. The Christian Medical Society, however, is not religiously pluralistic. Therefore we may opt for the Christian view of man straight off, though it is a question whether this will compound or simplify our task. At any event, as Christians we cannot approach our task from any other point of view than that of a Christian view of man. This view is implicit in the subject which I have been assigned: "The Relationship of the Soul to the Fetus." Here the assumption is being made that man is more than a complex chemical machine; he is, or has, a soul.

Presumably, if he is or has a soul from the earliest stages of fetal development, then, as a fetus he is a primordial person whose life cannot be taken with impunity. Hence the investigation of the question of the relation of the soul to the fetus, it is hoped, will illumine the degree of man's responsibility and freedom in the control of human reproduction during pregnancy.

Having defined the human fetus as living tissue with a unique genetic makeup, destined to become a fully developed human organism, we must now seek to define soul, the term which is really primary in our investigation. Aristotle affirmed long ago that to obtain knowledge about the soul is the most difficult thing in the world. Time has not altered this situation appreciably. Whether or not the soul exists, what it is and how it is related to the body are all questions for which answers, to date, have not been discovered by scientific investigation, nor demonstrated by rigorous philosophic analysis. By the same token, neither has scientific investigation discovered that there is no soul, nor has philosophic analysis demonstrated that the term is meaningless. Because of the limitation of time, we shall not pursue the question further from the perspective of science and philosophy, but only that of theology. In making this decision, we assume, on the one hand, the correctness of our affirmation that nothing in science or philosophy precludes a theological approach to this question. By investigating the concept of soul from a theological perspective, we are engaging in a procedure which cannot be invalidated in its method by science, nor falsified in its conclusions by philosophy. On the other hand, we admit that in making this decision, we must leave out of the discussion many aspects of the problem which are related to the findings of science and illumined by the conclusions of philosophy.

Even when we limit ourselves to theological considerations, the question of the soul and its relationship to the fetus must be discussed along several lines which may be distinguished as follows: Biblical theology offers the materials with which dogmatic theology must work; historical theology tells us how dogmaticians have done their work in the past; philosophical theology offers us criteria by which to criticize this effort of the dogmaticians; and moral theology suggests what we should do in the light of our dogmatic conclusions.

As for biblical theology, we shall begin our discussion of the meaning of the term soul by observing that, according to scripture, both men and animals share a common life which they receive from God the Creator. The word which the Israelites used to describe God, which we translate "spirit," is the same as the word for "wind" or "breath." Therefore every creature which breathes, in which there is the breath of life, was believed by the writers of the Old Testament to have received this animating principle from the Creator, the source of all life. Such creatures, including man, are "living creatures." As their life consists in receiving the living spirit (Spirit) from God, so, when he recalls his spirit (Spirit), they die.

Celebrating the glory of God revealed in the manifold works of wisdom with which he has filled the earth, the Psalmist speaks of the stork that nests in the fir tree and the wild goats that take refuge in the hills and the conies that gambol on the rocks and the young lions that roar after their prey, and man who goes forth unto his work and to his labor until the evening, and leviathan who plays in the sea. To all these God opens his hand and they are filled with good, or he hides his face and they are troubled. Thou (v. 29) takest away their breath, they die, and return to their dust. Thou sendest forth thy Spirit, they are created and thou renewest the face of the earth (v. 30). This is true of both man and beast; they both live when they have the breath of life; they die when it is taken from them. In an apparent moment of bitter resignation, the Preacher reflects on this idea, not from the perspective of the glory of God, the sovereign disposer of life and death, but rather from the perspective of the vanity of man's life. For that which befalleth the sons of men befalleth beasts; even one thing befalleth them. As the one dieth, so dieth the other; yea, they have all one breath, and man hath no preeminence above the beasts, for all is vanity (Eccl. 3:19).

But this is not the only word in scripture. While animals share with man in the mystery of life and death, and therefore are capable of a conscious response to their environment, there is that about man which makes his response to his environment unique. The life which he has from God, though like that of the animals, is at the same time qualitatively different from theirs. While it is true that man, like the beasts, is formed out of the dust of the ground and animated with the breath of life, he is, at the same time, unlike the beasts in that he is copied from his Maker. He is one who reflects his Creator's image and likeness. That is to say, he is not only living, not only conscious; he is, among all the living, conscious creatures, uniquely so. And in this unique form of consciousness he is like God. His *spirit*, or his *soul*, or his *heart* is a spirit of wisdom and understanding (Exod. 28:3, Job 30:3); he has the word lodged in him. Hence God brings the creatures to man, as the Bible says in its quaint and simple way, to see what man will call them (Gen. 2:19–20). His *soul* is a soul that is wronged by sin (Prov. 8:36), because his soul is given man that he may keep God's testimonies always (Ps. 119:129, 167). Hence God says to him, "Of every tree of the garden thou mayest freely eat, but of the tree of knowledge of good and evil, thou shalt not eat of it." (Gen. 2:16, 17) His *heart* is a heart with which he is to love God supremely (Deut. 13:3, Matt. 22:37); a heart which he should keep with all diligence, for out of it are the issues of life (Prov. 4:23).

Hence God walked in the garden, where he had put the man, in the cool of the day seeking him as his supreme and highest good (Gen. 3:8).

But it may be objected, while this review of the usage of Scriptures illumines the Christian doctrine of man's superiority over the lower orders of the animal world, it still does not seem to help us in our specific problem of the soul and the fetus. Is this marvelously endowed creature called man, whose intelligence reduces remote galaxies and minute atoms to the laws of reason; who lives in the realm of responsibility, knowing the commendation of a good conscience and the condemnation of an evil one; who, as Luther said, in his highest and noblest part is qualified to lay hold of the incomprehensible, invisible and eternal, in short, to become the house where faith and God's word are at home; is he or is he not a man while still in his mother's womb? If we take away the life of a fetus, is this or is it not an affront upon the divine image?

There is nothing in scripture bearing directly on the question of the participation of the fetus in the divine image. As we know, the narrative of man's creation contemplates him as full-fledged. The umbilical cord has been cut; even infancy and childhood are left far behind. It is as "man come of age" that Scripture presents to us the one who is made in the image and likeness of God. To the question "Does the unborn infant have the same relationship to his Maker?" one may infer a positive answer, but the inference would be more convincing if the data were less ambiguous.

Since the creation narrative speaks of God's "breathing into man's nostrils the breath of life," it might seem plausible to argue that the soul informs the fetus when the first breath is drawn, that is at birth. But it is doubtful that we can take a narrative which is so metaphorical in form and theological in content, and apply it with such scientific

precision and literalness. The difficulty with such a procedure is evidenced by the fact that the ancient Hebrews associated life in a unique way, not only with the breath, but
also with the blood. "The blood is the living being," we are
told in Deut. 12:23, 24. Therefore the blood of animals was
taboo as drink, and whoever shed *man's* blood was guilty
of a capital offense (Gen. 9:6). If one were to press this
teaching about blood, as literal science, it would yield the
result that the human fetus is informed with the soul, not at
the moment the first breath is drawn, but when the blood
system develops.

Not only do these data respecting blood and breath yield
different results, applied to our question, but even if they
did not, a convincing case could hardly be made, since the
animating "breath of life," and the "blood which is the
life," as biblical terms, are equally applicable to animals and
men. The biblical description of man's distinctiveness as "in
the divine image" refers to a quality of life which, though
it depends upon breath and blood, is not to be equated with
them. (This is evident from the fact that a man's blood can
be replaced with a completely different type, yet he is the
same person still.) The biblical data, in this respect, appears
to reflect the rough approximations with which antique
"science" conceived the physiological basis of life. If we
were to state the equivalent in contemporary scientific
idiom, we should have to argue that the soul is present to
the human fetus when the nervous system is developed.[2]
The fact that man's likeness to God, which is the ground
of reverence for his life, is qualitatively distinct from the
physiological basis of his life, means that all efforts to
identify the presence of the human soul in terms of some

---

[2] Since brainwaves are discernable through the maternal abdomen
shortly before viability, some have argued that the fetus should be
protected from the seventh month. See Granville Williams as quoted
by John Warwick Montgomery in "Fetus and Soul as Related to the
Abortion Question". (Chapter 4)

stage of physiological development must prove frustrating.

The difficulty remains when one examines the scripture that expressly alludes to human life in the fetal stage of development. In some instances the biblical usage reflects a distinct difference of value between an unborn child and the mother. According to the law of Exod. 21:22f, "If a man strive, and hurt a woman with child, so that her fruit depart from her," he shall compensate the husband with the payment of a fine as the judges shall impose. But if the woman herself be injured or die, then the offender shall give an eye for an eye and life for a life. Whatever the limitations may be of a concept of justice based on the *lex talionis,* this particular application plainly implies a greater worth in the mother, as human, than in the child which she carried.[3]

Yet to infer from this difference that the mother is human and the child is not, is more than the text will bear. Indeed to draw a sharp and heavy line between mother and fetus runs counter to other passages which presuppose that in some sense the fetus is human. We read for example, in Psalm 139:13–15, "For thou didst form my inward parts. Thou didst cover me in my mother's womb, my frame was not hidden from thee, when I was made in secret and curiously wrought in the lowest parts of the earth." (This last phrase, "lowest parts of the earth," is a Hebrew expression to describe the dark interior of the womb.) Here the psalmist is principally concerned to confess the divine omniscience. Even before he knew God, God knew him; even before his eyes opened on the light of day, while he was still being marvelously formed in the womb, God was there. But though the thrust of the passage is principally

---

[3] See Bruce K. Waltke for a fuller treatment of this passage, "Old Testament Texts Bearing on the Problem of the Control of Human Reproduction". (Chapter 1)

to confess a truth about God, it tacitly confesses a truth
about the psalmist, namely, that he regarded himself as a
self even before he was conscious of himself. *I*, the person,
was covered by thy hand, O Lord, in my mother's womb;
I was made in secret and curiously wrought in the inner re-
cesses of my mother's body. While this gives us no precise
information about the relation of the soul to the fetus, it
would appear that the psalmist did not think of his
humanity as uniquely tied to the moment of birth. The
events leading up to birth are a kind of primal history of
the self. In a similar usage, Psalm 51:5, the psalmist roots
the impulse to sin in this same primal history. "Behold I
was shapen in iniquity and in sin did my mother conceive
me." In an analogous way, Luke the Evangelist speaks of
the infant John as "leaping for joy" in his mother's womb
at the salutation of Mary. (Luke 1:41)

Yet one can hardly make such passages bear the weight
of a demonstration that the fetus is a personal self in the
fullest connotation of the term. Even as an ancient law concerning violently induced miscarriage does not make the
fetus other than human, so the language of the personal,
when applied to the fetus, does not erase all differences
between parent and child. The amount of scriptural data is
neither sufficient, nor is the direction in which it points so
unequivocal that one can be dogmatic.

As might be expected, the orientation of the biblical
materials in terms of mature manhood, and the paucity of
reference to human life in the prenatal period, have led
dogmaticians to give themselves over to inference and
speculation, resulting in an inevitable spectrum of opinion.

Tertullian, the first theologian to speak on the subject,
says that Christians abominate both infanticide and abortion as murder, the latter being a kind of murder in advance. For the embryonic man is as the fruit to the

blossom, destined in a little while to become a perfect man, if nature meets with no disturbance.[4] As a traducianist, that is, one believing that the soul, as well as the body, is derived from the parents, Tertullian naturally inferred that where there was the beginning of man on the physical side, there also man was present on the spiritual side.

Traditionally most theologians have espoused creationism, i.e., the view that God creates each individual soul directly, leaving only the body to develop by the laws of natural generation. Thinking of a person as a rational essence (it was commonly believed that thought was a pure act of the soul involving no bodily counterpart) the conclusion was reached that the fetus was informed by a rational soul shortly before birth. The Medieval Scholastics, employing Aristotelian distinctions, commonly spoke of a vegetative (nutritive) soul at the moment of conception, an animal (sensitive) soul at a later stage of embryonic development, followed by the impartation of a rational soul as the moment of birth drew nigh. On such a view, though deliberate interference with the life of the fetus was condemned, it was homicide only when the fetus was possessed of a human soul. Such was the view of Augustine and Thomas, neither of whom adventured an opinion as to exactly when this moment was reached, a reticence in which they have been often emulated through the centuries.

Turning from the past to the present, the uncertainty still prevails among Christian thinkers as to soul and fetus. I suspect it always will, inasmuch as the phenomena of self-consciousness—the rational, ethical and religious experience of the human I—are not in evidence prior to birth. We say "not in evidence" advisedly, for to say they do not exist, even in the earliest stages of fetal development, is to say more than we know. We must remember that it is a fallacy to which the mind is prone, to make the self the

---

[4] *Apology*, IX, VI–VII.

measure of all things. A person who is sleeping or unconscious is a person still, though he gives no express evidence
of it. And so it may be with the fetus. At least we can say
that a fetus is a potential person, and maybe it is a
primordial person, that is, a person in its most elementary
form.

Perhaps, to use an analogy, as the self cannot evidence
its presence when unconscious, so it cannot do so when still
in the womb. We do not judge that a person who is in a
coma has ceased to be a person. Can we, then, say that the
fetus has not yet become a person? If we have doubts about
terminating the life of one who has lost the ability to live
and act as a human subject, because he may still be a human
subject, though unable to act like one, should we not have at
least as much scruple to terminate the life of one who does
not yet have the ability to live and act as a human subject?
In fact, it would seem that an ability lost—the "human
vegetable," can make less claim to respect and reverence
than ability in prospect—the "human fetus." [5]

On the other hand, the analogy between a person-in-
embryo and a person-in-coma breaks down (as analogies are
wont to do) in at least one point. The existence of the
former is much less an existence in isolation than the latter.
The right of the fetus, therefore, to live, even if the fetus
be deemed a person in embryo with all that that means, is a
right which is held in conjunction with the right of another
person to live. The primordial person, if such the fetus be,
can never become a full-orbed person apart from another
person, the mother in whose womb he is conceived and at
whose breast he will be nourished. And while we may
question the humanity of the fetus, we cannot question the
humanity of the mother who conceives it. Furthermore, her

---

[5] This is not to suggest that all senior citizens, as soon as they
show senility, should be abandoned by those whom they love and deprived of the benefits of medicine and so eliminated from society.

life is not (ordinarily) as solitary as that of the life she
carries. She is a daughter, a wife, and perhaps a mother.
Her life has been wrought into the lives of others, who also
have claims upon her, which are more clearly human in
their "I-thou" nature, than the claims of the fetus. Recognition of these facts has led to near unanimity of opinion
that in case of life and death, the mother has the more
fundamental claim.

The present tendency to give the psychiatrist and even
the sociologist a part in defining *life* and *death* has indeed
complicated the picture, yet it cannot be doubted that this
extension of the terms is a valid one from a Christian perspective. *Life* as the Christian understands it, in its distinc-
tively human dimension, is more than biology; therefore the
physicians of the soul, like the physicians of the body,
should be heard when the question is raised as to whether
the life of the fetus must be surrendered to preserve the life
of the mother.

The problem, of course, is that it is enormously more
difficult to measure and evaluate the data in the area of
psychiatry and sociology than in the area of traditional
medicine. A physician of the body can give a relatively
precise judgment, from the perspective of the laws of
physical life, as to the threat which a pregnancy poses for
the mother. No such precision is possible from the perspective of the laws of the psychical life. Nor will we ever attain
such precise psychological knowledge in the future, if the
analysis which we have made above, of the nature of man is
true. Since man, according to the Christian view, is both
object (body) and subject (soul), the objective aspect of his
being is that aspect where causality and natural law are
most relevant. As body he will always be better understood,
in terms of science, than as soul or spirit, which is the seat
of his freedom as an individual self. To the extent man is a
free, responsible self, his behavior can never be reduced to

the alignment of a strict causality. This means that there will inevitably be an increased factor of uncertainty in every decision to sacrifice the life of the fetus to save the life of the mother, whenever the decision rests on psychological grounds.

The very fact, by the way, that psychiatric indications of abortion are so complex and uncertain (some practitioners almost never recommend it, contending that pregnancy represents virtually no additional stress, while others almost always do, as alleviating the incidence of mental illness [6]) should serve to humble the male of the species. It is something of an anomaly that women, who are the most immediately involved in the problem, can only ask, but never decide, what they ought to do, when those who presume to decide the question (theologians, physicians and psychiatrists) admit that they can reach no easy concensus of scientific objectivity.

As for the socio-economic indications for abortion, these are probably the most difficult of all to reduce to scientific objectivity, since they involve not only the mother, but the whole family, including the unborn fetus who will become a member of the family. But just because the decision is difficult, Christians should avoid simplistic answers, as though concern for the fetus' right to life before birth has nothing to do with the quality of life it will experience after birth. Too often those who oppose abortion because of the sanctity of fetal life seem impervious to the question of the quality of life open to one born of a dope addict, a prostitute or a destitute mother in the slums. Surely if one really believes in the sanctity of life, he should not be less concerned with the life of the child, who is certainly a person, than with the life of the fetus, who is possibly a person.

When, therefore, we analyze the difficulties that moral

---

[6] See M. O. Vincent, "Psychiatric Indication for Therapeutic Abortion and Sterilization". (Chapter 9)

theology, working with a Christian view of man, faces in the matter of abortion, whether we look at the question from the perspective of the mother or the fetus, it would seem that the Christian answer to the control of human reproduction must be found principally in the prevention of conception, rather than in the prevention of birth. The latter will always remain a last recourse, never to be denied out of hand, but only ventured in emergency, and burdened with uncertainty.

Chapter 4

THE CHRISTIAN VIEW OF
THE FETUS

SUMMARY

John Warwick Montgomery, Professor of Church History at Trinity Evangelical Divinity School, summarizes the history of theological debates relating to human personality, the origin of the soul and the culpability of abortion. Data from biological and psychological research is presented dealing with the nature of man and the origin of personality.

Dr. Montgomery delineates the creationist-traducionist controversy. He shows that both positions lead to the conviction that God is involved with the fetus from the time of conception.

Abortion is seen as an evil in any circumstances. Under some conditions, however, it may be a lesser evil than allowing a pregnancy to continue. Key biblical texts relating to the questions are interpreted.

JOHN WARWICK MONTGOMERY, A.B., B.L.S., M.A., B.D., S.T.M., Ph.D., D.Théol. *Dr. Montgomery is Professor and Chairman of the Division of Church History and the History of Christian Thought at Trinity Evangelical Divinity School, Deerfield, Illinois. He has also taught at the University of Wittenberg, the University of Chicago, and Waterloo Lutheran University in Ontario. An ordained Lutheran minister, his honors include membership in Phi Beta Kappa, and recognition of* Who's Who in America.

Among a number of books he has written are: The 'God is Dead' Controversy, The Shape of the Past, *and a chapter* "Toward a Christian Philosophy of History", *in the volume,* Jesus of Nazareth: Savior and Lord, *edited by Dr. Carl F. H. Henry.*

THE CHRISTIAN VIEW OF THE FETUS

by John Warwick Montgomery

INTRODUCTION

A superficial glance at the subject of this paper may suggest exactly that: superficiality. In the mid-20th century, is it really possible that theologians are still engaged in the kind of scholastic nit-picking that led St. Thomas,[1] following Aristotle,[2] to assert that the male receives his "rational soul" forty days after conception while the female has to wait eighty to ninety days for hers? Does our topic imply a revival of theological interest in intrauterine movement, such as led Samuel Pepys to write in his diary: "Lady Castlemaine quickened at my Lord Gerard's at dinner."?[3]

The relation of "soul" to "fetus" is of crucial importance

---

[1] *Summa Theologica*, Pt. I, quest. 75, art. i; cf. quest. 76, art. iii ad 3; quest. 118, art. ii ad 2.

[2] *Hist. Anim.*, vii. 3.

[3] Entry for 1 January 1662/3.

for the whole abortion issue. Is abortion morally wrong, and if so, *how* wrong? The answer to this question depends squarely on the nature of the unborn child. Is it in fact a person prior to attaining viability? In theological parlance, does it possess a soul? Is it a being destined for eternal life or merely a physiological growth within the mother (analogous to a tumor)? On the basis of responses to these questions the Christian will decide whether or not abortion is murder, and whether under any circumstances it can be morally justified.

The complexity, rather than superficiality, of our task comes from the necessity of interrelating at least five disciplines. First we must discuss the nature of the "soul" (theology), then the nature of the "fetus" (medical science). The answers to basic questions in those areas will force us to pose the ontological riddle concerning the nature of "personhood" (philosophy). And, finally, we must face the pressing moral and societal problem as to whether abortion ought to be allowed (ethics and the law).

WHAT IS THE SOUL?

As a descriptive tool Hegel's dialectic is not limited to history and economics. Most fields of endeavor manifest from time to time ideological trends that swing from one extreme (thesis) to another (antithesis). In medicine, for example, preventive tonsillectomy has been vehemently accepted at certain times ("yank 'em") and equally vehemently rejected at others ("forget 'em"). Theology is not immune from such trends, and the issue as to the nature of the soul is a good example demonstrating this.

The traditional, "orthodox" theology of the church, both Roman Catholic and Protestant, has maintained a trichotomistic (body, soul, spirit) or dichotomistic/dualistic (body, soul) view of man. In this conception, which has had definite historical alignments with "faculty psychology," [4] the soul has generally been regarded as the separable and immortal part of man, as contrasted with his mortal body.

Protestant liberalism of the early 20th century, which flowered on the soil of 19th century philosophical idealism, likewise stressed man's "immortal soul" (but for humanistic, rather than for strictly theological, reasons). Thus in the Neo-Orthodox reaction of liberalism (beginning in the 1920's), a powerful reaction to this entire mode of thinking entered the picture. In an effort to oppose the anthropocentrism of the liberals, and influenced by the salutary psychosomatic trend in the science and medicine of the time, Neo-Orthodox theologians and their compatriots in biblical studies (the so-called "biblical theology movement") argued for a totally monistic view of man. Undoubtedly the most influential product of this thinking in German has been the articles dealing with ψυχή, σῶμα, πνεῦμα, σάρξ, καρδία, etc. in Kittel's *Theologisches Wörterbuch zum Neuen Testament,* and in English the slim volume, *The Body,* by Bishop John A. T. Robinson (subsequently famous—or infamous—for his *Honest to God*). Here an attempt was made, conjointly with the emphasis in the biblical research of those decades, to distinguish as sharply as possible "Greek thinking" (supposedly foreign to the true biblical message) from genuine "Hebrew thought." One result was the rejection as a Greek import into Christian theology the entire concept of a separable, immortal soul. Thus Robinson categorically regarded the antithesis of body and soul as "foreign to the Hebrew," described the "Greek" dualistic position as the "angel in a slot machine," and asserted: "Man does not

---

[4] See Gardner Murphy, *Historical Introduction to Modern Psychology* (rev. ed.; New York: Harcourt, Brace, 1949), *passim.* This work is of particular interest because of Murphy's stature in the field of parapsychology (cf. his *Challenge of Psychical Research* [New York: Harper, 1961]).

have a body, he *is* a body. . . . The soul does not survive a man—it simply goes out, draining away with the blood." [5] In this view, the terms "body" and "soul" (as, indeed, such other expressions of biblical anthropology as "flesh," "spirit," "heart," and "will") do not designate separate ontological entities: they rather speak of the same "psycho-physical unity" from different angles. In recent years, this same position has been accepted and promoted by theological existentialists [6] and by a number of "new shape" Roman Catholic biblical scholars. [7]

Much can be said for this "holistic" understanding of man. The textual support for it in Scripture is powerful, and it has received qualified acceptance among conservative theologians. [8] The term "soul" both in the Old Testament (נֶפֶשׁ) and in the New (ψυχή) frequently designates simply an entity that breathes and therefore has life; both men and animals are so described. [9] Occasionally, "soul" is applied in a simple enumeration of persons, obviously without any attempt to delineate a separable aspect of man. [10] The vital biblical theme of the resurrection of the body argues in the strongest terms, over against the σῶμα-σῆμα motif in Eastern thought and Greek mysticism, that man's restoration in Christ must be a total, psychosomatic renewal. Liberalism deserved to be severely criticized for maintaining that man, because of his alleged native virtue, possesses a

---

[5] Robinson, *The Body: A Study in Pauline Theology* ("Studies in Biblical Theology," No. 5; London: SCM Press, 1952), p. 14.

[6] See Rudolf Bultmann, *Theology of the New Testament*, trans. Kendrick Grobel, I (London: SCM Press, 1951), 190–259.

[7] See, for example, Claude Tresmontant, *Essai sur la pensée hébraïque* (Paris: Éditions du Cerf, 1953), pp. 87–143. Tresmontant, significantly, has published an appreciation of the thought of Teilhard de Chardin.

[8] That this is no exaggeration may be seen by comparing the editorial notes at Gen. 1:26 and I Thess. 5:23—and even the index references to them in the editions of 1917 and 1967 (1st edition: "Man, tripartite nature of"; 2d ed.: "Man, nature").

[9] Gen. 2:7, 1:20 ff. (cf. Rom. 13:1 and Rev. 16:3); 9:12 ff.; Ezek. 47:9; Prov. 12:10 (cf. Gen. 44:30).

[10] Acts 2:41; 7:14.

natural immortality; Scripture makes the whole man totally
dependent on God not only for his present but also for his
future life. And the excuses offered by dualism for depre-
ciating the body (medieval monasticism and clerical celibacy) and avoiding dynamic involvement in the physical
secular world (blue-law fundamentalism) warranted the
most rigorous theological opposition.

Yet the "monists" must themselves be faulted for ex-
tremism. In their eagerness to make a legitimate point, they
committed the all-too-common human error of misusing and
ignoring evidence on the other side. James Barr, in his
epochal and badly needed critique of the methods of the "biblical theology movement," has shown that both the contrib-
utors to Kittle's *Wörterbuch* and Robinson's *The Body*
sadly misuse philological data in an effort to build a case for
the "Hebrew theological mentality." Barr rightly slaps
Robinson's attempt to obliterate distinctions between such
New Testament terms as σῶμα and σάρξ (so as to achieve
more "psycho-physical unity")—and the same judgment
could equally apply to σῶμα and ψυχή: "No one supposes that
the two words are completely synonymous in Paul." [11] For
Barr, Robinson manifests "a total neglect of linguistic semantics." [12] This point is well taken, for though there is
much scriptural evidence in behalf of the holistic view,
there are, at the same time, not only passages in which a
"faculty" approach is taken to man's nature,[13] but—even
more important—passages clearly showing that the soul can
be separated from the body and that it is capable of existence after the body's dissolution.[14] In Scripture all life
(whether here or hereafter) depends squarely on the God

---

[11] James Barr, *The Semantics of Biblical Language* (London:
Oxford University Press, 1961), p. 37.
[12] *Ibid.*, p. 35.
[13] Deut. 4:29; 26:16; I Kings 8:48; II Kings 23:25; Micah 7:1;
Mt. 16:26; 22:37 (cf. Deut. 6:5); Acts 4:32; Heb. 4:12.
[14] Mt. 10:28; Rev. 6:9; 20:4.

who creates and redeems it; [15] but an unqualified monism and a denial of life in the intermediate state between physical death and the general resurrection lose biblical warrant. It is highly significant in this connection that the force of total biblical teaching has led the world's foremost specialist on Luther's pneumatology to affirm a "dichotomisch (zweistufig)" theological anthropology.[16] The biblical scholar—or the lay Christian, for that matter—must take into account *all* scripture data in arriving at biblical teaching; as a faithful inductivist, he must not make his theories a procrustean bed into which some data are forced and from which others are selectively excluded.

But how can the "holistic" and the "dualistic" views be reconciled? If man is a body-soul unity, how can he continue to exist after the dissolution of his body? The best answer seems to be that during the intermediate state between death and the general resurrection, some kind of "clothing" is given to the soul, whose "nakedness" is an abnormal condition.[17] This "clothing" or "tabernacle" could

[15] Léon-Dufour makes the vital point, on the basis of James 1:21 and I Pet. 1:8–9, that the "souls under the altar" (Rev. 6:9; 20:4) are there only by "un appel à la résurrection, oeuvre de l'Esprit de vie, non d'une force immanente. Dans l'âme Dieu a déposé une semence d'éternité qui germera en son temps" (Xavier Léon-Dufour [ed.], "Ame," *Vocabulaire de Théologie Biblique* [Paris: Editions du Cerf, 1964], 29). Léon-Dufour, a French Jesuit, is, like Claude Tresmontant (see above, our note 7), a representative of the post-Vatican II "new shape" Roman Catholic theology, with both its positive and its negative characteristics (see my forthcoming book, *Ecumenicity, Evangelicals and Rome* [Grand Rapids, Michigan: Zondervan, 1969]).

[16] Regin Prenter, "Anthropologie. IV. Dogmatisch," *Die Religion in Geschichte und Gegenwart,* I (3. Aufl.; Tübingen, 1957), 420–24. Prenter's work on Luther, *Spiritus Creator,* contains detailed discussions of biblical anthropology.

[17] II Cor. 5:1–10; Rev. 6:9–11. This point has been well developed by Oscar Cullmann in his influential book, *Immortalité de l'âme ou Résurrection des morts?* (Neuchâtel & Paris: Delachaux & Niestlé, 1956; translated in *Immortality and Resurrection,* ed. Krister Stendahl [New York: Macmillan, 1965], pp. 9–53). It is too bad that Cullmann made such an invidious comparison between "immortality" and "resurrection" in his work; much of the criticism his book received has been due to unfortunate semantic overtones for which he was himself unwittingly responsible.

with some legitimacy be called a body (if we mean by "body" no more than a "soul covering"), for the New Testament makes clear that in God's creative activity there are many kinds of bodies, terrestrial and celestial.[18] On the other hand, it is definitely not the physical body of earthly life, since this has decayed; in this sense man's soul is most certainly separable from his body and can function in dualistic isolation from it. Assuredly this is not "normal": it is a temporary state, mitigated by temporary "clothing," and ending at the time of the general resurrection. But it cannot be ignored.

THE FETUS AND PERSONHOOD

Our examination of the biblical concept of the soul brought us to the conclusion that it is intimately, though not absolutely, connected with the life of the physical body. In general we may regard "soul" as a theological term for the "person"—who, though he exists without his earthly body after physical death, is "clothed" temporarily even in that condition. Evidently, then, to conceive of the "person" apart from any and every "body" is not a biblical mode of thought. So considerable is the importance of the earthly body that one thinks naturally of the intermediate "tabernacle" as having a close enough relation with it to maintain continuity of the total person.

The intimate connection of soul and body in scripture establishes a predisposition against the idea of a divine "superadding" of the soul to an already existent body, but such a possibility cannot be excluded *a priori*, since, as we have seen, the soul and the physical body must be considered ontologically distinct. The question of a possible superaddition of the soul to the fetus requires a brief glance at

---

[18] I Cor. 15:35–44.

the venerable conflict between the *creationists* and the *traducianists*.[19]

"Creationism," or (better) "concreationism," is a theological position held by Pelagius, Peter Lombard, St. Thomas, the Roman Catholic ordinary magisterium (though that Church has never given the position solemn definition), and by most Calvinists. This view affirms that God creates souls *ex nihilo* and supplies them to developing individuals at conception or during the intrauterine period.

Dissent has existed in the creationist camp in regard to the time when God supplies the soul to the developing person: Does this occur at the moment of conception or at a later point? Though St. Thomas, as we have noted, held to the latter viewpoint, the pressure of modern embryological knowledge has pushed creationist theologians more and more to the view that the soul is supplied by God when conception itself occurs. When sperm and ovum unite and the two pronuclei fuse, a process commences, governed by the DNA molecular pattern, that fixes the new individual's characteristics—and this occurs prior to the first division of the zygote. The following argument by the director of research at France's Centre National de Recherche Scientifique is typical of the judgments which have influenced creationists to focus their attention on the moment of conception:

> Cette [première] cullule est déjà le premier embryon d'un vivant autonome avec son patrimoine héréditaire bien à lui, tant et si bien que si l'on connaissait le spermatozoïde qui est venu et les chromosomes qui se sont rencontrés, on pourrait déjà prévoir le tempérament de cet enfant, la couleur future de ses cheveux et les maladies auxquelles il sera sujet. Dans la mère

---

[19] On the issue, see especially R. Lacroix, *L'origine de l'âme humaine* (Québec, 1945); R. Boigelot, *L'homme et l'univers* (Bruxelles, 1946); C. Fabro, *L'anima* (Roma, 1955; with valuable bibliography); and P. Overhage & Karl Rahner, *Das Problem der Hominisation* (Freiburg i.Br., 1961).

où il va croître et grandir, il prendra, non pas tout ce que celle-ci lui apportera, mais ce qui lui sera nécessaire: il réalisera son patrimoine héréditaire. En lui vient d'apparaître le dynamisme profond et l'orientation précise de la vie: un nouvel être est conçu. (. . .) Malgré sa fragilité et ses immenses besoins, un être autonome et bien vivant, dont on peut désormais briser mais non pas modifier le destin biologique, entre dans l'existence. (. . .) Il est assez surprenant de voir certains médecins parler ici de vie potentielle comme si l'ovule fécondé commençait sa vie réelle lorsqu'il s'est fixé sur l'utérus. La biologie moderne ne nie pas l'importance de la nidation, mais elle y voit seulement une condition, évidemment indispensable, pour le développement de l'embryon et la continuation d'une vie qui existe déjà.[20]

But does not the phenomenon of identical twins demand a later point for the introduction of the soul? Identical twins result—just as does the ordinary single individual—from the fertilization of one ovum by one spermatozoid; but splitting brings about *two* developing embryos with identical hereditary patterns.[21] Must not the soul therefore enter the picture at the point when the two individuals become truly distinct? And what can be done with the analogous conundrum posed by Ettinger?

Experiment 4. Applying biochemical or microsurgical techniques to a newly fertilized human ovum, we force it to divide and separate, thereby producing identical twins where the undisturbed cell would have developed as a single individual. (Similar experiments have been performed with animals.)

An ordinary individual should probably be said to originate at the "moment" of conception. At any rate, there does not seem to be any other suitable time—certainly not the time of birth, because a Caesarean operation would have produced a living individual as

---

[20] Jules Carles, *La fécondation* (5. éd.; Paris: Presses Universitaires de France, 1967), pp. 81–82.

[21] *Ibid.*, pp. 86–90. See also *L'hérédité humaine* by Jean Rostand of the Académie Française (7 éd.; Paris: Presses Universitaires de France, 1966), pp. 9–11.

well; and choice of any other stage of development of the foetus would be quite arbitrary.

Our brief, coarse, physical interference has resulted in two lives, two individuals, where before there was one. In a sense, we have created one life. Or perhaps we have destroyed one life, and created two, since neither individual is quite the same as the original one would have been.[22]

A minority of Roman Catholic theologians—the most persuasive being Hudeczek—have seen such arguments as definitive support for St. Thomas' mediate animation theory. But a close examination of Hudeczek's case reveals that it stands or falls on the scholastic principle that the soul, as a "rational" or "spiritual" entity, must be indivisible (*simplex*).[23] Our study of the biblical data on the soul certainly established no such *a priori* principle, and on what other ground could such a principle be asserted definitively? Perhaps the soul is as divisible as is the fertilized egg! If the resultant identical twins show remarkable affinities in appearance, temperament, habits, etc., and if (as we have seen) scripture sets forth an intimate soul-body relationship, perhaps one can as legitimately speak of "twin souls" as of twin bodies!

But as we have found ourselves imperceptibly moving back toward the motif of psycho-physical unity, we have in fact been approaching the domain of the theological traducianists. "Materialistic" traducianism holds either that parents generate from inanimate matter not only the body but also the soul of the child, or that the soul is actually contained in the sperm and conveyed by organic generation. More attractive by far has been "spiritual" traducianism,

---

[22] Robert C. W. Ettinger, *The Prospect of Immortality* (Garden City, New York: Doubleday, 1964), p. 132. I have discussed the central thesis of Ettinger's book in my article, "Cryonics and Orthodoxy," *Christianity Today*, XII (May 10, 1968), 816.

[23] M. Hudeczek, "De tempore animationis foetus humani secundum Embryologiam hodiernam," *Angelicum* (Roma), XXIX (1952), 162–81 (especially p. 175).

often called "generationism," which asserts that the soul of
the child derives from the souls of the parents. Augustine,
in opposing the Pelagians and in his insistence on man's
total depravity, held to generationism,[24] as did Luther and
most theologians influenced by him. The Roman Church,
while not solemnly defining creationism (as we noted), has
seen fit through its ordinary magisterium to condemn both
forms of traducianism.[25]

The contemporary orthodox Protestant systematician
Mueller is quite right to use the traducianist-creationist
dispute as an example of an "open question"—a question
"on which the Word of God is silent." [26] In a sense it is a
pseudo-problem: a special case of the more general question
as to whether the appearance of a new human individual is
an act of direct or mediate creation by God. But the conflict
is very instructive from the point of view of the abortion
question, for we see how, whether more obviously as in
traducianism or less obviously in creationism, the point of
origin of the individual is pushed backwards in time. For
the traducianist, it would be absurd to regard the individual
as commencing later than conception, for even his soul derives from his parents. For most creationists, the moment
of conception is the point when the soul is bestowed. Even
those theologians who follow Aquinas in his mediate animation theory now argue from the case of identical twins,
analysis of which leads directly to the original fertilized
egg as supplying what will become the total and identical
hereditary constellation of genes and chromosomes for both
individuals. Moreover, the Roman Church has long condemned the viewpoint that if one grants that the soul is

---

24 Augustine, *Epist.*, 166.8.25–26; 190.4.14–15.
25 See P. B. T. Bilaniuk, "Creationism," *New Catholic Encyclopedia*, IV (New York, 1967), 428–29; "Traducianism," *ibid.*, XIV,
230.

26 J. Theodore Mueller, *Christian Dogmatics* (St. Louis, Missouri:
Concordia, 1934), p. 58.

supplied subsequent to conception, abortion would not be murder. Pope Innocent XI, in a decree of 2 March 1679, condemned this position;[27] the encyclical *Casti connubii* (1930) reinforced the Church's unqualified opposition to abortion; and very recently (3 October 1964), Paul VI, in reviewing the doctrine for a group from the New England Obstetrical and Gynecological Society,[28] repeated Pius XII's condemnation of abortion (26 November 1951).[29]

But cannot the force of the embryological evidence be reduced simply by recourse to contemporary philosophical attempts at defining "personhood" functionally? Granted that from the moment of conception everything has been supplied to produce an individual; can it really be said to *be* an individual prior to, say, the onset of its brain functions, or its viability, or its manifestation of rational activity—in short, prior to its genuine *functioning* as a human being? Should we not, with Van Peursen, choose as our starting-point "the whole man in his ordinary, day-to-day conduct, attitudes and decisions. These things are not accretions to the human being who exists in himself *qua* substance (body plus soul), but they are the indispensable essence or core of man, without which he would not be man at all"?[30] If this is the case, abortion could hardly be murder, for the fetus lacks this "indispensable essence or core of man." Glanville Williams suggests brain-functioning as the *point de départ*:

---

[27] Condemned was the following proposition: "Videtur probabile omnem foetum (quamdiu in utero est) carere anima rationali et tunc primum incipere eamdem habere, cum paritur: ac consequenter dicendum erit, in nullo abortu homicidium committi" (Denzinger, *Enchiridion*, § 1052).

[28] *Pope Speaks*, X (1964), 1.

[29] *Discorsi e radio messagi di Sua Santità Pio XII*, 13.415. By the papal bull *Apostolicae sedis* (12 October 1869), the canon law penalty of excommunication was levied against those persons responsible for procuring abortions of nonviable fetuses.

[30] C. A. Van Peursen, *Body, Soul, Spirit: A Survey of the Body-Mind Problem*, trans. from the Dutch by H. H. Hoskins (London: Oxford University Press, 1966), p. 181 (cf. pp. 188, 193–94).

The soul, after all, is frequently associated with the mind, and until the brain is formed there can be no mind. By placing electrodes on the maternal abdomen over the foetal head, electric potentials ("brain waves") are discernible in the seventh month, i.e., shortly before the time of viability. If one were to compromise by taking, say, the beginning of the seventh month as the beginning of legal protection for the foetus, it would practically eliminate the present social problem of abortion.[31]

The answer to this is two-fold. First, even from a totally secular viewpoint, the "functionalist" definition of man will not wash. What functions will be regarded as *truly* human —as *sine quibus non* for genuine humanity? Movement? (But what about total paralysis?) Intelligence? (But what degree of it?) Personhood escapes all such definitional attempts, and the reason appears to be that personality is a transcendent affair: the subjective "I" can never be totally objectified without destroying it.[32] If this is true, then one can hardly look for the origin-point of personhood anywhere other than at the moment when all potentialities necessary for its functioning enter the picture: namely, at conception. To argue otherwise is to become caught inextricably in a maze which would deny true humanity to those who, through organic defect, are incapable of carrying out certain rational activities (e.g., some mental cases). The efforts of the Third Reich "eugenically" to eliminate such "non-humans" should give us no little pause here. Can we say that when a human being on the operating table undergoes suspension of activity he ceases to be human? As long as the native potentiality to function as a human being

---

[31] Glanville Williams, *The Sanctity of Life and the Criminal Law* (London: Faber & Faber, 1958), p. 210.

[32] See my treatment of the "irreducible I" in "The Theologian's Craft: A Discussion of Theory Formation and Theory Testing in Theology," *American Scientific Affiliation Journal*, XVIII (September, 1966), 74.

exists, one must be treated as human and must have his human rights protected.[33] Though the new-born child does little at the time to justify its humanity (except to make an immediate pest of itself), its potentiality to exercise a range of human functions later rightly causes the law to regard its wanton destruction as murder in the full sense; and the same may be said by simple extension for the nonviable fetus.

Theologically, the argument is even stronger. Man is not man because of what he does or accomplishes. He is man because God made him. Though the little child engages in only a limited range of human activities, Jesus used him as the model for the Kingdom [34]—evidently because, as one of the "weak things of this world that confound the wise," he illustrates God's grace rather than human works-righteousness. Even the term βρέφος, "unborn child, embryo, infant," is employed in one of the parallel passages relating children to God's Kingdom.[35] The same expression appears in the statement that when Mary visited Elizabeth, the unborn John the Baptist "leaped for joy" in Elizabeth's womb and she was filled with the Holy Spirit.[36] Peter parallels the ideal Christian with a βρέφος,[37] and Paul takes satisfaction that from Timothy's infancy (ἀπὸ βρέφους) he had had contact with God's revelation.[38] Moreover, the Bible regards personal identity as beginning with conception, and one's involvement in the sinful human situation as commencing at that very point: "Behold, I [not "it"] was shapen in iniquity; and in sin did my mother conceive me [not "it"]." [39]

---

[33] The legal practice of "ascription of rights" well illustrates this point (see especially the writings of H. L. A. Hart): though the fetus cannot defend himself in court (any more than an infant can), society ascribes genuine legal rights to him and seeks to uphold them.

[34] Mt. 19:13–15; Mark 10:13–16.

[35] Luke 18:15.

[36] Luke 1:41, 44.

[37] I Pet. 2:2.

[38] II Tim. 3:15.

[39] Ps. 51:5.

For the biblical writers, personhood in the most genuine sense begins no later than conception; subsequent human acts illustrate this personhood, they do not create it. Man *does* because he *is* (not the reverse) and he *is* because God brought about his psycho-physical existence in the miracle of conception.

ABORTION IN LIGHT OF THE CHRISTIAN ETHIC

We have now reached the point where ethical judgment can be made on the abortion question. Four considerations warrant the strongest possible emphasis.

1. Abortion is in fact homicide, for it terminates a genuine human life. God's revealed moral law in Holy Scripture, with its high view of the sanctity of life, is an absolute, and therefore to cut off human existence is always an evil, regardless of changing circumstances or "situations." [40]

2. Nonetheless, it must be clearly seen that Christians have no business "legislating morality" in such a way that their non-Christian neighbors are forced to adhere to laws which create impossible stresses for them. The divorce laws in some countries and in some states of the United States are of such severity that many non-Christians who never contracted their marriage on a proper foundation are forced to greater sin in attempting to circumvent the legislation against divorce. Abortion problems are often analogous: the individual has put himself or herself in a situation where abortion might conceivably be the lesser of evils. Still an evil, definitely, and the law of the land must unflinchingly say so; but the penalties could well reflect the ambiguity of the sinner's condition. As the law recognizes gradations of homicide, it should look with some under-

---

[40] The most effective presentation of this viewpoint in all its aspects is, in this writer's judgment, *Le respect de la vie* (Paris: Beauchesne, 1963), by the eminent French medical scientist Paul Chauchard. Cf. also Rousas J. Rushdoony, "Abortion," *The Encyclopedia of Christianity*, ed. Edwin H. Palmer, I (Wilmington, Delaware: National Foundation for Christian Education, 1964), 20–23.

standing on abortions where the lesser-of-evils principle unquestionably comes into play. Certainly there is some social difference between an abortion-homicide and the murder of a full member of society, whose life intermeshes with the lives of many others.[41] We are not here advocating legal laxity, but we are underscoring a fact often forgotten by Christians, namely that the purpose of a human court of law is not identical with that of the Great Assize.

3. Christians must not, however, tolerate the fallacious argument that the establishment of legal abortion would *per se* constitute a lesser of evils by allegedly eliminating illegal abortion. A recent and careful study of ten years of legal abortion practice in Sweden reached the conclusion the "the frequency of illegal abortion has if anything increased," [42] and recommended that "a more restrictive attitude should be adopted in the evaluation of the grounds for legal abortion." [43] The causes of legal abortion stem from much deeper considerations than can be touched through legalizing such operations. As a Planned Parenthood Federation conference on the subject recommended, sensing the underlying moral problems involved: "There

---

[41] The following judgment is admittedly overdrawn, but is there not some truth in it? "In comparison with other cases of murder, a minimum of harm is done by it [abortion]. . . . The victim's mind is not sufficiently developed to enable it to suffer from the contemplation of approaching suffering or death. It is incapable of feeling fear or terror. Nor is its consciousness sufficiently developed to enable it to suffer pain in appreciable degree. Its loss leaves no gap in any family circle, deprives no children of their breadwinner or their mother, no human being of a friend, helper or companion. The crime diffuses no sense of insecurity. No one feels a whit less safe because the crime has been committed. It is a racial crime, purely and solely. Its ill effect is not on society as it is, but in striking at the provision of future citizens, to take the place of those who are growing old; and by whose loss in the course of nature, the community must dwindle and die out, unless it is replenished by the birth and upbringing of children" (Charles Mercier, *Crime and Insanity* [London, 1911], pp. 212–13).

[42] Per Arén, *On Legal Abortion in Sweden: Tentative Evaluation of Justification of Frequency during Last Decade* ("Acta Obstetricia et Gynecologica Scandinavica," Vol. XXXVII, Supp. 1; Lund, 1958), p. 62.

[43] *Ibid.*, p. 70.

should be encouragement . . . of higher standards of sexual conduct and of a greater sense of responsibility toward pregnancy." [44]

4. The lesser-of-evils principle referred to above can (and frequently does) apply to Christian ethical decisions in abortion cases. The Christian, no less than the non-Christian, lives in an ambiguous and sinful world, where few decisions can be regarded as unqualifiedly good—untainted by evil consequences. Thus the Christian physician may be called on to sacrifice the fetus for the mother, or the mother for the fetus. Decisions in cases like this will be agonizing, but there is no *a priori* way of knowing what to do: given the particular medical problem, the Christian doctor will endeavor with all his skill to cheat the grim reaper to the maximum and bring the greatest good possible out of the given ambiguity.[45] And the Protestant, unlike his Roman Catholic confrère, will not casuistically endeavor to "justify" himself through his decisions. Though in particular instances the Protestant may well arrive at the very same action as his Catholic counterpart, he will find his decisions —in which lesser evils still remain evils—driving him continually to the Cross for forgiveness.[46] "Abortion" will

---

[44] Mary S. Calderone (ed.), *Abortion in the United States* (New York: Hoeber-Harper, 1958), p. 183.

[45] It is perhaps well to note that even for Protestant Christians (such as this writer) who are members of communions where infant baptism holds a place of great theological importance, the baptism issue does not automatically place the unborn child's welfare above the mother's. No possible interpretation of Scripture can yield the belief that children who die without baptism are ipso facto consigned to hell or to a "limbo" state, and even the most "orthodox" of Lutheran theologians (e.g., Martin Chemnitz) made this perfectly clear; the destiny of such a child, though beyond human ken (as is, note well, the specific destiny of every individual, old or young—Mt. 25:31–46), rests in the hands of the Father of all mercies. As Augustine and Luther rightly maintained: *Contemptus sacramenti damnat, non privatio.* Thus the Christian physician must not decide a question of physical life or death on the basis of the unknown quantity of a given individual's ultimate personal salvation. (Cf. Mueller, *op. cit.* [in note 26 above], pp. 499–500.)

[46] A point well made by George Forell in his writings on the Protestant social and individual ethic.

suggest to him first and foremost the total human drama as well as his own life: an "arrested development" due to neglect of God's creative love—yet wondrously redeemable through the sacrifice of Christ for us all.

ADDENDUM

The reader of the preceding paper will have observed that its author has become convinced of the truly human character of the fetus, and that he has reached this conclusion on the basis both of medical and of theological considerations. The essayist therefore looks with particular severity on the practice of abortion, allowing it only in instances where abortion unquestionably constitutes the lesser of evils. This is in substance the viewpoint held by medical scientists such as Dr. M. O. Vincent (whose papers on the subject appear in the present volume) and theologians such as Helmut Thielecke:

> The fetus has its own autonomous life, which, despite all its reciprocal relationship to the maternal organism, is more than a mere part of this organism and possesses a certain independence. . . . These elementary biological facts should be sufficient to establish its status as a human being. . . . This makes it clear that here it is not a question—as it is in the case of contraception—whether a proffered gift can be responsibly accepted, but rather whether an already bestowed gift can be spurned, whether one dares to brush aside the arm of God after this arm has already been outstretched. Therefore here [in abortion] the order of creation is infringed upon in a way that is completely different from that of the case of contraception. (Thielecke, *The Ethics of Sex,* trans. Doberstein [New York: Harper, 1964], pp. 227–28.)

It would be less than fair to imply, however, that this "strong view" was universally represented by participants at the Symposium on the Control of Human Reproduction. Some medical men (e.g., Drs. R. L. Willows and C. T. Reilly) and theologians (e.g., Drs. Bruce Waltke and Kenneth

Kantzer) have definite reservations as to the genuine humanity of the fetus and as to its possession of a human soul from the moment of conception. I shall not speak further in regard to the medical evidence bearing on this point, for I have already given a summary statement of what would appear to be the definitive considerations bearing on the question: the fact that the DNA molecular pattern, established at conception, is a package containing the entire hereditary makeup of the individual—the sum total of his characteristics as an independent individual (see above, the quotation from Jules Carles, corresponding to note 20). But an additional word is necessary in respect to a theological, or rather exegetical, argument introduced by Professor Waltke which strongly influenced the thinking of a number of Symposium participants (cf. the news report on the Symposium which appeared in *Christianity Today*, September 27, 1968, pp. 33–34).

This argument, contained in Dr. Waltke's paper (Chapter 1), regards Exod. 21:22–25 as definitive biblical proof that "in contrast to the mother, the fetus is not reckoned as a soul [*nephesh*]." But, wholly apart from specific exegetical considerations, one might raise the general hermeneutic question as to whether a statement of penalty in the legislation God gave to ancient Israel ought to establish the context of interpretation for the total biblical attitude to the value of the unborn child (including not only specific and non-phenomenological Old Testament assertions such as Ps. 51:5, but the general New Testament valuation of the βρέφος, as illustrated especially in Luke 1:41, 44). Should a passage such as Exod. 21 properly outweigh the analogy of the Incarnation itself, in which God became man at the moment when "conception by the Holy Ghost" occurred—not at a later time as the universally condemned and heretical adoptionists alleged? Do we not have in the very nature of Dr. Waltke's argument a common hermeneutical blunder:

the erroneous perspective that does not properly distinguish
Law from Gospel and that tends to view the New Testament in light of the Old, instead of the Old Covenant as
comprehensible only in terms of the New?

Moreover, even on strictly exegetical grounds, Exod. 21:
22–25 does not say what Dr. Waltke thinks it does. He follows the interpretation of David Mace [47] over against virtually all serious exegetes, classical and modern, in claiming
that the passage distinguishes between a pregnant mother
(whose life has to be compensated for by another life if
killed) and her fetus (unworthy of such compensation).
But Keil and Delitzsch,[48] after explaining that the passage
demands *exactly* the same penalty for injuring the mother
or the child ("but if injury occur [to the mother or the
child], thou shalt give soul for soul, eye for eye, . . . wound
for wound"), comment in a lengthy note as to how the Septu-
agint translation of the Hebrew text has misled vernacular
translators (and a few commentators like the Hellenizing
Jew Philo) to adopt the view that

> "the fruit, the premature birth of which was caused by
> the blow, if not yet developed into a human form, was
> not to be regarded as in any sense a human being, so
> that the giver of the blow was only required to pay a
> pecuniary compensation." [49]
> "But," continue Keil and Delitzsch, "the arbitrary
> character of this explanation is apparent at once; for
> יֶלֶד only denotes a child, as a fully developed human
> being, and not the fruit of the womb before it has
> assumed a human form. . . . The omission of לֹא,
> also, apparently renders it impracticable to refer the
> words to injury done to the woman alone." [50]

The full meaning of the passage is, then: "If men strove

[47] David Mace, *Hebrew Marriage*, note 6, p. 11.
[48] C. F. Keil and Franz Delitzsch, *Biblical Commentary on the Old
Testament: The Pentateuch*, trans. James Martin, II (small reprint
ed; Grand Rapids, Michigan: Eerdmans, [n.d.]), 134–35.
[49] Keil and Delitzsch, *op. cit.*
[50] *Ibid.*

and thrust against a woman with child, who had come near or between them for the purpose of making peace, so that her children come out (come into the world), and no injury was done either to the woman or the child that was born, a pecuniary compensation was to be paid. . . . A fine is imposed, because even if no injury had been done to the woman and the fruit of her womb, such a blow might have endangered life." [51] But where injury occurred either to mother or unborn child (as we have noted), the *lex talionis* applied indiscriminately—to the genuinely human fetus as well as to his genuinely human parent.

This interpretation is presented not only by a classic Old Testament scholar such as the 19th century Protestant Delitzsch, but equally by such contemporary Jewish exegetes as Cassuto, whose *Commentary on the Book of Exodus* is a landmark. Here are the relevant portions of Cassuto's explanatory rendering:

> "When men strive together and they hurt unintentionally a woman with a child, and her children come forth but no mischief happens—that is, the woman and the children do not die—the one who hurt her shall surely be punished by a fine. But if any mischief happen, that is, if the woman dies or the children die, then you shall give life for life." [52]

To interpret the passage in any other way is to strain the text intolerably, and efforts at emendation (such as what S. R. Driver commended as Budde's "clever" suggestions) are neither necessary nor helpful. The original text places a value on fetal life equal to that accorded to adult life, and in doing so perfectly conjoins with the rest of Holy Writ.

---

[51] *Ibid.*

[52] Umberto Cassuto, *Commentary on The Book of Exodus* translated by Abrahams Jerusalem: Magnes Press, The Hebrew University, 1967, p. 275.

Chapter 5

THEOLOGICAL PRINCIPLES IN THE CONTROL OF HUMAN LIFE

SUMMARY

The author describes a Christian view of man. This concept is set against the somber background of multiple realities which seem to demand that man control both the quantity and the quality of his offspring. Eugenic schemes for achieving utopia are considered, ranging from Plato to science fiction.

Man is seen as a sovereign, creative being, created in God's image. When the dimension of dependence on God is denied or ignored, distortion, alienation and perversion inevitably result. Human schemes for controlling human reproduction founder on the ineradicability of human sinfulness and the necessity for giving final authority to men who are both sinful and mortal.

The Christian is both pessimistic about the possibility of solving the problem in history and optimistic in view of God's promise for eternity. Utopia is contrasted with the biblical picture of the Kingdom of God.

PHILLIP EDGCUMBE HUGHES, B.A., M.A., D.Litt., Ph.D.
*Professor Hughes is an Anglican clergyman. He was born
in Australia, educated in South Africa and England, and has
served in a number of academic and ecclesiastical posts.
His books include:* Theology of the English Reformers, But
for the Grace of God, *and* Christianity and the Problem of
Origins. *He holds degrees from the University of London,
the University of Cape Town, and the Australian College
of Theology.*

*Currently living in the U.S., Dr. Hughes served as Guest
Professor of New Testament at Columbia Theological Seminary in Georgia until 1968, when he was appointed Professor of Historical Theology and Chairman of the Department
of Theology at Conwell School of Theology in Philadelphia.*

THEOLOGICAL PRINCIPLES IN THE CONTROL OF HUMAN LIFE

by Philip Edgcumbe Hughes

INTRODUCTION: THE NATURE OF MAN

The theme of this paper raises at once the question concerning the propriety of the human control of human life, for the term "control" in the title intends the control *by man* of human life. Within this perspective, then, *man* is both the controller and the controlled. The consideration of this prospect in the light of *theological* principles declares the desire to place man in his ultimate and only true perspective, namely, as *man under* God, and indicates the importance of a right understanding of *the Christian doctrine of man*. Despite the assumptions of many today (and in the past), man is not and cannot be autonomous and an end in himself, for there are two frustrating and inescapable factors: his finitude and that final negation of his adequacy, his death. Death and the despair that accompanies it are, indeed, written over the whole of merely human history; and not only over the past but over the future as well. The desperate self-assertion of the existentialist is an extreme manifestation of the revolt of man against the futility of his finitude and his mortality. More subtle, but still illusory, is the form of anthropocentric philosophy which is man-centred rather than self-centred, in the sense that its hope is focussed on the eventual progress and perfectibility of mankind, of Man spelt with a capital M. The whole, it is chanted, is greater than the parts; the mystique of Man will somehow compensate for the paltriness of men. So all but a hundred years ago, on the occasion of the First Vatican Council (1870), the poet Swinburne composed his defiant Hymn of Man and propounded in superb measures the philosophy of human adequacy:

> But God, if a God there be, is the substance of men
> which is man.
> Our lives are as pulses or pores of his manifold body
> and breath;
> As waves of his sea on the shores where birth is the
> beacon of death.
> We men, the multiform features of man, whatsoever
> we be,
> Recreate him of whom we are creatures, and all we
> only are he.
> Not each man of all men is God, but God is the fruit
> of the whole;
> Indivisible spirit and blood, indiscernible body from
> soul.
> Not men's but man's is the glory of godhead . . .
> Men are the thoughts passing through it, the veins
> that fulfil it with blood,
> With spirit of sense to renew it as springs fulfilling
> a flood.
> Men are the heartbeats of man . . .
> Men perish, but man shall endure; lives die, but the
> life is not dead.

This same philosophy of man motivates the idealism of many of the advocates of the eugenic control of human life. The framework of their thinking is that of progressive

evolutionism. Man, as they conceive him, is a merely biological phenomenon. The Christian thinker, however, cannot leave out of account the important fact that in the
structure of man theological as well as biological principles
are involved and closely interrelated—that biology and theology, in fact, are not disparate fields. This is clearly indicated in the biblical doctrine of the creation of man. Three
principles in particular demand emphasis in this connection.

Man is God's creature

It should be unnecessary to add that this doctrine inevitably involves the primacy of God, in being and in power.
The supremacy of God's being and power is the basis and
background of man's existence. The being and power of
man are dependent on and derivative from God. This means
that man cannot have a proper understanding of himself
and his world if he ignores the Creator-creature relationship which is fundamental to his being. For man to place
himself instead of God at the centre of reference can only
lead to a complete distortion of perspective. Indeed, as St.
Paul says, suppression of the truth about God is at the root
of all man's problems. Nothing shows the illogical nature of
sin more starkly than the denial of the Creator who is the
sole source of man's being and man's wisdom (Rom. 1:18).
A return to theology, the knowledge and acknowledgment
of God, is essential if man is to return to his true self and
to recover the fulness of his humanity.

Man is created in the image of God

This image in which man is created is marred by man's
rebellion against God, by his refusal to honour God as God
(Gen. 1:27; 3:17–19; Rom. 1.21) ; but it is restored in Christ
Jesus, the incarnate Son and Redeemer of man, who Himself is the the image of the invisible God (Col. 1:15; 2 Cor.
4:4), and into whose image the Christian believer is being

transformed (2 Cor. 3:18). In Christ, the God who creates
re-creates; in Him, the divine voice is heard again creative-
ly, renewing the creature and restoring all the purposes of
creation. That is why St. Paul affirms that "the same God
who said [that is, at creation], 'Out of darkness let light
shine', has caused his light to shine within us, to give the
light of revelation—the revelation of the glory of God in the
face of Jesus Christ" (2 Cor. 4:6, NEB).[1]

This doctrine of man's creation in the image of God
means that man cannot possibly escape from his inner
knowledge and awareness of God because it is part of his
very constitution as man. For man to deny or defy God,
then, is to do violence to himself in that those qualities
which set man apart from the rest of the created order are
implanted by God and reflect the glory of the divine character. Not that there is an analogy of being between God and
man, for the being of God is uncreated, eternal, and sovereign, whereas the being of man is created, finite, and dependent, and the two beings are not to be fused or confused.
The true glory of man resides in this divine imprint at the
very heart of his being. Wilful disavowal of this image con-
ducts man not to richer humanity but to subhumanity and
inhumanity.

In what, then, does the image of God in man consist? The
following are some important aspects of its manifestation
which are at the same time relevant to the theme of this
paper.

Personality

Man is a *personal* being, and his personality is a reflection of the personal character of the divine nature. It
is, indeed, possible to use the term "man" generically to

---

1 "The man who is an image of Christ is an image in the specific
sense which is the true and original sense for those familiar with the
Bible, namely, the sense of Gen. 1:27", Gerhard Kittel, *Theological
Dictionary of the New Testament*, Vol. II, Grand Rapids, 1964, p. 396.

signify the totality of men, that is, mankind. Mankind, however, is compounded of *men*. The essential personality of
man consists not in the mass but in the individual. To treat
man as a transient nameless cypher, as a mere component
of the mass, is to depersonalize him. Personality is the potential of freedom, freedom to be oneself, freedom to emerge
rather than be merged and dehumanized in the faceless mob.
But personality is also the potential of responsibility, the
responsibility to respect the persons of others, and above
all to honour the Person of Him who is the source of all
personality. Freedom is the ability to act responsibly, and
responsibility is freedom to have concern for others. To
rob a man of freedom is to rob him of responsibility, and
vice versa.

The personality of man mirrors the personality of God;
for the God of the Bible is not some nebulous concept of
theology or some remote world force, but the personal God:
Creator, Redeemer, Judge, who reveals Himself in Jesus
Christ and indwells as Holy Spirit, and who is both free
and concerned. The depersonalization of man is symptom-
atic of rebellion against the personal God and a mutinous
attempt to delete the image of this personal God in man.

Rationality

The personality of man finds expression in this and in all
the aspects that follow. Man could not be rational in an irrational world. The world is a cosmos, not a chaos; a universe, not a jumble. Its structure bears the impress of the
rationality of its Maker. It is patterned in accordance with
the logic of the Supreme Mind. Were it not so, logical
thought and communication would be impossible; rational
behaviour would be inconceivable; for man himself would
belong to the prevailing chaos, and each man would be an
irrational non-person. But the world is an ordered whole,
and man is a part of the order of things. The philosopher

seeks for the key to the meaning of the whole because he knows instinctively that there is a harmony which unites all the parts into a grand unity. The scientist pursues facts wherever they may lead him because he knows instinctively that all facts are interrelated and that one fact must lead on to another—that there is no such thing as a bare or isolated fact. Indeed, it is the logical interrelatedness of things which makes rational thought and speech and behaviour and the pursuit of scientific knowledge possible. Man's instinctive recognition of this truth is a manifestation of the image of God in which he is constituted. The philosopher or scientist who denies the existence of the divine Creator is undermining the only foundation on which he can consistently construct the system of his thought.

Morality

Morality, too, is an essential element of the human personality. Man's sense of justice and fair play, his awareness of the distinction between right and wrong, his conscience; all this is part of his structure as a person and a reflection of the divine image. It is a part also of the moral fabric of the whole created order which in turn is an expression of the absolute morality, holiness, and justice of the Creator. Morality, properly understood, is reverence for God and concern for others: the desire to honour God with one's whole being and to be just in one's dealings with men. It is not bondage but freedom: freedom to enjoy the dignity of living as a responsible being.

Morality is also submission to the law of God. The positive fulfilment of the law is nothing other than the manifestation of love (Rom. 13:8–10). That is why the law in its totality may be summarized in the two injunctions, "Love God and love your fellow man" (Mark 12:30f.). The negative prohibitions of the law are but the obverse side of this same coin, for to go after false gods and to murder, steal, commit adultery, and cheat display the contrary of love. Law and love, then, are not antithetical to each other; and the expression of love in morality is essential if human society is to be livable. The increasing advocacy in our day of amorality and immorality is a symptom of man's alienation from God and his revolt against the divine image stamped on his being. It is a dehumanizing assault on the dignity of the person and can lead only to the disruption of society.

Sovereignty

Man is sovereign among creatures. His sovereignty, however, is not absolute but derived. He is sovereign *under God*, the supreme Sovereign of all. Hence the divine mandate to man to "subdue" the earth and "have dominion" over the rest of creation (Gen. 1:28). This kingly function of man is seen in the organization and government of society which we call civilization, in the taming and domestication of animals for uses advantageous to man, in the cultivation of the soil, in the moulding and transformation of materials into utensils and tools and machines, in the harnessing of the elemental forces and energies of nature, and in the exploration and conquest of land, sea, air, and outer space. In this lordship of man the divine similitude is once again displayed. Indeed, the kingly potential of man seems almost boundless. His dominion over nature is advancing in spectacular fashion in our day. Yet this master of so much else fails to be master of his own self. Twentieth-century man is as much a slave to irrational impulses and passions as ever his ancestors were. Mankind is threatened by the abuse of power in the form of tyrannical domination of the few over the many in a manner unprecedented in history. The prospect of the virtual enslavement of the minds and bodies of millions is neither apocalyptic nor future; it is taking place now. The dominion of man is being replaced by the subjection of man, and this deprivation of dominion is an affront to the dignity of the person and a reprehensible diminishment of his humanity. Moreover, the perversion of man's sovereignty is exhibited by the misapplication of his conquest of the physical world in the production of fiendish armaments for the destruction of his fellow men, the employment of communications media for the propagation not of truth but of lies, and the prostitution of politics for the acquisition of despotic power.

Creativity

The image of God in man is seen in man's capacity to create. This, like all other human endowments, is not an absolute but a relative and finite capacity. Man's creativity is derived, and is limited to the fashioning of the materials which are given in the realm of God's created order. By the exercise of the creative faculty in music and literature, painting and sculpture, drama and architecture, and cultural activity in a great variety of manifestations the human race has been enriched through the centuries. The tragedy of man is apparent even here in that this ennobling faculty also is profaned and inverted. Preoccupation with lechery and excrement may be a projection of the shame of man in his fallenness and a defiant or desperate attempt to affirm the self-adequacy of the human spirit even when the meaning of things has been lost, but it is a terrible defilement of the divine image and an insult to the true nature of man. The creative faculty of man is used in its full propriety only when it is exercised to the glory of the Creator and the ennoblement of the human spirit.

Man is created male and female

The distinction between male and female, though not peculiar to man, may also be regarded as in some measure an aspect of the image of God in man—only by a more remote analogy, however, since it is not a distinction which belongs to the being of God. But to the extent that man was not created in solitude but with woman as his partner, and the two to be one, the analogy is justifiable. God, though One, is not alone in Himself; He is unity in plurality, three persons in one essence, Father, Son, and Holy Spirit coexisting in a Trinity of being. Because "it is not good that man should be alone" (Gen. 2:18) God created both male and female, husband and wife, who by sexual union become "one flesh" (Gen. 2:24). Sexuality, accordingly, points to the plurality and the unity of man—though in a manner of being quite other than that of God.

The ideal union of love and harmony between husband and wife, however, becomes something more than a relationship of two in one and one in two, for it involves procreation. Thus it leads to what may be called a human trinity, namely, father, mother, and child(ren), who together constitute the solidarity of the family. Though it does not pertain uniquely to man, this power of procreation is a wonderful facet of man's faculty of creativity. Yet the difference between man and the lower creatures does obtain here too, because man is required to exercise this power responsibly and with proper respect for the sanctity of the family. This is plain from beginning to end of Holy Scripture; and nothing could emphasize the sacredness of the marriage bond more graphically than the description of the Church as the Bride of Christ and their marriage as a union for eternity (Eph. 3:25–32; 2 Cor. 11:2; Rev. 19:7ff.; 21:2). Within the framework of the "one flesh" concept and the sacred solidarity of the family the creation mandate to man to "be fruitful and multiply and fill the earth" (Gen. 1:28) is carried out.

THE POPULATION EXPLOSION

We are now confronted with the problem of a "population explosion" which, we are told, will mean that very soon there will be more people in existence than our planet can sustain unless the rate of increase is drastically checked. Man has been so successful in the matter of fertility and reproduction that the world is now in imminent danger of being filled to overflowing. A rate of population growth of two per cent per annum does not in itself sound alarming, but it is a compounding rate and the statisticians assure us that by the year 2,000 A.D. the number of persons inhabiting the earth will be double what it is at present. In fact the world may already be regarded as over-populated since the majority of its inhabitants suffer from inadequacy of food and care. Can the prospect of an increase of world population from $3\frac{1}{2}$ billion to 7 billion in the next thirty odd years be contemplated with complacency? Has the time come when the creation mandate should be rescinded? This question becomes very much more insistent when the estimate that within two centuries the number of the earth's inhabitants will have soared to more than 150 billion is taken into account.[2]

The problem is not at all just one of accommodation or living space for such vast numbers. Immense tracts of the earth's surface are still uninhabited and unproductive; and, even so, the tendency is for people to live together in urban aggregations of constantly increasing density. Dwelling and working in "high-rise" apartment and office buildings is commonplace today. The pattern of the skyscraper metropolis pioneered by Manhattan is already being imitated in great cities all over the world. In the foreseeable future a world population several times the size of what it is now may well be living in hundreds of Manhattan-like conurbations without encroaching unduly on the great open spaces which will be under cultivation.

Nor would the problem necessarily be the production of

---

[2] For fuller statistics see Malcolm H. Merrill, "An Expanding Populace in a Contracting World" in the *Journal of the American Medical Association*, Vol. 197, No. 8 (1966), pp. 632–637.

sufficient food for maintaining the life of so many persons. Striking progress is even now being made in the irrigation and reclamation of hitherto infertile areas in many parts of the world. The food resources of the oceans, which cover more than two-thirds of the earth's surface, are as yet largely unexploited. So many essential components of a balanced diet are now being synthesized in the laboratory that no great flight of the imagination is needed to envisage the possibility of providing nutriment for multitudes in concentrated or capsule form. Edmund Leach has assessed the situation in the following way:

> The circumstance that, in the future, social life as we now know it may be impossible is irrelevant. The human species is very versatile. Over a long period it has been evolving new types of social organization which permit denser and denser aggregates of population; at each stage in this process the people concerned have very quickly adapted themselves to the idea that this new style of living is normal and comfortable. . . . This is a value problem, not a food problem. If human beings were content to live on a diet of modified plankton, I suppose that it would be scientifically feasible to have ten or twenty times as many people living on the earth as there are now, but they would have to live their lives in an entirely different way under conditions which all of you would consider perfectly horrible. And yet, if that Brave New World actually came into being, its inhabitants would think that everything was perfectly normal. This strange form of existence would correspond to what they had been taught to expect. They would enjoy living that way.[3]

The problem is seen rather in the fact that the people who can least afford to do so are reproducing themselves at a rate far in excess of those who have an abundance of good things. The problem is compounded by the greed,

---

[3] Edmund Leach, Provost of King's College, Cambridge, Reith Lectures for 1967, *The Listener*, London, Vol. 78, No. 2016, 16 November 1967, pp. 622f.

graft, and callousness which keep on coming to the surface of human nature. There is, moreover, another ironic factor, namely, that the conquest of formerly lethal diseases in underprivileged countries has led automatically to the increase of population and by the same token to an intensification of poverty and destitution. Kenneth Boulding comments:

> Today . . . we face an appalling demographic crisis in the poor countries, partly a result of the World Health Organization, which went round the world about 1950 eliminating malaria, thereby almost eliminating infant mortality, without affecting the birth rate. As a result of this, most of the poor countries today have enormous generations of teenagers and almost 50% of the total population under the age of twenty. . . . At the moment, therefore, the poor countries are faced with an almost insoluble problem, with a small proportion in the labor force and an enormous generation of children to feed, educate, and bring into the modern world. I am inclined to think that unless we have a birth reduction campaign of major magnitude in the next five years, the situation in many of these countries is almost hopeless for the next fifty years. We will have anarchy, famines, disorganization, and perhaps a nightmarish retrogression from poverty into destitution.[4]

The figures substantiate this judgment. It is estimated, for example, that if things continue on their present course the population of Latin America will by the year 2,000 have increased by 200 per cent from 200 million to 600 million, while in the same period the population of North America will have increased by but 50%, from 200 million to 300 million. Kenneth Boulding's assessment of the situation, given above, is confirmed by Malcolm Merrill (and many others) as follows:

> The rate of world population growth has increased so spectacularly in recent years chiefly because man has

---

[4] Kenneth E. Boulding, "The Prospects of Economic Abundance", in *The Control of Environment* (A Discussion at the Nobel Conference, Minnesota, 1966), Amsterdam, 1967, pp. 53f.

controlled famines and mass killer diseases. He has managed to produce a sudden and sharp decline in death rates but has not effected any corresponding decline in birth rates. . . . The population growth that the world is experiencing threatens to nullify all efforts to bring about economic development and higher living standards in the poor countries of the world. If unchecked it can have disastrous effects. The poor nations are even now unable to provide adequate food, housing, health services, and education for their children or productive employment for new entrants into their labor force.[5]

Under the shadow of the forebodings engendered by such a prospect a pessimistic view of the future would seem also to be a realistic view. There are some, however, who seem determined to practice optimism at all costs and in spite of the depressing evidence to the contrary—Kenneth Boulding for one, who offers the following confession of faith:

For the long run, I am prepared to be more optimistic, simply because I think the processes of increase of knowledge are almost irreversible. Once we have wised up, it is very hard to wise down, particularly once knowledge becomes widespread. Knowledge, in fact, reproduces itself even more efficiently than the gene.[6]

René Dubos, however, finds little cause for encouragement in the development of our modern world. "For some three centuries," he remarks, "western man has believed that he would find his salvation in technology." But an increase in wealth and health have not meant an increase in happiness. In any case, if some diseases have been driven back, others have advanced, especially degenerative diseases and chronic complaints, so much so that, "despite the spectacular progresses in prophylactic and therapeutic medicine, . . . we are still a disease ridden society." Con-

---

[5] Malcolm H. Merrill, *loc. cit.*, pp. 633f.
[6] Kenneth E. Boulding, *loc. cit.*, p. 54.

temporary man, despite all his scientific advances, appears
to be trapped in some vicious spiral, since

> the increase in the prevalence of degenerative and
> other forms of chronic ailments is due in part to the
> fact that more people escape death from nutritional
> and infectious diseases.

Other factors which contribute to the creation of a disease
ridden society, with malignancies, vascular disorders, al-
lergic conditions, and mental illnesses constantly increasing
in frequency, are our manner of living, great numbers of
people in our sophisticated society being dependent in their
day-to-day existence on cigarettes and sedatives, and the
pollution of our environment by exhaust fumes, factory
smoke, and industrial waste products. It is a startling fact
that chronic pulmonary disease has now become the greatest
and most costly single medical problem in Northern Europe,
and may be expected to spread to all areas undergoing industrialization.[7]

ENVIRONMENTAL POLLUTION

As the effluvia or harmful waste-products of our industrialization cannot be eliminated they must at least be
controlled. But their control is not in fact a solution of the
problem. At best it is a postponement, and in the meantime
a new factor of deleteriousness is building up. This is how
René Dubos sees the situation:

> Wherever convenient, chemical pollution of air,
> water, and food will be sufficiently controlled to pre-
> vent the kind of toxic effects that are immediately
> disabling and otherwise obvious. . . . But it is prob-
> able that continued exposure to low levels of toxic
> agents will eventually result in a great variety of de-
> layed pathological manifestations, creating physio-
> logical misery and increasing the medical load. The
> point of importance here is that the worst pathological

---

[7] René Dubos, "Adaptation to the Environment and Man's Future",
in *The Control of Environment, ut supra*, pp. 62ff.

effects of environmental pollutants will *not* be detected at the time of exposure; indeed they may not become evident *until several decades later*.[8]

The accumulating menace from the pollution of the atmosphere alone is startlingly underlined by the estimate that if we go on burning coal, oil, and natural gas at the present rate of six billion tons a year between now and the year 2000 there will be an increase of 25% in the quantity of carbon dioxide in the earth's atmosphere. This, quite apart from its effect on the health of mankind, will lead to uncontrollable changes in climate. The question arises whether man is capable of developing other and less noxious sources for the provision of energy than the somewhat crude methods of combustion to which we are accustomed. This is a possibility which René Dubos has apparently failed to take into account, with the result that his prognosis is probably over-pessimistic. The use of nuclear energy for peaceful purposes may well supersede combustion as the main source of power in the foreseeable future. It hardly needs saying that this is a matter of urgency if the situation is to improve rather than deteriorate. The attitude of Glenn Seaborg at any rate is one of optimism. With reference to this problem posed by the pollution of our environment, he writes:

> I think the growing use of nuclear energy may provide one of a number of solutions to this problem. Since nuclear power does not involve combustion, it can cleanly produce electric power for industry, homes and transportation, and possibly provide space heating for all three, either directly, as is currently being done by the Swedish reactor at Farsta, or through electricity. The possibility of electrically powered automobiles, operating on batteries which could be charged at service stations receiving nuclear-generated electricity, might also help to solve air pollution problems. I believe that these are important contributions which the atom could make to man.

[8] René Dubos, *loc. cit.*, p. 67.

Beyond that there lies the challenge of manipulating the heavy hydrogen atom, known as deuterium, which is found in common sea water, with its promise of a virtually limitless source of energy; and, further still, the conquest of the direct harnessing of the energy which daily pours forth from the sun.[9]

René Dubos might well retort that new technical and scientific achievements are likely to bring with them new menaces of deterioration, such as the deleterious effects of atomic radiation which may be expected to follow the general use of nuclear energy. Be that as it may, few would deny that our western civilization enjoys great benefits thanks to the progress of science and technology—good food, good clothing, good housing, good schooling, good working conditions, high standards of hygiene and sanitation, immunization against dangerous and once common diseases, and the availability of expert medical care for all. Still, there is the ominous shadow of a built-in recessive factor; and it is particularly in this respect that René Dubos should gain our serious attention. To quote him again:

> There is no doubt, in fact, that higher living standards have rendered the population more resistant to various infections and other stresses. But there is reason to fear that we have now reached a phase of diminishing returns in this regard. Furthermore, the high level of prosperity is creating a new set of medical problems. Environmental pollution, excessive food intake, lack of physical exercise, the constant bombardment of stimuli, the inescapable estrangement of civilized life from the natural biological rhythms, are but a few among the many consequences of urbanized and industrialized life that have direct or indirect pathological effects. . . .[10]

---

[9] Glenn T. Seaborg, "The Control of Energy", in *The Control of Environment, ut supra*, pp. 110f.
[10] René Dubos, *loc. cit.*, pp. 70f.

To be forewarned, then, is no longer to be adequately forearmed. Indeed, an intensification of the problem may be anticipated through the escalation of sheer economic pressures.

> It had been assumed a few years ago that, as medical care becomes more widely available, the demand for it would decrease because the population would become healthier. Unfortunately, the opposite has happened. The pattern of diseases is constantly changing and new and more exacting kinds of demands for medical care are constantly arising. In fact, it is to be feared that the medical burden will become so heavy in the future that medical ethics will have to be recast in the harsh light of economics.[11]

SOCIAL REGIMENTATION

There is another disturbing prospect, namely, the virtual inevitability, as the structures of community existence become more and more complex, of the intensive regimentation of society. This in turn threatens a devastating assault on that sacred fortress of the human personality, the privacy and independence of the individual. Of all the serious problems portended by the over-crowding of society this is regarded by René Dubos as the most alarming:

> In this regard, the most alarming problem posed by over-population is the likelihood that the ever increasing complexity of the social structure will impoverish life by imposing on it a kind of regimentation. Food, natural resources, and other elements involved in the operation of the body machine and of industry are not the only factors to be considered in determining optimum population density. Just as important are the social amenities that make it possible to satisfy the longing for quiet, empty spaces, privacy, independence, and other conditions essential for preserving and enlarging the peculiarly *human* qualities of life. . . . As these commodities disappear, so will many of the con-

---

[11] René Dubos, *ibid.*, pp. 72f.

ditions that have enabled human life to transcend brutish existence; privacy and freedom, in particular, will become antisocial luxuries.[12]

The development of such a situation would bring us at least close to the nightmare of the tyrannical regimentation of society depicted in George Orwell's *1984*. The *Report from Iron Mountain* of cryptic origin (it might suitably have been named Irony Mountain), an essay in laconic realism, offers the following prognostication:

> Another possible surrogate for the control of potential enemies of society is the reintroduction, in some form consistent with modern technology and political processes, of slavery. Up to now, this has been suggested only in fiction, notably in the works of Wells, Huxley, Orwell, and others engaged in the imaginative anticipation of the sociology of the future. But the fantasies projected in *Brave New World* and *1984* have seemed less and less implausible over the years since their publication. The traditional association of slavery with ancient preindustrial cultures should not blind us to its adaptability to advanced forms of social organization, nor should its equally traditional incompatibility with Western moral and economic values. It is entirely possible that the development of a sophisticated form of slavery may be an absolute prerequisite for social control in a world at peace. As a practical matter, conversion of the code of military discipline to a euphemized form of enslavement would entail surprisingly little revision.[13]

The invasion of our privacy is already proceeding at a shocking rate. We all know that telephone tapping, concealed microphones, electronic listening devices, telescopic photography, one-way "mirrors", and other prying devices are rapidly becoming an accepted part of our "culture". The equally menacing compilation and electronic storage by government and bureaucratic departments of detailed in-

---

[12] René Dubos, *ibid.*, pp. 77f.
[13] *Report from Iron Mountain*, New York, 1967, p. 70.

formation concerning the lives of individual citizens is increasing. The intimate questionnaires of health agencies, insurance firms and sales networks are familiar to all. The prospect, as Harry Kalven has observed, is one of "a formidable dossier on every member of the society," with the disturbing result that "everyone will live burdened by an unerasable record of his past and his limitations;" indeed, "the threat is that because of its record-keeping the society will have lost its benign capacity to forget." [14] Then, too, there are the investigations of personality and aptitude tests, now commonplace in educational institutions as a means for placing people in pigeon-holes, and the use of drugs, hypnosis and Freudian techniques to assist in the process of laying bare the secrets of the individual with a view to determining what role he may be permitted to play in the community.

GENETIC DYSTROPHY

A further aspect of the problem confronting us is found in the ironic fact that the conquests of modern preventive medicine must be held responsible to a large degree for the genetic deterioration of the human species. The *Report from Iron Mountain,* for example, referring to "the regressive effect of certain medical advances", observes that pestilence is no longer an important factor in population control and that the problem is aggravated by the increase in life expectancy.[15]

The effective treatment of diabetics is frequently adduced to illustrate this degenerative trend. The position has been summarized by Paul Ramsey:

> Diabetics formerly died early. After a cure was found
> in insulin, they were enabled to survive and lead use-

---

[14] Harry Kalven, Jr., "The Problems of Privacy in the Year 2000", in *Daedalus* (Journal of the American Academy of Arts and Sciences), Boston, Summer 1967, pp. 877f.

[15] *Report from Iron Mountain,* pp. 50f.

ful lives. Since, however, they were not generally able to have children, these individuals were as genetically dead as if they had been stillborn. Now the safe delivery of the children of diabetic mothers is a commonplace in all our hospitals; and as a consequence the incidence of diabetes in the population is irreversibly increasing.

He goes on to quote the warning of Frederick Osborn that there is a limit beyond which this process cannot be carried and that if we consider not diabetes alone, but all the other ills to which the human race is genetically heir, that limit is not far away.[16]

AGING

This genetic dystrophy, complicated by environmental pollution and radiation and by the diseases and psychoses of our urbanized society, is accompanied by the increasing level of senility in the population. Today the man of our western civilization has a life expectancy which exceeds that of his grandparents born in 1890 by no less than 25 years (67 as compared with 42).[17] "The cause of the world population explosion," according to William Shockley, "has been the technology explosion, particularly the explosion of death control due to the advances in medical technology." [18] From this the conclusion may be drawn that death control necessitates birth control. But the effect on the structure of society which the postponement of death coupled with the diminution of reproduction now so widely demanded can easily be imagined. Edmund Leach describes it in the following manner:

Modern medicine has given the doctor almost unbelieveable powers to preserve alive creatures that nature

---

[16] Paul Ramsey, "Moral and religious implications of genetic control", in *Genetics and the Future of Man* (A Discussion at the Nobel Conference, Minnesota, 1965), p. 112.

[17] See William Shockley, "Population Control or Eugenics", in *Genetics and the Future of Man, ut supra*, p. 79.

[18] William Shockley, *ibid.*, p. 80.

would previously have destroyed, power to change the life prospects of children still in the womb, to alter the personality of the living, and to extend the life span of the senile. But if these powers of preservation are exercised in uninhibited fashion while, at the same time, we try to tackle the population explosion by reducing the birth-rate, then the outcome will be a very decrepit conservative society in which all the political and economic advantages lie with the very old. Most people will dodder on until they are nearly 100 and half the adult population will be well past retiring age.[19]

Men, he maintains, offered by science the total mastery over their environment and over their destiny, have become like gods; and it is the function of gods not only to create but also to destroy. "We too," he says, "must accept our dual responsibility and come to terms with the fact that the total elimination of disease would be an entirely intolerable blessing." [20]

THE MODERN DILEMMA

The assertion that "the total elimination of disease would be an entirely intolerable blessing" serves to throw into relief the dilemma in which modern man continually finds himself. The conquest of disease is the primary incentive of medical research, with the ultimate objective, utopian though it may be, of the elimination of disease. The attainment of such an objective would presumably require the nullification of all noxious germs and viruses, the cleansing of the environment from everything that is harmful, and the complete insulation of society against accidents of any kind, whether individual or communal. This would be a tall order by any standards! But, even if it were achieved, there would still remain the most baffling problem of all: that of

---

19 Edmund Leach, *loc. cit.*, Vol. 78, No. 2019, 7 December 1967, p. 751.
20 Edmund Leach, *ibid.*, also No. 2016, 16 November 1967, p. 621.

aging and death. At this point the optimism of humanists like Edmund Leach inexorably breaks down. Aging and death constitute the ultimate frustration which makes nonsense of the confident claim that modern men have become like gods and have "the total mastery over their environment and over their destiny" within their grasp. It is a claim that is utterly refuted by the startling admission that "the total elimination of disease would be an entirely intolerable blessing"; for, by Edmund Leach's reckoning, society would then have an unduly large proportion of individuals in a state of senile decrepitude. The hesitation to do more than darkly hint that old people be eliminated is understandable; but, given the premise that the species is infinitely more important than the individual, it is far from fantastic to envisage the enactment of a law which would prescribe that on reaching a set age persons should be "put to sleep." Thus modern man could exercise his godlike mastery by ridding society of senility.

But he would find it a tougher problem to rid society of the psychoses which would unbalance the personalities of so many as they approached the date of their liquidation or as they were forced to see the last of loved ones. Indeed, even as things are now, our modern society, for all its science, is becoming more and more a psychotic society in which the psychiatrist's prestige is outstripping the pastor's. How does the humanist propose to deal with the human psyche and with all the frightening ailments which it is capable of inducing? The elimination of germs, pollution, and accidents would not dispel the neurotic mentality; on the contrary, the more human society is controlled from birth to death the more neurotic it is likely to become and the worse afflicted with somatic illnesses of a psychological origin. Moreover, as we have seen, the conquest of one disease, while laudable in itself, only seems to leave the door open for the incidence of some new form of illness. The ability to reproduce their kind bestowed by modern therapeutic medicine on those with transmissible ailments and defects is leading to the genetic entropy of the species.

It is a matter of historical experience, further, that those who by one means or another exercise absolute control over their fellow men have a propensity to exempt themselves from the restrictions and prohibitions which they impose on others. They above all wish to act as gods—decreeing, but not themselves submitting to the decrees they enforce. In controlling the lives of others they will themselves be uncontrolled. But not ultimately; for they are not really gods, but men; and however impregnable their tyranny may be it is ultimately subject to the control of death and of judgment at the throne of the one true God. But meanwhile the urge of unregenerate man is to be as God and to exercise plenipotentiary authority over his fellow creatures, as though he himself were creator and lord of all. Unregenerate man hates the divine image in which he is created. The resulting corruption of his nature guarantees the corruption of the power he seizes. Hence the nemesis by which his footsteps are dogged. The idealistic utopia he first envisioned becomes a place of torment and brutality. Hitler the redeemer becomes Hitler the monster and the destroyer. The Nazi utopia, originally so bright and beckoning, is stamped not with the image of God but with the mark of the beast; its incense is the stench of corpses. Of all individuals the most psychotic is the one with the mania for power. The façade of his own impregnability can be propped up only by the control not merely of the bodies but also of the minds of those whom he wishes to dominate. Mental manipulation which reduces persons to puppets and the insecurity which is bred from the knowledge that everybody is trained to be an informer have already become commonplaces in the totalitarian régimes of our day. The philosophy of *1984* has ceased to have a futuristic ring:

> Power is tearing human minds to pieces and putting them together again in new shapes of your own choosing. Do you begin to see, then, what kind of world we are creating? It is the exact opposite of the stupid hedonistic Utopias that the old reformers imagined. A world of fear and treachery and torment, a world of trampling and being trampled upon, a world which will grow not less but *more* merciless as it refines itself. . . . Already we are breaking down the habits of thought which have survived from before the Revolution. We have cut the links between child and parent, and between man and woman. No one dare trust a wife or a child or a friend any longer. But in the future there will be no wives and no friends.[21]

The futilities and frustrations by which man is hounded when he wishes to act as his own god are inescapably in evidence too as he faces the problem of the abolition of war. So far from being diminished as a result of the phenomenal scientific progress of our supposedly enlightened modern age, the problem of war has become greatly intensified and the prospect for world peace is continually getting darker. The stockpiling of thermonuclear weapons by the so-called great powers forebodes a holocaust of indescribable dimensions. It is plain that man's wisdom does not keep pace with his knowledge.

At root, of course, the problem is that of the alienation and hostility in the depth of man's being. Hostile to God, man is alienated from the central and only point of reference for the meaning of his existence. And his sense of alienation generates in turn all the hostility which he displays to his fellow men. Man's basic need is that of reconciliation—reconciliation to God and thereby to his fellow

---

[21] George Orwell, *1984*, New York, 1961 edition (first published in 1946), p. 220.

men—and the Christian message is that this reconciliation
is available, by the free grace of God, in and through Jesus
Christ. So long as the Prince of Peace does not rule in the
hearts of men it is vain to look for the abolition of enmity
and warfare in human society. In our day, however, thanks
paradoxically to the brilliant advances in technological invention and global transport the situation has reached an
unprecedented degree of instability and explosiveness. By
assuming the front place in international economics, war-
preparedness has made peace more improbable than ever.
The *Report from Iron Mountain,* to which reference has
already been made, is specifically "on the possibility and
desirability of peace". As a document it is eloquent of the
frustration and despair which have taken hold of modern
man. Its cynical realism is well summarized by Leonard
Lewin in his foreword:

> Lasting peace, while not theoretically impossible, is
> probably unattainable; even if it could be achieved it
> would almost certainly not be in the best interests of
> a stable society to achieve it. . . . War fills certain
> functions essential to the stability of our society; until
> other ways of filling them are developed, the war sys-
> tem must be maintained—and improved in effective-
> ness. . . . the long-range planning—and 'budgeting'
> —of the 'optimum' number of lives to be destroyed
> annually in overt warfare is high on the Group's list
> of priorities for government action.[22]

Again, deplorable as it is in itself, war has been an important factor in the ecological sense that it has served to
keep the population growth in check. Thus, to quote from
the body of the *Report:*

> War has not been genetically progressive. But as a
> system of gross population control to preserve the
> species it cannot fairly be faulted.[23]

---

[22] *Report from Iron Mountain,* pp. x, xii.
[23] *Ibid.,* pp. 72f.

EUGENICS AND UTOPIA

Looked at in this perspective, the mass destruction effected by a third world war, this time with the widespread use of thermonuclear weapons, might well be regarded as a blessing rather than a curse. A drastic remedy indeed, but within a few short hours it could, by the indiscriminate slaughter of millions, solve the fearsome problem of the population explosion. It might also afford at one stroke, as it were, a new and otherwise unavailable opportunity for the eugenic control of society. Daunted by the intractable realities of a situation that seems to be getting further and further beyond control, some scientists seem to be focussing desperately on the intervention of some huge catastrophe which would enable the human race, or such remnants of it as were left, to make a fresh start. This, at any rate, seems to be seen by Kingsley Davis as the best hope for the future:

> Under the circumstances, we shall probably struggle along with small measures at a time, with the remote possibility that these may eventually evolve into a genetic control system. We shall doubtless increasingly seek to restrain reproduction in those cases in which there is patently a large risk of grossly defective offspring. . . .
>
> It seems more likely, however, that the change will be precipitated more suddenly by something new in human history, a genetic crisis. The survivors of a nuclear holocaust might prove willing to adopt a thorough system of genetic control in order to minimize the horrifying effects of radiation on the next generations. Once the barriers inherent in the existing social organization of human life were thus broken, genetic control would probably persist because of the competitive power it would give to the societies that maintained it.[24]

William Shockley also seems to discern a ray of hope

---

[24] Kingsley Davis, "Sociological aspects of genetic control", in *Genetics and the Future of Man, ut supra*, pp. 203f.

piercing through the mushroom-shaped cloud. Speaking of
"the threat of enormous genetic damage from a nuclear
war", he finds a promise beyond the threat:

> Eugenics would then be forced upon the human race in
> much the same way as infanticide was in more primi-
> tive times, as a necessary step in the struggle for
> existence.[25]

The concept of eugenics is not, of course, peculiar to our
modern age, though the development of the exact science of
genetics has understandably provided it with an impetus
and a significance not known in earlier eras. In the ancient
world the most celebrated blueprint for a eugenic utopia
was propounded by Plato in his *Republic*. Taught by the
example of the animal breeder, who selects only the best
specimens for reproduction and rejects those that are weak
and inferior, Socrates advocated the "nationalization" [26]
of marriage, or more accurately of mating, in accordance
with which those men and women who are fit to become
parents were to be designated by the state. These approved
propagators were to share a communal life together, without the privilege of private possessions. The matings were
to take place at prescribed times which would coincide with
certain religious festivals, in conformity with the principle
that

> the best of either sex should be united with the best as
> often, and the inferior with the inferior, as seldom as
> possible; and that they should rear the offspring of the
> one sort of union, but not of the other.

It is provided, further, that

> the number of weddings is a matter which must be
> left to the discretion of the rulers, whose aim will be
> to preserve the average of population.

---

[25] William Shockley, *loc. cit.*, p. 100.
[26] To use a modern term; Plato was thinking in terms of the city-
state rather than of the nation.

Other factors to be taken into account include

> the effects of wars and diseases and any similar agencies, in order as far as possible to prevent the state from becoming either too large or too small.[27]

Family life and the attendant responsibilities of parenthood were to be abolished. Parents would not know who were their children nor children who were their parents, and the upbringing of the children would be entirely in the hands of the state. Sub-standard infants were to be "put away".

> The proper officers will take the offspring of the good parents to the pen or fold, and there they will deposit them with certain nurses who dwell in a separate quarter; but the offspring of the inferior, or of the better when they chance to be deformed, will be put away in some mysterious, unknown place, as they should be. . . . They will provide for their nurture, and will bring the mothers to the fold when they are full of milk, taking the greatest possible care that no mother recognizes her own child; and other wet-nurses may be engaged if more are required.[28]

Parenthood would be permissible only within certain age-limits fixed by the state, namely, 20 to 40 for women and 25 to 55 for men, these being regarded respectively as the years of maturity or the prime of life.

> Any one above or below the prescribed ages who takes part in the public hymeneals shall be said to have done an unholy and unrighteous thing; the child of which he is the father, if it steals into life, will have been conceived under auspices very unlike the sacrifices and prayers, which at each hymeneal priestesses and priests and the whole city will offer, that the new generation may be better and more useful than their good and useful parents, whereas his child will be the offspring of darkness and strange lust. . . . And the same law shall apply to any one of those within the

---

[27] Plato, *Republic*, V, 458ff. (Jowett's translation).
[28] Plato, *ibid.*, 460f.

> prescribed age who forms a connection with any
> woman in the prime of life without the sanction of the
> rulers; for we shall say that he is raising up a bastard
> to the state, uncertified and unconsecrated. . . . This
> applies, however, only to those who are within the
> specified age: after that we allow them to range at will.
> . . . And we grant all this, accompanying the permis-
> sion with strict orders to prevent any embryo which
> may come into being from seeing the light; and if any
> force a way to the birth, the parents must understand
> that the offspring of such a union cannot be main-
> tained, and arrange accordingly.[29]

To the Athenians, for whom the family was an integral
part of the structure of society, this must have seemed a
startlingly radical scheme, proposing as it did the elimination of the family, rigidly enforced control of population,
and the wholesale practice of abortion or infanticide in
every case of conception not sanctioned by the government.
As has often been pointed out, Plato was influenced by the
pattern of society so carefully developed by the republic
of Sparta in which from infancy to old age physical culture
and civic virtue were pursued with singleness of purpose.
Benjamin Jowett has commented pointedly on Plato's mistake in looking to Sparta for the inspiration for his ideal
commonwealth:

> Least of all did he observe that Sparta did not really
> produce the finest specimens of the Greek race. The
> genius, the political inspiration of Athens, the love
> of liberty—all that has made Greece famous with
> posterity, were wanting among the Spartans. They had
> no Themistocles, or Pericles, or Aeschylus, or Sophocles,
> or Socrates, or Plato. The individual was not allowed
> to appear above the state; the laws were fixed, and he
> had no business to alter or reform them. Yet whence has
> the progress of cities and nations arisen, if not from
> remarkable individuals, coming into the world we know
> not how, and from causes over which we have no con-
> trol? Something too much may have been said in modern

---

[29] Plato, *ibid.*, 460f.

times of the value of individuality. But we can hardly condemn too strongly a system which, instead of fostering the scattered seeds or sparks of genius and character, tends to smother and extinguish them.[30]

There is, indeed, an element of ruthlessness and inhumanity in the Spartan system. Society loses something essential to its humanity when its members are manipulated like a herd of prize cattle. The physical result may be impressive (and the physical side is not unimportant) but what does it guarantee for the truest spirit of humanity? The question has well been asked, by Frederick Copleston: "Does a beautiful soul always go with a beautiful body or a good character with a strong body?" [31]

It is precisely at this point that any programme for eugenics which is concerned with the selection of those types which are regarded as most fit to survive and most likely to benefit posterity, comes face to face with a fundamental problem. This is the difficulty, admitted by William Shockley, of reaching "agreement as to what does constitute the ideal type of man". [32] The perfect man is an abstraction that does not belong to the world of real experience. Even the greatest of men in the world's history have had their areas of vulnerability; all have suffered from defects of character and physique which, in the eyes of the eugenist, might have disqualified them for the role of the ideal man. Socrates was wise but ugly; Alexander was bold but intemperate; Savonarola was righteous but celibate; Byron was poetic but club-footed. Indeed, it must be said that the noblest figures in human history are men who have achieved greatness by rising superior to their disabilities. They have been realists first, and only then idealists. The improvement

---

[30] Benjamin Jowett, in the Introduction to his translation of *The Republic of Plato*, Oxford, 1888, p. cxc.

[31] Frederick Copleston, *A History of Philosophy*, Vol. I, London, 1946, p. 230.

[32] William Shockley, *loc. cit.*, p. 98.

of the human race and of the conditions in which man lives is a legitimate concern, but one of the first principles of eugenic planning should be the realistic renunciation of the kind of idealism that looks on man as perfectible to an infinite degree. Man is sinful, and because he is sinful he is a bundle of contradictions. Discoveries and advances that promise so much for the betterment of mankind he invariably perverts to purposes of evil and inhumanity. The sinfulness of human nature is the ever present barrier which inexorably blocks the progress of human nature to higher things. One of the great fallacies of our day is to confuse scientific progress with human progress. The failure of human nature is visible on every side in the horrifying mess that man has made of this world—the inequity, the misery, the cruelty, the bloodshed, the futility, and the purposelessness by which the lives of such multitudes are blighted.

The eugenist, of course, wishes to improve the lot of the human race. To this end he advocates the imposition of certain controls which according to his reckoning will produce beneficial effects in due course: Negatively he would gradually eliminate deleterious elements which at present threaten the well-being of future generations. Positively he proposes immeasurably to improve the human stock, in character as well as in physique, through a selective and thorough limitation of procreation to only the best types. Immediately, however, a further problem arises: how and by whom are these controls to be enforced? As we have seen, Plato's answer is, by the highest authorities of the state, whose rulings may not be questioned or disregarded. As Werner Jaeger has observed:

> None of his regulations shows more bluntly, and for us more shockingly, how he demanded that his ruling class should surrender all personal interests to those of the state. This destroys the last relic of individuality, the right which no other state has ever ventured to challenge, the individual's right to his own body.

> For when Plato in another context describes the prop-
> ertyless state of the guards [33] by saying they literally
> own nothing but their bodies, he is really exaggerating,
> considering his own views on the relation of husband
> and wife. He can only have meant that they 'possessed'
> their bodies, not that they could use them freely.[34]

It is somewhat ironic that these words were written at a
time when the totalitarian régimes of German Nazism and
Russian and Chinese communism were being manifested in
their full ruthlessness and brutality to the world. The cry
of liberty and plenty for all which rang out so clearly at the
beginnings of these movements has a hollow mocking ring
now, since never before in history have the dignity of the
person and the sanctity of the individual been so savagely
and systematically assaulted. Yet the world has had to wait
till the dawn of our much vaunted twentieth century for the
appearance of these monstrous tyrannies, in which not only
politics and economics but even literature, music, art, and
scientific research have been forced to prostitute themselves and lose their honour by submitting to the imposi-
tions prescribed by the state. This consideration in itself
should serve at least as a curb to humanistic arrogance and
optimism.

Needless to say, things are very different now from what
they were in Plato's day. Plato's vision was of an ideal city-
state with a citizenship limited, by population control
effected through abortion, infanticide, and restriction of
parenthood, to an optimum figure of 5,040 persons. We are
faced with a global population explosion which, as things
are now going, will mean a doubling of the world's inhabitants by the end of this century. When Plato was
writing, some 2,300 years ago, there was no such thing as a

---

[33] Or "guardians", the superior class of Plato's ideal society, who
are dedicated to the preservation of the principles on which the
republic is founded and from whose ranks the rulers are chosen.

[34] Werner Jaeger, *Paideia: The Ideals of Greek Culture*, Vol. II,
Oxford, 1944, p. 248.

science of genetics; but in our time genetics, though still
a young science, is a discipline through which a great deal
of important knowledge concerning the mechanics of heredity is being built up. How, if at all, should this knowledge be
applied as the attempt is made to meet and solve the problem
of over-population and all its attendant disabilities? Of those
who give thought to such a question, many today pin their
faith on the effectiveness of applied genetics. There is wide
acceptance of the judgment of Kingsley Davis that

> deliberate genetic control certainly appears to be the
> 'absolute weapon', the most powerful means for sur-
> vival yet contemplated.

He urges the enormous potential gain that may be expected
from systematic improvement of human inheritance.

> It holds the promise of transforming human society in
> precisely those ways in which purely cultural change is
> impotent. . . . It would reverse the present tendency
> to eliminate the selective bars against physical defect
> and mental mediocrity. It would save the species from
> its lop-sided dependence on cultural props for biological
> inadequacies.

This hopeful prospect, however, is qualified by uncertainty;
for Davis admits that "genetic regulation, like any other
human effort, runs the risk of failure"; he acknowledges
the possibility that "the artificially created thoroughbreds
of the species might prove less viable than the mongrels." [35]
    Kingsley Davis's delineation of a eugenic utopia is along
the lines advocated with such fervour by H. J. Muller. The
first step, he says, is to decide whether the entire population
or merely an élite is to have its heredity improved. Then a
"social adjustment" would be necessary, to be achieved by
educating couples no longer to have a preference for children genetically their own, but "to welcome a child which
comes from artificial insemination or, better, from an im-

---

[35] Kingsley Davis, *loc. cit.*, pp. 202f.

planted fertilized ovum" derived from donors of superior quality.

> The parents would thus regard the child as their own
> —much as a purchased house or car becomes a source
> of pride to its new owners, regardless of the fact that
> they themselves did not manufacture it.

It is added that

> the nation could maintain a board of geneticists to
> determine who should furnish the sperm and the ova
> and what crosses should be made in the artificial
> mating.

As for those males in the population not required to supply sperm to the official "sperm-banks", they would all be sterilized, while the females not supplying ova would have their ovulation suppressed or diverted.

> The board of supervising geneticists would have con-
> fidential records on the pedigree of all persons born in
> the population, as well as records of their traits and
> achievements. On this basis it would determine who is
> to be sterilized and who is to furnish sperm or ova.[36]

The assertion that "such a scheme would keep marriage and the family as a means of rearing children, and so would do minimum violence to traditional social structure" [37] is extraordinarily naïve. The father would be father in name only and not in any sense in deed. The mother would be a mere lodging-house proprietress, a passive hostess, a vehicle of sophisticated parthenogenesis. The instinct for one's own flesh and blood, so constant throughout human history, would now be suppressed and relegated to the museum. Indeed, Kingsley Davis speaks of the family as "a very primitive mode of social organization" and its retention as "a curious fact." [38] Edmund Leach suggests

---

[36] Kingsley Davis, *ibid.*, pp. 195ff.
[37] *Ibid.*, p. 197.
[38] *Ibid*, p. 183.

in similar vein the need for a change in the accepted idea
of the family and complains of "so much soppy propaganda
about the virtue of a united family life" emanating from
"psychologists, doctors, schoolmasters, and clergymen."
His judgment that, "far from being the basis of the good
society, the family, with its narrow privacy and tawdry
secrets, is the source of all our discontents," borders on the
hysterical. To propose, as he does, the Chinese commune as
an example to be followed betrays an extraordinary failure
to acknowledge the chaotic and disastrous state of affairs
that has followed from the policy of community of children
practiced by Chinese communism.[39] Children that belong to
the state belong nowhere; they are rootless and, deprived
of the intimate centre of security and affection that the
family affords, they seek acceptance by the formation of
mobs of their own tender age which, as current events have
demonstrated, become a fearsome and uncontrollable element of society.

Over and over again, the replacement of the natural by
the artificial has led to consequences which are anything
but beneficial—monstrosities, deformities, deficiencies; but
modern scientism, with its pretensions to ultimate omniscience and omnipotence, shows an unwillingness to learn
this lesson. Even, however, if it were granted that problems
of this kind could be overcome and foolproof methods devised, there would remain one deep-seated obstacle with
which science is incapable of dealing: The fact that it is impossible to breed sin out of the species. The choice, as
donors of spermatozoa and ova for the projected eugenic
"banks", of men and women who not only are fine physical
specimens but also persons of moral integrity, emotional
stability, and intellectual capacity will not begin to scratch
the surface of this fundamental problem of the human
race. Genetic surgery for the correction of faults or un-

[39] Edmund Leach, *The Listener, ut supra*, Vol. 78, No. 2018, p. 695.

desirable combinations in the units of heredity is already in the experimental stages; but the geneticist cannot extend his operations to the surgery of the human soul. The thoroughbred society that he hopes to produce might well turn out to be a generation of vipers, capable of wickedness hitherto unknown. Certainly, the increase in scientific knowledge in our age has not led to a decrease in human depravity; on the contrary, it has been the occasion for the invention of new techniques of oppression, falsehood, and destruction. Let us suppose that by the rigid enforcement of eugenic control the genetic specialists succeeded in manipulating man's heredity in such a way that a generation was produced at last which was conditioned to respond and act only in accordance with a predetermined pattern of social behaviour. This generation would no longer be human, but an assembly of automata without minds or wills of their own, and those who brought about this state of affairs would themselves have become monstrous and inhuman, guilty of the appalling sin of the dehumanization of their fellows.

I am aware that it is fashionable in some scientific and philosophical circles to scoff at talk of human sinfulness as defeatist talk and the relic of an outmoded religious past. We are supposed to have reached an era of enlightenment in which man has at last come of age. It is only a matter of realism, however, quite apart from the theological considerations which quite definitely are involved, for one is brought face to face with the abject sinfulness of man, displayed in an almost endless variety of forms of selfishness, dishonesty, violence, and depravity, every time one opens a daily newspaper. The evidence is on every hand, and to close one's eyes to it is as stupid as it is unscientific and unrealistic. The *Report from Iron Mountain* approves as "a universal requirement" the limitation of procreation to the products of artificial insemination on the ground that such a reproductive system would have the "advantage of being susceptible of direct eugenic management," and adds that

> its predictable further development—conception and embryonic growth taking place wholly under laboratory conditions—would extend these controls to their logical conclusion.[40]

The logic of such a conclusion resides only in the mentality of the planner and not at all in the realities of human nature. It would be far more logical to conclude that the generation, or more accurately manufacture, in the grand cause of a eugenic utopia, of babies in test tubes will predictably lead to a calamitous condition of mass neurosis.

The achievement of a situation in which babies are produced and reared under laboratory conditions should, of course, be the *ultima thule*, the *ne plus ultra*, for those who clamour for complete equality of the sexes. Once the stage was reached at which all babies were brought into being through the culture of an approved ovum fertilized by an approved spermatozoan selected from a refrigerated "bank," the donors of which could have lived and died centuries earlier, any differentiation between the sexes would become meaningless. Parenthood would no longer be a thing of the present. In fact, sexuality would then be an anachronism as it would no longer be needed. The aging bishop who, when assailed in his study by a formidable female campaigning for equal rights for women with the question, "After all, bishop, what difference is there between you and me?", muttered, "Madam, I can't conceive," would no longer be considered a wit.

In predicting that

> responsiveness to the world situation may take the form of a new willingness to assume responsibility for supporting massive dependence on modern scientific methods for the control of conception and the use of such inventions as artificial insemination, artificial lactation, and perhaps extra-uterine gestation.

---

[40] *Report from Iron Mountain*, p. 73.

Margaret Mead envisages the sex-equality that might follow from such a sociological transformation:

> There would be a growing disregard for sex as a basic mode of differentiation. Boys and girls would be given a similar education and like demands would be made on them for citizenship, economic contribution, and creativity. . . . Boys and girls would be differentiated not by sex-typed personality characteristics, but by temperament. The two-sex exclusive pair model of human relationships would lose its power. Instead, companionship for work, play, and stable living would come to be based on many different combinations, within and across sex lines. . . .[41]

The enforcement, by one method or another, of universal sterilization for the purpose of safeguarding eugenic purity would open the way for "safe" and unrestricted promiscuity, both heterosexual and homosexual. It is also predictable, however, that this in turn would lead to an appalling increase in the incidence of venereal disease and that this would be a ghastly Achilles heel of the process of the neutralization of the sexes.

If there is one thing that is unpredictable about man it is his behaviour, and this must be a major concern of the eugenist. The variety of patterns of behaviour and temperament in human society is virtually limitless, and this complexity belongs to the individuals as well as to the group. The complexity is compounded, moreover, by the factor of contradiction. While it is possible to classify people in accordance with certain character types, it is a matter of everyday experience that persons can and do act "out of character." There is general agreement, too, that certain kinds of behaviour and temperament are undesirable because they are harmful or anti-social, and that their elimination would be requisite before an ideal society could be achieved. Some utopian planners have hopes that this

---

[41] Margaret Mead, "The Life Cycle and its Variations", in *Daedalus, ut supra*, pp. 872f.

elimination will in time become possible by resort to genetic recombination—a device which is dismissed by Gardner Quarton as "rather wild speculation," especially as the contributions of the genes to behaviour and personality are exceedingly complex and all experiments on transformation in mammals have so far been negative.[42] In any case, however much the cast of our temperament may be genetically determined, it would be foolish and undignified to blame our misdemeanors on our chromosomes. The distinctive worth of man is apparent in the fact that he is a responsible creature, able to distinguish between good and evil and to respect the rights of his fellow men, and endowed with the faculty of the will which makes him master of his conduct. Of course, there are other factors which may influence a man's behaviour, such as environment and upbringing and abnormal functioning of the endocrine glands. But it is a fundamental element in the structure of society that men are answerable for their conduct. We must emphasize again that behind all human misbehaviour is the deep-seated factor of sin, which is inimical to the good of society, a violation of one's own being and an affront to one's Creator.

There is very little indication, however, that the eugenic visionary is inhibited by considerations of this order. It is fair to say, I think, that in the utopia which he foresees, the solution to the problem of aberrant human behaviour will be sought by removing responsibility from the individual and placing it in the hands of the society, or rather of those who wield the power over society. To suggest the techniques by which this is likely to be accomplished is not difficult, for at least some of them are already commonplace in totalitarian states, such as massive indoctrination and brain-washing, additives to the diet and the drinking supply, administration of hormones and drugs, the conditioning

---

[42] Gardner C. Quarton, "Deliberate Efforts to Control Human Behaviour and Modify Personality" in *Daedalus, ut supra*, pp. 840f.

of reflexes along Pavlovian lines, neurosurgery, stimulation of the brain by remote electronic instruments, and protracted surveillance of a man's actions and reactions by means of specialized and computerized monitoring devices. Gardner Quarton envisages the use of techniques in combination:

> The most efficient utilization of behavior-control technology would involve mixing techniques. If, for instance, a human subject had electrodes implanted in such a way that any ongoing action could be rewarded, punished, or prevented, and if microtransmitters and receivers made external wires and apparatus unnecessary, he could be placed in a learning situation, and selected patterns of behavior could be encouraged or discouraged automatically. With effective monitoring and computing equipment, much of the process could be controlled automatically.[43]

The planners assure us that manipulations of this kind are justified on the grounds of humanitarianism and the improvement of the race. But, as every person has undesirable tendencies in his make-up, where is it all going to stop? The utopia could not be attained except by the comprehensive control of society. We should all then be like experimental mice in a laboratory labyrinth, rewarded if we take the right route and penalized if we fail. This means, once again, that the process will in the end be one of dehumanization. As a completely controlled being, from his conception in a test tube to his conduct as an adult, man will have been deprived of his freedom, his responsibility, his individuality, his dignity. In short, he will have lost his humanity. And there is the ever-recurring question: Who will control the controllers?

A further question of control which must arise is that of the organization of society for the performance of the various tasks that are necessary for the proper functioning

---

[43] Gardner C. Quarton, *ibid.*, pp. 846f.

of the life of the community. The projected utopia will presumably have educators and industrialists, business men and technologists, writers and mechanics, artisans and labourers. Are these diverse duties and abilities to come under the cover of genetic manipulation? Will every individual born in the utopian community possess a genetically predetermined aptitude which will qualify him to fulfil a particular function? Will each megalopolis be like a human ant-heap? The enforcement of the eugenic system, as Kingsley Davis has remarked, will require "tight control."

> This would be particularly true if human breeding were used to produce diverse types in the population for special tasks, somewhat analogous to the division of labour in insect societies.[44]

The prospect of predestination by genetic selection is no more alluring than the other features of the eugenic paradise envisioned by would-be beneficiaries of the human species. The regimentation of society along fixed tracks of routine may promise super-efficiency, but it also promises monotony and frustration which could rapidly produce devastating psychological effects. It would, in fact, amount to little more than a development, on a grander and more sophisticated scale, of the social pattern of Plato's ideal republic with its arbitrary stratification of the populace into a hierarchical structure of, at the top, the privileged class of the guardians, below them the militia, then the artisans, and, lowest of all, the substratum of unprivileged slaves. There really is not a great step between Plato and *1984*!

It must be said that Kingsley Davis is not hopeful about the early achievement of a eugenic society. "Human beings are still a long way from such self control," in his view; and he adds the explanation: "A species which cannot as yet

---

[44] Kingsley Davis, *loc. cit.*, p. 197.

even control its own sheer numbers is obviously not likely
to control its own genetic constitution." As we noticed
earlier, he sees, paradoxically, the main chance for comprehensive eugenic advance in the incidence of some
cataclysmic disaster, such as a nuclear holocaust. He reminds us that the process of social change may be "salta-
tory" as well as gradual. "It is possible," he says, "to
imagine a catastrophe so great that it would spark a eugenic
transformation" by way of producing a genetic crisis, and
"the only one that suggests itself is one produced by the
use of nuclear weapons in a third World War."

> Under such circumstances, faced with generations
> burdened with countless horrifying mutations, nations
> possessed of modern genetic science would be likely to
> overcome all traditional obstacles in favor of a com-
> prehensive genetic control system.[45]

Evidently by "self control" Kingsley Davis means control
by society of itself, or, put in another way, the willingness
of society to submit to the imposition of strict genetic control through the enactment by its rulers of specific laws
designed for this purpose. William Shockley affirms that "it
is clear that man's destiny will be shaped by the acts of
man"; [46] and Edmund Leach emphasizes the responsibility
of man for his own future in the following terms:

> It is not vanity to say that man has become like a
> god; it is essential to say it and also to understand
> what it means. Since, god-like, we can now alter
> nature, including that part of nature which is man
> himself, we can no longer console ourselves with the
> thought that a search for scientific knowledge is its
> own justification. It has ceased to be true that nature
> is governed by immutable laws external to ourselves.
> We ourselves have become responsible.[47]

Men like these, who are unwilling to abandon their dedication to the governing concept of evolutionism, have now, it

---

[45] Kingsley Davis, *loc. cit.*, p. 201.
[46] William Shockley, *loc. cit.*, p. 104.
[47] Edmund Leach, *The Listener, ut supra*, Vol. 78, No. 2016, p. 624.

seems, taken mankind out of the hands of Evolution and placed evolution in the hands of Mankind. Evolution, which has worked hitherto and got us thus far from the humblest of origins, cannot now be relied on. No longer is Evolution working its purpose out as age succeeds to age. After all these inconceivable eons of time Nature Selection has packed up. Everything now depends on Human Selection. Failure by man to control his destiny will mean devolution and doom.

The high-priest of neo-evolutionism is the Jesuit Pierre Teilhard de Chardin, who died, little known, scarcely a dozen years ago in New York. He propounded the revised evangel that man is the master of a glorious future, and the visionary poeticism of his message has now captivated the minds of intellectuals seeking a new prophet. Societies called by his name have sprung into being on both sides of the Atlantic with a strangely mixed but devoted membership of Catholics, atheists, Protestants, Marxists, theologians, scientists, and academics of many varieties.

Teilhard is a passionate advocate of the gospel of "the continuation of the evolutionary movement at the heart of Humanity," even though his eschatological perspective is somewhat deficient in definition. It has become "the matter of fundamental importance," according to Teilhard, "to ensure, rationally, the progress of the world of which we are a part."

> How—not only, as hitherto, for our little individual life, for our little family, for our little country—no longer even only for the entire earth—but for the salvation and the success of the Universe itself—how ought we, men of today, to organize around us the preservation, the distribution, and the progress of the Energy of Humanity for the better?
> That is the whole question.[48]

There is, Teilhard maintains, "no essential difference"

---

[48] Pierre Teilhard de Chardin, *L'Energie Humaine*, Paris, 1962, pp. 153ff.

between physical energy and moral force. This follows from the premise that the stuff of the Cosmos is spiritual. The domain, therefore, of the Energy of Humanity is that of the "physico-moral." [49] It is "an immense task" which confronts the "technician of the Energy of Humanity" in the realm of biology, physiology, and medicine:

> not only to overcome scientifically the maladies and the phenomena of counter-evolution (sterility, physical enfeeblement) which threaten the increases of the Noosphere; [50] but by various means (selection, control of the sexes, administration of hormones, hygiene, etc.) to set free a superior type of man. A like ambition has for long seemed, and still seems to many, fantastic or even impious. On the part of some there is resistance to the thought of any change in what seems 'always to have been'; on the part of others there is a mistaken religious fear of violating the imprescriptible rights of the Creator over his work of flesh and thought: for a complex of obscure reasons our generation still regards with mistrust every attempt devised by science to intervene in the sphere of heredity, of the determination of the sexes, and of mental development. As though Man had the right and the power to handle all the affairs of the World except those which concern his own constitution! And yet it is in this field that we must attempt *everything,* right to the end. [51]

Teilhard speaks with appreciation of the imaginative attempts of men like H. G. Wells and Aldous Huxley to portray, "somewhat satirically," the shape of man's future, urging us to retain the idea without being disconcerted by details in the picture they paint. "The idea," he says, "is just and grand, and its realization, like everything of which life is compounded, will succeed in escaping from the caricature." [52]

---

[49] *Op. cit.,* p. 158.

[50] By the term "Noosphere" Teilhard intends "the world of Thought" which transcends and crowns the "Biosphere" or world of physical life.

[51] *Op. cit.,* pp. 159f.

[52] *Ibid.*

The "profound metamorphosis" which Teilhard presages will come about, he explains, through the development of our modern consciousness of "a special sense for laying hold of the Totality in which alone the marvel of our mutual liberation and compenetration (or transparence) can operate."

> Nothing seems to me more important, from the point of view of the Energy of Humanity, than the spontaneous appearance and, eventually, the systematic cultivation of such a 'cosmic sense'. By it Men ascend explicitly to the perception of their 'molecular' nature. They cease to be individuals shut off in separation. In them, from then on, the elementary spiritual energy becomes specifically ready for integration into the Total Energy of the Noosphere.[53]

Teilhard's vision is of the totality of mankind acting as a single organism motivated by a collective consciousness and emotion. He believes that there would be no limit to the spiritual expansion, penetration, and fusion that would result from such coherence of the mass of humanity.

> To conquer and harness the forces of the ether and the sea is fine. But what is this triumph compared with the global mastery of human thought and love? Truly, never has an opportunity more magnificent than this been presented to the hopes and endeavours of the Earth.[54]

Turning to the theme of eugenics, Teilhard complains, "We are incredibly slow in promoting (and even in conceiving) the realization of a 'body' of humanity" and deplores "the anomaly of a society which concerns itself with everything except organizing the recruitment of its own elements." It seems that Teilhard would have concurred with Edmund Leach's judgment that man, now god-like, must destroy as well as create. Eugenics, he points out, "is not confined to a simple selection of births." What attitude

---

[53] *Op. cit.*, pp. 163f.
[54] *Op. cit.*, p. 165.

should be adopted towards unprogressive ethnic groups? The earth's surface is confined and limited. "To what degree, racially or nationally, should areas of inferior activity be tolerated?" What justification is there for the multiplication of effort expended in the preservation of what is often no more than the fag-end of life?

> Something profoundly fine and true (I would say faith in the irreplaceable worth and the incalculable resources contained in each personal element) is apparently concealed beneath this obstinate determination to sacrifice everything in order to preserve a human existence. But ought not this solicitude of Man for his individual neighbour to be balanced by a higher passion, engendered by faith in this other superior personality which is anticipated, as we shall see, from the terrestial success of our evolution? To what point ought the development of the strong (to the extent that this may be clearly defined) to take precedence over the preservation of the feeble? [55]

The organization of the human race demanded by Teilhard will be, first, international, and then, in the ultimate issue "totalitarian." [56] The way ahead requires not the limitation of Force, which in any case Teilhard regards as both impossible and immoral, but its controlled direction into channels which will be for the benefit of all. "The cure for our ills" (*notre guérison*), he affirms, lies in the discovery of a natural and fruitful cause into which "the super-abundance which oppresses us" can be channelled.

> An ever greater excess of free energy, made available for ever vaster conquests: this is what the world is waiting for from us and this is what will save us. [57]

But the development of the external, material solidarity of mankind is no more than the pointer to something far

---

[55] *Op. cit.*, p. 166.
[56] *Op. cit.*, p. 167. Totalitarian (*totalitaire*) is intended, of course, without the pejorative connotation now frequently attached to it.
[57] *Op. cit.*, p. 168.

more profound which is going on, namely, the organization, inner and psychical in character, of the Noosphere. The mingling and fusion of the races is leading directly, says Teilhard, to a community and equality, not only of language, but of morality and idealism.

> Beneath the combined effect of the material needs and spiritual affinities of life Humanity is beginning to emerge all around us from the impersonal in order to take on, as it were, a heart and a form. . . . The organization of the Energy of Humanity, taken in its totality, is directed, and urges us, towards the ultimate formation, over and above each personal element, of *a common human soul*.[58]

Teilhard posits as a necessity the consummation of Evolution in a universal Personality which is the product of and "ultra-concentration" of the personal human elements in a higher consciousness. "The world would not function," he asserts, "were it not for the existence, somewhat in advance of time and space, of a 'cosmic point Omega' of total synthesis." The unitive influence or energy which leads to the achievement of this "Point Omega" and the formation of the Noosphere is Love.[59] "Love one another" is the fundamental principle and the key to the future of man and the world. The goal is "the totalization, in a total love, of the total Energy of Humanity." [60] This brings us to what Teilhard presents as the Gospel, "the essential message of Christ," which is to be sought not in the Sermon on the Mount, nor in what took place on the Cross. Teilhard's gospel "consists in its entirety in the proclamation of a 'divine Fatherhood' "; in other words, in the affirmation that "God, personal being, is presented to Man as the goal of a personal *union*." He ventures the definition that

---

[58] *Op. cit.*, p. 171.
[59] *Op. cit.*, pp. 178ff.
[60] *Op. cit.*, pp. 189ff.

"Christianity is nothing but a 'phylum' of love in Nature." [61] It is Christian love that will bring us to a further and ultimate metamorphosis: "the awareness of an 'Omega' at the heart of the Noosphere—the passage of the circles to their common centre: *the appearance of the 'Theosphere.'* " [62]

The ultimate end of the long process, it seems, is a sort of Pythagorean paradise in which matter and individuality have disappeared from the scene and Mind and Spirit hold the stage. This would be the consummation of what Teilhard has called elsewhere "the general 'drift' of matter towards spirit." "This movement," he explains, "must have its term: one day the whole divinisable substance of matter will have passed into the souls of men; all the chosen dynamisms will have been recovered: and then our world will be ready for the Parousia." [63] And so we are back again with Plato and his ascent from matter to spirit and final absorption into the World-Soul! It is the cosmic pilgrimage of Man and Woman described by Lilith in George Bernard Shaw's *Back to Methuselah:*

> After passing a million goals they press on to the goal of redemption from the flesh, to the vortex freed from matter, to the whirlpool in pure intelligence that, when the world began, was a whirlpool in pure force.[64]

But what in the meantime has happened to Man?

CONCLUSION

We must ask, finally, what the Christian perspective is in confrontation with all this planning and preaching and speculation; for Christianity does have a perspective which embraces the entire history of man, including his future.

In the first place, it must be said with emphasis that the

[61] *Op. cit.*, pp. 193ff.
[62] *Op. cit.*, p. 198.
[63] Pierre Teilhard de Chardin, *Le Milieu Divin*, London, 1960, p. 94.
[64] George Bernard Shaw, *The Complete Plays*, London, n.d., p. 962.

frequent affirmation that man is the master of his own
destiny and that his future lies squarely in his own hands
is entirely alien to the Christian view of the human situation. No Christian would wish to deny, of course, that man
is a responsible being and that there is a logical sequence of
cause and effect in the sphere of human conduct. A man
reaps what he sows; sin pays its own wages; and man has
only himself to blame when he comes under judgment. The
Bible, however, does not see man as the centre and sum
of things. In the biblical perspective, God and God alone
is the sovereign Lord of the whole universe: sovereign in
creation, sovereign in providence, sovereign in judgment,
and sovereign in redemption; and sovereign also over all
human history. The staggering problems with which the
foreseeable future, like a dark cloud, is freighted, and which
are so threatening to man, are quite certainly not problems
to God. The frustration of man is not the frustration of
God. In the ultimate issue, the future rests in God's hands.
This means, for the Christian, that his very proper concern
for the progress and well-being of his fellow men is
tempered by a calm confidence which springs from his
knowledge that God is in control. This is not pietistic
escapism; it is getting the over-all picture into true focus—
and that, surely, is the first essential for the person who
wishes to take life and humanity and the world seriously.

Secondly, it should be said that, in the proximate issue,
the future does rest with man. Man, fallen though he now
is, still has a mandate to fulfil; and this mandate, as we
have seen, involves in its various requirements cultural,
social, and scientific tasks. Man, created in the image of
God, has a responsibility not only for his own self but also
for the state of the world and the society of which he is a
part. He has a duty to promote decency and order, and to
ensure as far as he possibly can that human affairs are
governed and controlled in such a way as both to benefit

and ennoble the commonwealth and also to safeguard the rights and freedoms of the individuals of whom it is composed. It is within this framework that the practice, for example, of medicine and surgery have their proper setting and that the questions posed by the population explosion and the genetic deterioration of mankind demand to be sympathetically considered. The Christian is the last person who should shrug off such questions as though they are no concern of his. The second of the two great commandments is that he is to love his fellow man as himself. Disease, poverty, unemployment, tyranny he recognizes as evils which he must strive to remedy and eliminate. Injustice and brutality are abhorrent to him. The dignity of the person, each person, is precious to him.

But, thirdly, the Christian is the only true realist. He is precisely this because he brings God into the picture as well as man. To leave God out of account means that the whole human situation must inevitably vacillate between optimism and despair. Some will stake all on optimism, expressing an invincible confidence in the ultimate indefectibility of evolution or natural selection or fortuitous mutation, or some other *tertium quid*, assisted by the accumulation of man's technological expertise, for the achievement after long ages of a state of utopian perfection. Others, unable to close their eyes to the depressing evidence of the wickedness and irreformability of the human heart, will conclude that pessimism regarding the future of mankind is alone justified. Contemporary existentialism is a defiant manifestation of despair about man which is candidly realistic in its assessment of the hopelessness of the human situation, but unrealistic because it suppresses the truth about God. Some abandon a blandly optimistic attitude, as, for example, H. G. Wells did at last, in favour of the deepest gloom and foreboding. Others again attempt to temper pessimism with optimism by issuing admonitions to the effect that mankind will be overtaken with irretrievable disaster if steps are not taken forthwith to control human life and reproduction.

The Christian is the true realist, moreover, because he recognizes that man, by reason of the sinfulness which perverts his nature, is incapable of producing, by his own effort and planning, the utopia for which he longs. He knows that human endeavour to this end, admirable though it may be in so many respects, is doomed to frustration. He points man away from himself to God, from whom alone salvation and reintegration can come. In particular he points to Christ, the incarnate, crucified, risen, and glorified Son of God, as the One in whom God reconciles the world to Himself. The Christian future, further, does indeed include a "utopia," but it is something induced neither by man nor by natural selection. Christian optimism rests on the sovereign purpose of God in Christ for the establishment of an everlasting kingdom, the setting of which will be the new heavens and the new earth. What this means, in other words, is the restoration and the fulfilment in Christ of all God's purposes in creation. The citizens of this kingdom are the twice-born, those who have been regenerated by the grace of God through faith in Jesus Christ. They are the new men in Christ, renovated in the image of God in which they were made, and rejoicing in the purpose and potential of their reintegrated manhood. In the kingdom of God they are full persons, redeemed in body as well as soul, exulting in the dignity of their being as they do everything to the glory of God. They are not dehumanized automata or brutalized serfs; nor are they some sort of dematerialized humanity whose identity has been dissolved in a nebulous realm of thought. Through union with Christ they have become the heirs of all things. Their enjoyment of that heritage will be spoiled by no illness or disease; it will not be clouded by any sorrow; it will not be frustrated and lost through death. For all these things which are enemies to our self-fulfilment and our delight in others here and now will then have passed away; and in the unending summer of the divine love redeemed humanity will blossom into the full fruition of its innate potential in the joyful service and praise of God. This is the glorious hope of the Christian, a hope that is assured in Christ.

Alongside of this grand purview of optimism, however, there is a Christian pessimism regarding the world and society as we now know them. The Bible stresses over and over again the futility of unregenerate human effort to control and master the destiny of man. Every utopian dream is a mirage without substance. The constant lesson of history is that there is a nemesis that overtakes and distorts each achievement of man. The phenomenal technological advance of our age has brought with it a phenomenal increase in destruction and suffering. The evil outweighs the good. And the reason for this is in man himself, not outside of him. It is the inevitable consequence of his alienation from his Creator and his desire to invert the fundamental order of things by suppressing the truth about God and foolishly presuming to behave as though he can sovereignly control the course of history. That is why the entropy of cosmic energy is matched by the entropy of human society. The problem is essentially a human problem, and it is basically no different today from what it was in Plato's day or in any other period of the history of man.

Christian optimism, then, flows from the knowledge of the sovereignty and goodness of God and the indefectibility of His purposes. Christian pessimism flows from the knowledge of the fallenness of human nature and its incapacity to achieve the perfect society. As Paul Ramsey has said, "We have to contrast biblical or Christian eschatology with genetic eschatology." [65] The outlook for society, in terms of

---

[65] Paul Ramsey, *loc. cit.*, p. 132.

biblical eschatology, was described by the apostle Paul in
the following words, which, though written nineteen hundred years ago, apply in every detail to the human situation
of our own time:

> The final age of this world is to be a time of troubles.
> Men will love nothing but money and self; they will be
> arrogant, boastful, and abusive; with no respect for par-
> ents, no gratitude, no piety, no natural affection; they
> will be implacable in their hatreds, scandalmongers,
> intemperate and fierce, strangers to all goodness, trai-
> tors, adventurers, swollen with self-importance. They
> will be men who put pleasure in the place of God, men
> who preserve the outward form of religion, but are a
> standing denial of its reality.[66]

In a measure unknown before in human history our
twentieth century has experienced the reality of the
eschatological prediction of Christ that "even your parents
and brothers, your relations and friends, will betray you"
and that "on earth nations will stand helpless, not knowing
which way to turn from the roar and surge of the sea,"
while "men will faint with terror at the thought of all
that is coming upon the world." [67] According to the Christian eschatology, the consummation of this age is not a
man-devised utopia but the sudden breaking of the Day of
the Lord, marked by the coming again of Christ, this time
as Judge and King, to set up the unending perfection of the
kingdom of God, a kingdom from which all evil will be
eliminated. This is the Christian "utopia," and because it is
brought about by God it cannot fail of fulfilment.

In the meantime the Christian has to live in the world
as it exists between the two comings of Christ, knowing
both that the source of redemption is available by the free
grace of God in the crucified and risen Saviour and also that
the aspirations of unregenerate man for a perfect world,

---

[66] 2 Tim. 3:1ff. (New English Bible).
[67] Luke 21:16, 25f. (New English Bible).

even if he be scientist or philanthropist, will meet with frustration and failure because of the invalidating contradictions at the root of fallen human nature. In this world the Christian is commanded to love and serve his fellow man. He shares in the longings of others for an ideal society. He too yearns for a time when sickness, infirmity, cruelty, sorrow, and enmity will be banished from the human scene. He cannot approve, however, of the employment of means for the attainment of the utopia goal which have the effect of dehumanizing and depersonalizing the individual components of society. He cannot approve of such means, moreover, because they are inexorably self-defeating. He agrees with Paul Ramsey who says, "The Christian knows no such absolutely imperative end that would justify any means." [68] Eugenic programmes designed to improve the quality of mankind, to ensure an optimum size and balance of population, and ultimately to usher in the ideal society are prompted by excellent intentions; but if they involve the dissolution of the family, the refusal of parenthood to all but an élite few, mass sterilization, the production of babies from sperm and ova banks under laboratory conditions, and the rigid regimentation of society, then the Christian must demur. This may be eugenics from some strictly clinical point of view, but a scheme that cannot work without what is nothing less than a gross perversion of sexuality and an assault on the dignity and freedom of the person, indeed on the image of God in man, cannot be for the good of humanity. In the end it is as inhumane as it is inhuman.

Writing on "The Ethics of Genetic Intervention", Dwight J. Ingle asserts, "The idea of forcing a program of eugenics on any population is a threat to basic freedoms." He continues:

------

[68] Paul Ramsey, *loc. cit.*, p. 139.

Some governmental interventions in basic freedoms at the social level are even now models of injustice. Guided by social scientists, theologians, and jurists without competence in testing claims to knowledge, with little information and too little wisdom, governments are already fostering social malignancy, and without the general consent of the populations. Biologists are not enlightened by a greater wisdom; those asking for large-scale programs now, and especially for forced intervention through eugenics, should be rebuffed.

He pleads for the reasonableness of steering a course between laissez-faire and totalitarian methods of dealing with social and biomedical problems, and expresses the belief that "intervention with the biologic endowment of man requires consent, freedom from government control, and guidance by physicians trained in human genetics." [69]

It is unnecessary for me to belabour the emphasis that is placed on the sanctity of the marriage bond in Scripture. Not sexuality alone, but its purpose, the "one flesh" of the marriage union and the benediction of children proceeding from that union, is something constitutive of man himself. It is a principle which is there from the very beginning. The seventh of the ten commandments is a terse reminder that permanence and fidelity are essential ingredients of true marriage. The family unit is in a very special sense the sphere of God's covenant of grace. Throughout the centuries they have been among the most precious and ennobling of the institutions of society. They provide man with that sense of belonging which is so necessary to the flowering and fulfilment of personality and for which the organization of clubs and the regimentation of society in different ways can never be a substitute. A population deprived of the relationships expressed in the terms husband and wife, father and mother, parent and child is little

[69] Dwight J. Ingle, "Ethics of Genetic Intervention," in *Medical Opinion and Review*, Vol. 3, No. 9, September 1967, p. 61.

better than an assemblage of Pavlovian animals. To quote
Paul Ramsey again:

> To put radically asunder what God joined together in
> parenthood when He made love procreative, to pro-
> create from beyond the sphere of love (AID,[70] for ex-
> ample, or making human life in a test tube) or to posit
> acts of sexual love beyond the sphere of responsible
> procreation (by definition, marriage), means a refusal
> of the image of God's creation in our own.[71]

This is not, of course, to deny the importance of genetic
research or the beneficial contribution that genetics has to
make to the knowledge of mankind. Nor is it to belittle the
necessity of an ethics of genetic duty [72] which should be observed by all reasonable people, Christians not least. This is
really an ethics of self-control, not imposed arbitrarily on
society, but self-imposed by the individual on himself (or
herself) both inside and outside of marriage. Selfish and
irresponsible indulgence in the sexual act irrespective of the
consequences it may have is inexcusable. A person who
knows that he (or she) carries a defect or a disease which
is transmissible to the children he (or she) may have
should be prepared to forgo, in the interests both of the
family and of the race, the privilege and the pleasure of
marriage and parenthood. Married couples who discover
that they will pass on to their posterity seriously harmful or
deforming characteristics should refrain from having children of their own. In some cases at least voluntary
sterilization may be a right and proper course to follow.
Advance in genetic knowledge will certainly mean the opportunity for advance in genetic responsibility. Whether
that opportunity will be taken is another question. But in
this, as in other matters which affect the welfare of the
community, Christians should be prepared to give a lead
and fulfil their duty.

---

[70] That is, artificial insemination with the semen of a donor other
than the husband.
[71] Paul Ramsey, *loc. cit.*, pp. 147f.
[72] *Ibid.*, p. 166.

Finally, while marriage is an institution of this life and not of the next—"those who are accounted worthy to attain to that age," Christ taught, "and to the resurrection from the dead neither marry nor are given in marriage" [73]—the kingdom of God represents the triumph of love, the love of God in Christ and the responsive love of the redeemed, and the consummating event is going to be that of a marriage, the marriage of Christ with His bride the Church. That union will be infinitely more sacred and intimate than any union of husband and wife in this present age; and it will be an eternal union, for it will never be terminated by death. Here and now, death is the inescapable surd which unfailingly writes frustration across all merely human endeavour and which means that, even if a human utopia were attainable, it would be enjoyed only by some distant future generation, but still subject to the human life-span. Death would have excluded all previous generations from it. But the kingdom of God will have a citizenship which embraces all the generations of human history and all the races of mankind, "a great multitude which no man could number, from every nation, from all tribes and peoples and tongues." [74] The vision of the aged apostle is still the vision of the Christian Church:

> I saw a new heaven and a new earth; for the first heaven and the first earth had passed away, and the sea was no more. And I saw the holy city, new Jerusalem, coming down out of heaven from God, prepared as a bride adorned for her husband; and I heard a great voice from the throne saying, 'Behold, the dwelling of God is with men. He will dwell with them, and they shall be his people, and God himself will be with them; he will wipe away every tear from their eyes, and death shall be no more, neither shall there be mourning nor crying nor pain any more, for the former things have passed away'.[75]

---

[73] Luke 20:35.
[74] Rev. 7:9.
[75] Rev. 21:1ff.

SECTION 2

PERSPECTIVES
FROM THE
HEALTH SCIENCES

Chapter 6

MEDICAL INDICATIONS FOR CONTRACEPTION

SUMMARY

The goal of birth control is that every child be wanted and planned. This objective is assumed in this chapter as an acceptable guideline for the couple and the physician called to make decisions related to contraception or sterilization. Significant medical statistics are presented. Diseases which are indications for prevention of conception are enumerated. The thesis "for every life saved in an overpopulated world a new life should be prevented" is advanced. The physician is encouraged to be involved in all facets of birth control in keeping with the purpose of treating the whole person.

Harold W. Hermann, M.D. *The author of this paper is currently the Associate Director of the Medical Research Department in the Mead Johnson Research Center, Evansville, Indiana. He is a pediatrician, having been chief of pediatrics at Methodist Hospital in Minneapolis and on the teaching staff of the School of Medicine of the University of Minnesota, and was in private practice in Minneapolis for fifteen years.*

MEDICAL INDICATIONS FOR CONTRACEPTION

by H. W. Hermann

Birth control is an accepted technique of modern preventive medicine. Not only is it *accepted*, but it is becoming increasingly *essential* as an important constituent of population control plans. The goal of birth control is that every child be wanted and planned.

The safest years for childbearing for the mother are the ages of 20 to 30. There is a recognized increase in the rate of stillbirths and congenital malformations in children fathered by men over 45 years of age or born to women in their teens or over forty years of age. The president of the Planned Parenthood Federation of America states:

> "Beyond the fourth child, maternal and perinatal mortality rates rise slowly through the sixth pregnancy, moderately through eighth, and relatively

rapidly thereafter. The best pregnancy interval from the viewpoint of infant survival is two to three years between the end of one pregnancy and the beginning of the next. The physician knowing the health of the woman should advise against further pregnancies if, in his judgment, medical contraindications exist." [1]

Contraceptive advice rendered by the physician can be based on sociological, economic, medical, or purely personal reasons. In defining medical care as therapy of the total person, each of these categories can rightfully be considered medical indications. However, when restricting the topic to medical indications for contraception on the basis of physical health, we immediately face the issue of whether the fertility control should be temporary or permanent.

Short of an operative procedure or destruction of the organs of reproduction, such as by radiation, contraceptive methods are considered temporary. The choices of temporary methods available are continually increasing, ranging from the highly effective estrogenic agents taken by mouth to the less reliable rhythm method to the least effective post-coital douche methods and withdrawal.

Temporary methods of contraception are medically indicated in those circumstances where the wife may have increasingly severe diabetes, active tuberculosis, disability from the consequences of poliomyelitis, progressive cardiovascular disease amenable to surgical prosthesis, or progressive neuromuscular disease—or any medical condition that limits her activity. In these instances, spacing of the children is the key consideration. Even in such cases the advisability of temporary methods could be seriously questioned but may be considered acceptable when the desire for a child or children exceeds the risk to the mother after being medically assessed. The actual pregnancy and delivery are rarely fatal or disabling to the mother with modern obstetrical care, but

---

[1] Alan F. Guttmacher, *Minnesota Medicine*, January, 1968, page 138.

the ability of an already disabled or activity-limited woman coping with three or more children demands its share of consideration by the responsible physician. Thus, temporary methods are rarely medically justified.

Before a "permanent" fertility control procedure is performed, the couple must have adequate consultation with knowledgeable personnel. Voluntary sterilization is legal in all fifty states, with only two states, Connecticut and Utah, restricting the reasons for its performance. "Informed consent" by both partners is an essential of honesty as well as for the medico-legal safety of the advising physician. This sterilization route of contraception is preferred by many because of its permanence and degree of completeness. Its risk is limited to a period of surgical intervention, and its cost is not a continuing factor. Even surgical methods are not 100% effective.

We Protestants have been silent too long in addressing ourselves to this moral-religious issue. The Bible admonishes, "Be fruitful, and multiply, and replenish the earth and subdue it" (Genesis 1:28). Because of our familiarity with the first four words of that scripture, we have not seen the responsibility further extended in the challenge to "subdue it" as related to overpopulation and its earthly problems. The Christian Medical Society has actively propounded the thesis that one of our medical tasks in aiding an underdeveloped society is that for every life saved through advancing medical therapeutics, epidemic control or prevention, a new life should be prevented.

Thus, in summary, although there are physical-medical indications for contraception, the physician's involvement with and ministrations to the "whole person" demands our increasing support in world-wide assistance toward population control. Where these medical indications do exist, a permanent type of contraception is the most practical.

Chapter 7

MEDICAL INDICATIONS FOR THERAPEUTIC ABORTION AND STERILIZATION

SUMMARY

The historical evolution of the practice of induced thera-peutic abortion as performed by medical doctors in treating diseases complicated by pregnancy are reviewed. The author then discusses those medical entities which require abortion for the preservation of the life of the mother, or the preservation of her health if it is seriously threatened by the diseases under consideration. Reference is also made to indications that relate primarily to the unborn child. Medical indications for sterilization are also examined, with reference to those indications which are enumerated for abortion. It is shown that medical progress has re-duced conditions that justify abortion or sterilization only to a few, and that even in these, interruption or prevention of the pregnancy is indicated only when the disease is of a very severe nature.

Eugene B. Linton, M.D., F.A.C.O.G. *Dr. Linton is assistant professor in the Department of Obstetrics and Gynecology of the Bowman Gray School of Medicine at Winston-Salem, North Carolina. He has also held an academic appointment in obstetrics and gynecology at the University of Tennessee. He was granted a B.S. degree from Davidson College and earned his medical degree at the Medical College of Virginia. Dr. Linton is a son of missionaries and was born in Kunsan, Korea, where he received most of his earlier education. Dr. Linton is a Fellow of the American College of Obstetricians and Gynecologists.*

MEDICAL INDICATIONS FOR THERAPEUTIC ABORTION AND STERILIZATION

by Eugene B. Linton

INTRODUCTION

In ancient times, therapeutic abortion was done to save the life of the mother. One Greek school of philosophy gave serious consideration to certain eugenic aspects of the procedure. Early in the Christian era, toward the end of the fourth century, the leading physician, Priscianus, recommended abortion to save the life of the mother. However, as the influence of the Roman Catholic Church became more widespread, physicians were threatened with eternal punishment for taking the life of an unborn child. After the tenth century, medical writings contained no mention of the subject. The question was re-opened at the beginning of the 18th century. In 1772 William Cooper, speaking of the bad results of Cesarean section in cases of contracted pelvis, stated "in such cases where it is certainly known where a mature child cannot possibly be delivered in the ordinary way alive, would it not be consistent with reason and conscience, for the preservation of the mother, as soon as it can conveniently be done, by artificial modus to attempt to produce an abortion?"

Dewees in 1843 quotes with approval Alfred Delpeau, who had said "for my own part, I confess I cannot possibly balance the life of a fetus of 3, 4, 5, or 6 months, a being which so far scarcely differs from a plant, and is bound by no ties to the external world, against that of an adult woman who a thousand social ties engage us to save; so that in case of extreme contraction, if it were mathematically demonstrated the delivery at full term would be impossible, I would not hesitate to recommend abortion in the first months of gestation."

In England and France many obstetricians accepted these suggestions, but in Germany it was not until the beginning of the 19th century that Kiwisch, Scanzoni and others advocated the therapeutic abortion. During the latter half of the 19th century, and especially in Germany, the indications were extended to include tuberculosis, heart disease, nephritis and certain forms of psychosis. In the present century, particularly since World War I, there has been increasing tendency to extend the indications to eugenic and socio-economic factors.

Hasseltine, Adair and Boynton define therapeutic abortion as follows: "Therapeutic abortion means the termination of an apparently normal intrauterine pregnancy before the period of viability in an effort to save or prolong the life of a mother." [1]

In order to limit the scope of this paper, only those medical entities which necessitate abortion for the preservation of the life of the mother, or in cases where pregnancy

---

[1] Colpills, R. V. "Trends in Therapeutic Abortion". *American Journal of Obstetrics and Gynecology.* Vol. 68:988, 1954.

seriously threatens to affect the health of the mother will be considered.

CARDIAC DISEASE

Whether inherited or acquired, cardiac or heart disease comprises the most common medical indication for therapeutic abortion. The cause of the lesion in the heart or its exact location is not as important as the classification or the results of the lesion in terms of residual function of the heart. The classification used by most clinics is that of the New York Heart Association as follows:

> Class I—Patients with a cardiac disorder without limitation of physical activity. Ordinary physical activity causes no discomfort.
> Class II—Patients with a cardiac disorder with a slight to moderate limitation of physical activity. Ordinary physical activity causes some discomfort.
> Class III—Patients with a cardiac disorder with moderate to great limitation of physical activity. Less than ordinary physical activity causes discomfort.
> Class IV—Patients with a cardiac disorder who are unable to carry on any physical activity without discomfort.[2]

Another factor to be considered is the age of the patient. There is a much greater risk in pregnancy when patients have passed 35 years of age and also in the presence or precedent of irregularities of rhythm of the heart.[3]

Interruption of pregnancy should be seriously considered in all Class III and Class IV patients with heart disease. Those patients who have a lesion which can be corrected by surgery have been operated upon during pregnancy, and there are reports in the literature indicating that a successful outcome of the pregnancy is possible following surgery

---

[2] Guttmacher, A. F., Rovinsky, J. J., *Medical, Surgical and Gynecological Complications during Pregnancy*. New York. Williams and Watkins, 1961.
[3] *Ibid.*

during pregnancy. If, however, the patient falls in the Class IV group with a lesion that can be corrected, therapeutic abortion might be considered, followed by surgery that would correct the condition of the heart, and then the patient would be encouraged to become pregnant again after surgery.

Where a patient in early pregnancy has acute and active abnormalities of the heart due to rheumatic fever, or where the situation has degenerated to heart failure that is difficult to control, interruption of the pregnancy should be considered.[4] This is also true in the patient seriously ill with bacterial endocarditis, which is an inflammation of the inner layers of the heart due to bacterial organisms. A study by Chelsey at the Margaret Hague Maternity Hospital shows that the life expectancy of women with rheumatic heart disease is not altered by pregnancy.[5] Myocardial infarction (acute coronary heart disease) in the child-bearing age group is exceedingly rare. In a review of the literature and case report by Mendelson, a 24% mortality was found among patients who had coronary or artery disease.[6] It would seem, then, that interruption of pregnancy should be seriously considered in a patient who has definite coronary artery heart disease, if proved by usual, definitive diagnostic procedures.

DISEASES OF THE KIDNEY

Advancing pregnancy makes increasing demands on kidney function. Those women who have a marked decrease in a kidney's ability to function normally (renal reserve)

[4] Ueland, K., Metcalf, J., "Acute Rheumatic Fever in Pregnancy". *American Journal of Obstetrics and Gynecology.* Vol. 95:586, 1966.

[5] Chesley, L. C. "Rheumatic Cardiac Disease and Pregnancy": *Obstetrics and Gynecology,* Vol. 29:560, 1967.

[6] Mendelson, C. L. "Coronary Artery Disease in Pregnancy". *American Journal of Obstetrics and Gynecology.* Vol. 63:381, 1952.

should be considered for interruption.[7] This impairment of renal function can be due to infection, diseases of the blood vessels supplying the kidney which cause high blood pressure (hypertensive cardiovascular renal disease), a complication of long-standing diabetes, inherited lesions of the kidney, such as polycystic kidneys, or loss of renal function due to disease of the small blood vessels, called periarteritis. The classical urinary determinations that show a fixed specific gravity of the urine plus the presence of abnormal concentrations of albumin, should be reinforced by other laboratory diagnostic aids, including chemical, radiologic and radioisotopic determinations.[8]

DISEASES OF THE LUNG

Tuberculosis of the lung as an indication for interruption of pregnancy is almost non-existent unless the pulmonary reserve (capacity of the lungs to function in the oxygenation processes of the body) of the patient is seriously impaired due to destruction of the lung or deforming surgery.[9] The same principle applies in other lung diseases, including emphysema, bronchiectasis, abnormalities of the bony structures of the chest or the back and other inherited lesions where an enlarging uterus would seriously impair the required expansion of the lungs. Those who have chronic lung disease of an obstructive nature and who suffer from oxygen starvation, a low oxygen level in the blood, as well as a high retention rate of carbon dioxide, do poorly during pregnancy and probably should have it interrupted. In a disease called primary pulmonary hypertension, in which there is an abnormally high blood pressure in the arteries supplying the lungs, a maternal mortality of 53%

---

[7] Guttmacher and Rovinsky, *op. cit.*
[8] *Ibid.*
[9] *Ibid.*

is reported. Interruption of pregnancy would be indicated in patients with this disease.[10]

MALIGNANT DISEASES

With the exception of malignant tumors of the breast and cancer of the neck of the uterus, malignant tumors are not adversely affected by pregnancy. Even in the case of cancer of the breast it is a subject of some controversy whether pregnancy has an adverse effect on that disease. Many feel that if the patient becomes pregnant within two years of a diagnosis of carcinoma of the breast, she should not be allowed to continue with a pregnancy.[11] Hagenson, on the other hand, feels that there is not enough data to support this thesis and cites several case histories in which patients have had several pregnancies following a radical removal of the breast because of cancer without any apparent unfavorable effect. He feels that pregnancy does not affect cancer of the breast. He points out that the late stage in which cancer is usually diagnosed in that young age group of patients comes with a lower rate of salvage five years after diagnosis, which is reported in many series.[12]

Most authorities agree that when cancer of the cervix (neck and opening of the uterus) is diagnosed at an early stage of pregnancy, that pregnancy should be ignored and treatment instituted immediately whether it be by irradiation (x-ray therapy) or radical surgery.[13] Either of these alternatives in therapy would interrupt a pregnancy; abor-

---

[10] McCaffrey, R. M., and Dun, L. V. "Primary Pulmonary Hypertension in Pregnancy", *Ob-Gyn Survey* 19:567, 1964.

[11] Robinson, D. W., "Breast Carcinoma Associated with Pregnancy". *Obstetrics and Gynecology*, Vol. 23:99, 1964.

[12] Haagensen, C. D. "Cancer of the Breast in Pregnancy and during Lactation". *American Journal of Obstetrics and Gynecology.* Vol. 98:141, 1967.

[13] Kinch, R. A. H., "Factors Affecting the Prognosis of Cancer of the Cervix in Pregnancy". *American Journal of Obstetrics and Gynecology.* Vol. 82:45, 1961.

tion usually occurs rather promptly following external x-ray therapy.

DISEASES OF THE LIVER

A marked and persistent reduction of normal functioning of the liver is called severe chronic hepatic failure. There are many possible causes of such failure. This condition is usually incompatible with a normal function of the ovaries and is therefore rarely complicated by pregnancy. However, if pregnancy does occur and is allowed to progress, the incidence of subsequent complete failure of the liver is quite high. Total hepatic failure is not compatible with life. Therapeutic abortion would be advised in the interest of prolonging a mother's life. It would be most unlikely that she would tolerate the burden of pregnancy in the presence of her liver disease.

Acute infectious hepatitis, a condition in which there is widespread inflammation of liver cells, is not an indication for abortion. Pregnancy does not alter the course of this disease.[14]

DISEASES OF THE NERVOUS SYSTEM

Diseases of the nervous system complicated by pregnancy are rare. From all reports, their course is unaffected by pregnancy. Some authorities feel that repeated pregnancy is contraindicated in a patient with a disease called multiple sclerosis, and such repeated pregnancies may precipitate an aggravation of the disease. However, the low number of cases reported and the extremely variable natural history of the disease make good statistical analysis and definitive conclusions difficult.[15]

DISEASES OF THE GASTROINTESTINAL SYSTEM

Two diseases of the gastrointestinal system have been

---

[14] Guttmacher and Rovinsky, *op. cit.*
[15] *Ibid.*

cited as reasons for therapeutic abortion. One is ulcerative colitis (a chronic, ulcerating disease affecting the large bowel), and the other is regional ileitis, which is a non-specific inflammatory disorder of the portion of the small intestine called the ileum. Because there is a definite correlation between the psychic state of the patient and her disease in both conditions, it is extremely difficult to evaluate the effect of pregnancy on them. Some mothers do quite well through pregnancy, others deteriorate and become extremely ill. The latter usually require therapeutic abortion. There is general agreement that when ulcerative colitis appears during pregnancy, it is apt to be extremely severe, and in such cases, an abortion is indicated.[16]

THE PREGNANT SURGICAL PATIENT

From time to time, it is necessary to perform major surgery in various degrees of importance on a patient who is pregnant. It is impossible to make generalizations about instances in which the nature of the surgical intervention or the consequences of it might constitute an indication for therapeutic abortion. There are no rules of thumb in this confrontation of priorities which the attending physician faces. The variables which relate to the surgery itself (nature of procedure, health of the patient, the underlying disease, etc.) must be evaluated together with variables that are less tangible but which are, nevertheless, important. These latter variables include the number of children which the mother has had, the desire of the parents to have the infant whose life is in question, the religion of the parents, etc. Decisions in such situations require great maturity in judgment and should preferably be made in consultation with specialists in more than one field of medicine.

---

[16] *Ibid.*

INDICATIONS RELATED TO THE FETUS

Any medical condition in one or both parents which results in a high incidence of abnormalities of the fetus constitutes a medical indication for therapeutic abortion. Examples are rubella (German measles) in the mother during the first seven weeks of gestation, intake by the mother of drugs which have been proven to cause fetal abnormalities (teratogenic drugs) and in the presence in one or both parents of hereditary conditions which have a high risk of recurrence in subsequent generations. (The reader is referred to discussion of this and other papers found in Part V, Appendix 4 of this book.)

MISCELLANEOUS

There are a number of conditions which are rare, or rarely complicated by pregnancy, in which the course of the disease in the presence of that present pregnancy is not truly known. The following is a list of diseases in which the evidence suggests that they are adversely affected by gestation. These are aplastic anemia,[17] acute pancreatitis, esophageal varices, collagen disease not affecting the function of the kidney, rare eye lesions, abnormalities of the blood vessels of the brain, etc. Isolated case reports are scattered throughout medical literature, but each case has to be considered on its own merit, and no categorical statements can be made concerning these entities.

MEDICAL INDICATIONS FOR STERILIZATION

Indications for sterilization are present in any of the conditions discussed earlier, where there is no hope of recovery or improvement of the disease for which the abortion is done. It seems obvious that prevention of pregnancy is indicated in women suffering from an incorrectable

[17] Rosner, F., Sussman, S. N., "Aplastic Anemia in Pregnancy". *Obstetrics and Gynecology*, Vol. 23:99, 1964.

heart lesion or in severe chronic diseases of the kidney or the liver.

Sterilization is also indicated where one or both parents are carriers of hereditary disease. The indication is present when it has been demonstrated objectively that there is a continuing risk of severe hereditary abnormalities in subsequent children. An example of a disease which not uncommonly causes such situations is cystic fibrosis of the pancreas.

CONCLUSION

It is often difficult in the individual patient to determine if there is a pure, clear-cut clinical indication for abortion and/or sterilization. Medical progress has reduced these conditions to only a very few. Even in these, the indication is present only when the disease is of a very severe nature. Recent summaries of the experience in induced therapeutic abortion as practiced in leading hospitals of the country show that these comprise but a small percentage of the total number of therapeutic abortions performed today.[18]

---

[18] Hall, R. E., "Therapeutic Abortion, Sterilization and Contraception". *American Journal of Obstetrics and Gynecology*, Vol. 91:518, 1965. Rovinsky, J. J., Gusberg, S. B., "Current Trends in Therapeutic Termination of Pregnancy". *American Journal of Obstetrics and Gynecology*, Vol. 98:11, 1967.

Chapter 8

THREATENED HEALTH OF MOTHER AS AN INDICATION FOR THERAPEUTIC ABORTION

SUMMARY

The current status of the law concerning therapeutic abortion as it relates directly with threatened health of the mother is examined briefly. The following reasons for abortion are considered: Medical, fetal, psychiatric, moral, philosophic, legal, religious and socio-economic factors. Factors are noted that are affecting incidence of induced abortion in different parts of the United States.

The threatened health of the mother as an indication for induced abortion is discussed in the context of all indications for that procedure. In this connection, it is noted that many induced abortions performed allegedly for psychiatric reasons are really done for socioeconomic considerations. Evidence suggesting that such is the case is given.

A description of various methods of induced abortion written for the non-medical layman helps the reader understand the nature of the decisions made by physicians confronted by difficult clinical alternatives. The complications that follow an induced abortion, as well as the consequences of not doing one when it might be indicated, are evaluated and compared.

The author concludes that while there are some clear-cut indications for induced abortion to preserve the health of the mother, they are becoming quite rare. He also underlines that the latest medical advances make induced abortions as safe as carrying a pregnancy to term. Morbidity and mortality when the operation is performed under ideal conditions are probably uncommon.

Christopher T. Reilly, M.D., F.A.C.O.G. *The author of this paper is in private practice in Ridgewood, New Jersey, and is an attending Surgeon of the Department of Obstetrics and Gynecology of the Valley Hospital at Ridgewood, New Jersey. He has been clinical assistant professor of obstetrics and gynecology at the New Jersey College of Medicine since 1965. He was director of the New Jersey Study of Maternity Utilization. Dr. Reilly did his undergraduate studies at New York University and was granted the M.D. degree from the Long Island College of Medicine (now State University of New York) in 1949. He became a Fellow of the American College of Obstetricians and Gynecologists in 1957 and is secretary-treasurer for District III of that college at the present time.*

THREATENED HEALTH OF MOTHER AS AN INDICATION FOR THERAPEUTIC ABORTION

by Christopher T. Reilly

INTRODUCTION

Each state in the United States has, in one form or another, a law concerning therapeutic abortion. In most cases it is permitted only to preserve the life of the mother. In some states the permission for abortion appears to be somewhat broader in that it includes the health of the mother as an indication. The terminology used is frequently vague and, of course, anything that would affect the mother's health would ultimately have an effect on her life. As a result, when to perform a therapeutic abortion has been left largely in the hands of the medical profession and it has been felt that current medical practice does not completely conform with the intent of the law unless one stretches the imagination. Some consciously feel that the dichotomy between the requirements of the law and current medical practice in abortion is of sufficient importance to suggest possible legislative revision.[1]

No attempt will be made here to moralize on this subject. Our purpose is to outline the indications and incidence of therapeutic abortion, the current methods that are used to perform the procedure, and the complications that have occurred. Naturally, it is almost impossible to divorce oneself completely from the ethical considerations. Medical factors are not only influenced by contemporary ethics but they, in turn, have their influence on these standards. The aspects of abortion which have emotional overtones are: medical, fetal, psychiatric, moral, philosophic, legal, religious, and socio-economic.[2] Before discussing the medical dimensions of this subject it will be helpful to review the other aspects. Some of these have stimulated trends in public opinion which are pertinent to this presentation.

The term, "induced abortion" will be used in this presentation, rather than therapeutic abortion. It has been chosen because the word therapeutic assumes the procedure will be curative, a result which cannot be guaranteed. Any time one must decide whether an induced abortion should be performed, the anticipated curative effects must be considered in relation to the potential risks of the procedure.

The existing attitudes toward induced abortion over the last 3500 years have been amply reviewed by others.[3] Robert F. Drinan, Dean of the Boston College Law School,[4]

---

[1] Gampell, R. J., "Legal Status of Therapeutic Abortion and Sterilization in the United States", *Clinical Obstetrics & Gynecology* 7:22, 1964.

[2] Barno, A., "Criminal Abortion Deaths, Illegitimate Pregnancy Deaths, and Suicides in Pregnancy", *American Journal of Obstetrics & Gynecology* 98:356, 1967.

[3] Eastman, J. N., "Induced Abortion and Contraceptions: A Consideration of Ethical Philosophy in Obstetrics", *Obstetrics and Gynecology Survey* 22:3, 1967; and Lister, J., "Medicine, Morals and Money", *New England Journal of Medicine* 276:971, 1967.

[4] Drinan, R. F., "Strategy on Abortion", *America*, Feb. 4, 1967. p. 177.

in an attempt to establish a stand which the Catholic Church could take concerning changes in laws involving induced abortion, discussed the results of a little publicized survey conducted by the National Opinion Research Center. A large percentage of the population favors permission for induced abortion to preserve maternal health, rape and genetic factors. Only a very small percentage of the population would care to legalize abortion for socioeconomic reasons or on demand. See Table 1.

	Yes	No	Don't Know
If the woman's own health is seriously endangered by the pregnancy	71	20	3
If she became pregnant as a result of rape	56	38	6
If there is a strong chance of a serious defect in the baby	55	41	4
If the family has a very low income and cannot afford any more children	21	77	2
If she is not married and does not want to marry the man	18	80	2
If she is married and does not want any more children	15	83	2

The Position of the American College of Obstetricians and Gynecologists

Significant action did occur in 1968. A committee of The American College of Obstetricians and Gynecologists prepared a statement on "therapeutic abortion" which was

circulated to their membership. It was approved in principle
by the majority of their members and finally, officially approved by their Executive Board on May 9, 1968. Included
here is the full text of the "Introduction to Statement on
Therapeutic Abortion" and the "Statement on Therapeutic
Abortion."

Introduction to Statement on Therapeutic Abortion

The American College of Obstetricians and Gynecologists,
cognizant of its responsibility for defining the standards of
maternity care, believes it has a responsibility to the profession
and public to state not only its recommendations with respect
to the laws governing therapeutic or medical abortion, but to
offer an interpretation of these recommendations. Moreover, the
College believes that it also has a duty to state what its membership will or will not condone or support.

First, The American College of Obstetricians and Gynecologists regards therapeutic or medical abortion as primarily a
medical responsibility. Secondly, any law concerned with therapeutic abortion should view as relevant that excessive numbers
of pregnancies and resultant offspring may cause social economic erosion of the family. All too often when the anticipated
family size has been exceeded, the patient in desperation may
resort to dangerous measures in an effort to terminate the pregnancy. In this regard, mention is rarely made of the numbers of
intrauterine lives lost through failure to react to this medical
problem.

In broadening the law to take into account the patient's
entire environment, actual or reasonably foreseeable, in assessing maternal risk, the medical profession must consider and
give thoughtful evaluation to each individual request. Experience will support the concept that physicians can convince
patients to continue an unplanned pregnancy provided steps will
be taken to prevent future unwanted pregnancy; and society
should provide the necessary economic support for the patient
so that she will continue and complete the pregnancy.

The foregoing leads to the suggestion that clinics be established within existing maternity sources to provide care and
consideration of patients with unplanned pregnancies. With the
assistance of special agencies, it is envisioned that the patient
will not take those measures that will be detrimental not only
to her immediate health, but which may cause physical and psychological sequelae.

*It is firmly stated that the College will not condone nor sup-
port the concept that an abortion be considered or performed
for any unwanted pregnancy or as a means of population control* (Italics ours, ed.). It is emphasized that the inherent risk
of such an abortion is not fully appreciated both by many in the
profession and certainly not by the public. Where abortion may
be obtained on demand, as in Japan and the Soviet Union, medical authorities of both these nations indicate that the physical
and psychological sequelae are still to be determined. Moreover,
where abortion is so practiced it can be said that the mortality

and morbidity rates are difficult to ascertain. Further, the public should realize that in countries or societies that permit abortion on demand, many, if not the majority, are performed in physicians' offices. Under these circumstances, it is reasonable to conclude that the mortality from this operation may exceed the maternal mortality of the United States and Canada while the incidence of serious complications is substantial.

Statement on Therapeutic Abortion

Termination of pregnancy by therapeutic abortion is a medical procedure. It must be performed only in a hospital accredited by the Joint Commission on Accreditation of Hospitals and by a licensed physician qualified to perform such operations.

Therapeutic abortion is permitted only with the informed consent of the patient and her husband, or herself if unmarried, or of her nearest relative if she is under the age of consent. No patient should be compelled to undergo, or a physician to perform, a therapeutic abortion if either has ethical, religious or any other objections to it.

A consultative opinion must be obtained from at least two licensed physicians other than the one who is to perform the procedure. This opinion should state that the procedure is medically indicated. The consultants may act separately or as a special committee. One consultant should be a qualified obstetrician-gynecologist and one should have special competence in the medical area in which the medical indications for the procedure reside.

Therapeutic abortion may be performed for the following established medical indications:

1. When continuation of the pregnancy may threaten the life of the woman or seriously impair her health. In determining whether or not there is such risk to health, account may be taken of the patient's total environment, actual or reasonably foreseeable.
2. When pregnancy has resulted from rape or incest: in this case the same medical criteria should be employed in the evaluation of the patient.
3. When continuation of the pregnancy is likely to result in the birth of a child with grave physical deformities or mental retardation.

Although the Statement by The American College of Obstetricians and Gynecologists only suggests consultations from two licensed physicians other than the one who is to perform the procedure, there are many who have recommended that applications should be submitted to a hospital committee on abortion and sterilization.[5] Hall observed that

[5] Eastman, N. J., "Obstetrician's Obligation to Provide Abortion, Sterilization, and Contraception", *Ob. & Gyn. Survey* 20:944, 1965; Russell, K. P., "Therapeutic Abortion in a General Hospital", *Am. J. Ob. & Gyn.* 62:434, 1951; Savel, L. E., "Adjudication of Therapeutic Abortion and Sterilization", *Clinical Ob. & Gyn.* 7:14, 1964.

at Sloane Hospital in New York City the incidence of abortion, five years following the establishment of a formal board for review, was almost precisely one-third of that during the previous five years.[6] One questions whether the formation of such committees would involve more individuals whose personal prejudices would prevent them from acting favorably on such applications.

FACTORS THAT AFFECT THE INCIDENCE OF INDUCED ABORTION

There seems to be a marked disparity between the incidence of induced abortions in various cities of the United States, in the various hospitals within one city and in the same hospital from one year to another. It is understandable that such is the case because frequently there is little objective evidence and so much depends on subjective factors. On the other hand, there have been some advances, trends, and factors which could have an influence on the incidence of induced abortion:

1. Changes in attitude.

2. Changes in the law.

3. Medical advances in the treatment or cure of diseases previously considered indications for abortion.

4. Medical advances which have made abortions safer, such as the use of blood transfusions, better anesthesia, and the discovery of antibiotics and chemotherapeutic agents.

5. A greater variety of methods to accomplish an induced abortion. (These methods will be discussed later.)

6. The discovery of new indications for abortions such as the effects of drugs and viruses on the fetus.

7. Improved contraceptive techniques reducing the occurrence of unwanted pregnancies.

8. Permissiveness in society (new morality?) resulting in

---

[6] Hall, R. E., "Therapeutic Abortion, Sterilization and Contraception", *Am. J. Ob. & Gyn.* 91:518, 1965.

more out-of-wedlock pregnancies which occur despite the availability of contraceptive methods.

9. Concern over the population explosion.

Indications for Induced Abortion

The indications for induced abortion can be classified into five broad categories: Psychiatric, general medical, due to malignancy, genetic, and socioeconomic. There is no doubt that the first three are concerned primarily with the threatened health of the mother. It is very difficult, however, for physicians to differentiate between a psychiatrically contraindicated pregnancy and an unwanted pregnancy.[7] Both the unwanted pregnancy or the medically (psychiatric) contraindicated pregnancy produced a severe psychologic reaction.[8] Rape and incest have a profound emotional effect whether the pregnancy be terminated by induced abortion or by term delivery. Even the genetic factors can have an effect on the mother's emotional health because many informed mothers are aware of the reported rate of abnormalities with German measles. Much has been written on the effects of drugs and inherited genetic defects. These women require considerable support and at times their emotional health is profoundly affected by the circumstances.

Rates of abortion are generally reported as a number per thousand live births. A review of the literature will reveal widely different rates in various reports. The overall ratio in the United States in 1966 and 1967 was approximately 2.5 per thousand live births.[9] In another study involving 60 outstanding American hospitals in 1965, Hall reported an

[7] Moore, J. G. and Randall, J. H., "Trends in Therapeutic Abortion. A Review of 137 Cases", *Am. J. Ob. & Gyn.* 63:28, 1952.

[8] Kretzschmar, R. M. and Norris, A. S., "Psychiatric Implications of Therapeutic Abortion", *Am. J. Ob. & Gyn.* 98:368, 1967.

[9] Spivak, M. M., "Therapeutic Abortion. A Twelve Year Review at the Toronto General Hospital, 1954–1965", *Am. J. Ob. & Gyn.* 97:316, 1967.

overall ratio of 3.6.[10] The ratio of abortions at certain specific hospitals are as follows: The University of Pennsylvania 4.6, Beth Israel Hospital, Newark 4.3, New York Mount Sinai 5.7, and the Toronto General Hospital 5.8.[11] It is interesting to note that there has been a definite increase in the number of induced abortions at the Toronto General Hospital during a 12-year period included in their report.[12] This increase is due almost exclusively to the acceptance of psychiatric indications for induced abortion. Buffalo also reports an increased incidence of induced abortion in contrast to the experience reported in other cities in the United States.[13] The ratio of therapeutic abortions per thousand live births in New York City has gradually decreased from 5.1 to 1.8 over a 20-year period from 1943 to 1962.[14]

Medical indications for induced abortion are generally cardiac, renal, pulmonary, malignancy and a variety of other miscellaneous conditions (See Chapter 7). Most authors report that medical non-psychiatric indications account for less than 50% of their induced abortions.[15] The incidence of induced abortion for medical reasons during the past two decades has either remained the same or decreased.[16] Tuberculosis and benign neoplasms have almost

[10] Hall, R. E., op. cit.

[11] Spivak, M. M., op. cit.

[12] Ibid.

[13] Moore, J. G. and Randall, J. H., op cit.; Niswander, K. R., Klein, M. and Randall, C. L., "Changing Attitudes Toward Therapeutic Abortion", Journal of American Medical Association 196:1140, 1966.

[14] Gold, E. M., Erhardt, C. L., Jacobziner, H., M.D. and Nelson, F. G., "Therapeutic Abortions in New York City: A Twenty Year Review", American Journal of Physiology 55:964, 1965; Tietze, C., "Therapeutic Abortions in New York City, 1943–1947", Am. J. Ob. & Gyn. 60:146, 1950.

[15] Russell, K. P. and Moore, J. G., "Maternal Medical Indications for Therapeutic Abortion", Clinical Ob. & Gyn. 7:43, 1964; and Spivak, M. M., op. cit.

[16] Gold, E. M., et al., op. cit.; and Rovinsky, J. J. and Gusberg, S. B., "Current Trends in Therapeutic Termination of Pregnancy", Am. J. Ob. & Gyn. 98:11, 1967.

been eliminated as a reason. One observer noted that virtually all of the abortions for the more debatable indications such as arthritis, inactive tuberculosis, and rubella were performed on private patients, whereas most of the induced abortions performed on ward or charity patients were for the less debatable indications such as rheumatic heart disease and hypertensive cardiovascular disease.[17] This difference between the management of the ward patient and the private patient will be reviewed in more detail later.

The incidence of abortions for genetic reasons has not changed much over the last two decades.[18] Yearly differences are usually the result of sporadic epidemics of rubella (German measles). The incidence for genetic reasons may change as the result of marked advances being made in the field of teratology (the study of hereditary abnormalities), discovery of the effects of some of the newer drugs upon the fetus and development of immunologic methods which make possible a more specific diagnosis in the case of virus infections. The genetic fetal indications for abortion have been thoroughly reviewed in the literature [19] and are mentioned here only because of their effect on the patient's emotional stability. Even for genetic indications there seems to be a higher incidence on the private service than on the ward service. Perhaps the private patients present themselves earlier during their pregnancy for care and have better documentation of rubella. The private patients might also be better educated regarding other genetic factors.[20] It is quite possible, however, that the psychiatric aspects of this indication could also be influential in increasing the rate.

---

[17] Hall, R. E., *op. cit.*

[18] Gold, E. M., *et al.*, *op. cit.*

[19] Moloshok, R. E., "Fetal Considerations for Therapeutic Abortion and Sterilization", *Clinical Ob. & Gyn.* 7:82, 1964.

[20] Rovinsky, J. J. and Gusberg, S. B., *op. cit.*

Psychiatric indications are accounting for an increasingly greater proportion of all induced abortions. Currently they account for 30% to 50% of all abortions performed.[21] In many institutions with declining abortion rates there has been very little change in the incidence of induced abortion for psychiatric reasons and in some there has been a marked rise.[22] At Mount Sinai Hospital, New York, the incidence of induced abortion for psychiatric reasons doubled from 1953 to 1964.[23] At the Toronto General Hospital during their 12 year series from 1954 to 1965 the percentage of abortions done for psychiatric reasons rose from 15% to 46% of all abortions.[24] *It is generally felt that there is not really an increase in psychiatric disease but the socio-economic reasons for induced abortion are placed into this group, in order to make them appear to be legal.* Some of the evidence for this will be presented.

The difference between the abortion rate on the ward and private services is one example of the inconsistencies that exist. Although a few institutions such as Mount Sinai Hospital in New York and the Toronto General Hospital record almost identical abortion rates on the ward and private services [25] *in most cases the incidence of induced abortion on the private service is 2 to 4 times more frequent than on the ward service.*[26] In addition, it is done more frequently among the white population than among the non-white groups. Is it because they are less prone to psychiatric problems or are they deprived of proper psychiatric care?

---

[21] Russell, K. P. and Moore, J. G., *op. cit.;* and Spivak, M. M., *op. cit.*

[22] Gold, E. M., *et al., op. cit.;* Rovinsky, J. J. and Gusberg, S. B., *op. cit.;* and Spivak, M. M., *op. cit.*

[23] Rovinsky, J. J. and Gusberg, S. B., *op. cit.*

[24] Spivak, M. M., *op. cit.*

[25] Rovinsky, J. J., and Gusberg, S. B., *op. cit.;* and Spivak, M. M., *op. cit.*

[26] Gold, E. M., *et al, op. cit.;* and Hall, R. E., *op. cit.*

Many have recommended that abortions be permitted in this country for socioeconomic reasons. Advocates of this change note that five to ten thousand deaths occur annually from criminal abortion in the United States and for public health reasons this should not be permitted. It is alleged that patients are forced to resort to situations which threaten their health or life and abortions should be allowed under more ideal conditions. Others have questioned the figure given for criminal abortions. Based on five to ten thousand deaths for the country, Minnesota should experience 98 to 198 deaths per year from induced abortion but only has two.

There is circumstantial evidence that abortions for socioeconomic reasons are being performed and classified frequently as being done for psychiatric reasons. There was a greater increase in the number of abortions in women under 20 years of age in Buffalo from 1943 to 1964 than in any other group.[27] Induced abortion has become more frequent with advancing age and also in most recent years for the teenage group.[28] Marked increases in the incidence of abortion for single, separated, widowed and divorced women from 1943 to 1964 have been reported.[29] *Such evidence has seemed to indicate that we are not "calling a spade a spade."* However, in countries where more liberal laws have been passed there has been a very marked rise in the incidence of induced abortion. In the Scandinavian countries the incidence is about 45, in Switzerland 67, in Chile 850 and in Japan there are probably more abortions than there are live births.[30] More specifically, in Denmark

---

[27] Niswander, K. R. *et al.*, *op. cit.*

[28] Gold, E. M. *et al.*, *op. cit.*

[29] Niswander, K. R. *et al.*, *op. cit.*

[30] Greenhill, J. P., "World Trends of Therapeutic Abortion and Sterilization", *Clinical Ob. & Gyn.* 7:37, 1964; and Spivak, M. M., *op. cit.*

from 1940 to 1956 the incidence of abortion per thousand live births rose from 7 to 60, in Sweden from 1941 to 1956 it rose from 5 to 35.[31]

There is little doubt that abortions are being performed in this country for socioeconomic reasons. Are we really weeding out those out-of-wedlock or unwanted pregnancies that are having a profound adverse psychiatric effect on the patient? Or, are we doing abortions only on those who have sufficient knowledge, education, background and money to obtain proper consultation and ultimately obtain a so-called legal induced abortion in a hospital?

METHODS OF INDUCED ABORTION

A discussion concerning the health of a mother and induced abortion would not be complete without some consideration of the methods that are used to accomplish this procedure. The most popular approved medical and surgical methods of terminating pregnancy are six:

1. Dilatation and Curettage (evacuation) of the uterus.
2. Suction evacuation.
3. The use of concentrated oxytocic drugs.
4. The injection of hypertonic solutions into the amniotic sac.
5. Hysterotomy (intervention through the wall of the uterus).
6. Vaginal or abdominal hysterectomy (removal of the uterus).

A permanent surgical sterilization may be combined with any one of the above methods which are not sterilizing in themselves. If the indication for abortion is such that all future pregnancies would be ill advised and provided the patient is in sufficiently good health to withstand an abdominal operation, sterilization may be done concurrently.

---

[31] Greenhill, J. P., *op. cit.*

Hysterectomy, of course, is sterilizing in itself. *It should be remembered that an indication for abortion, however, is not necessarily an indication for permanent sterilization.* Such statements have been made in the past and cannot be justified medically.

The medical reader is referred to detailed descriptions of the various methods of accomplishing induced abortion by many authors.[32] However, for those not medically oriented a brief summary of each procedure will be given with a statement concerning its advantages.

Dilatation and curettage of the uterus, commonly called D & C, has probably been the most popular method. This operation is performed almost daily in our hospitals for various conditions not related to pregnancy as well as for completing an otherwise incomplete spontaneous abortion. It is relatively simple and has a low incidence of complications. The cervix (mouth of the womb) is dilated and a curette or forceps is used to empty the uterine cavity of its contents. When performed on a healthy pregnant uterus, however, the procedure usually involves much more blood loss, the uterus is softer, there is a much greater danger of perforation and, of course, there is the ever present chance of infection. In general, if the pregnancy exceeds 12 to 14 weeks in duration this is not the method of choice because of a greater chance of complications.

A more recently described method of induced abortion is by suction evacuation of the uterus.[33] With this method the cervix or mouth of the womb is dilated sufficiently to allow a hollow tube to be placed into the uterine cavity. Sufficient suction is then used to evacuate the uterus. The advantages

---

[32] Guttmacher, A. F., "Techniques of Therapeutic Abortion", *Clinical Ob. & Gyn.* 7:100, 1964; and Peretz, A., Grunstein, S., Brandes, J. M., & Paldi, E., "Evacuation of the gravid uterus by negative pressure (suction evacuation)", *Am. J. Ob. & Gyn.* 98:18, 1967.

[33] Peretz *et al., op. cit.;* and Vladov, E., "The vacuum aspiration method for interruption of early pregnancy", *Am. J. Ob. & Gyn.* 99: 202, 1967.

listed for this procedure are: 1. Less dilatation of the cervix is needed. 2. An anatomic (natural) separation of the placenta occurs. 3. The operating time is one to three minutes. 4. Very little analgesia and anesthesia is needed. 5. There is very little blood loss. 6. There is a decreased risk of infection. 7. There is less chance of trauma to the uterus. This, perhaps, in the near future will become the most popular method of induced abortion in the first trimester of pregnancy.

Oxytocic drugs cause the uterine muscle to contract. They are very useful in more advanced pregnancies particularly after 16 weeks and may be all that is needed to complete the abortion. Pitocin, placed in a liter of 5% glucose in water and administered intravenously over a period of time, occasionally more than 24 hours, stimulates the uterus to expel its contents. There is usually very little success in accomplishing an induced abortion by the use of concentrated oxytocic drugs alone during the first trimester. But this method is used in conjunction with the other techniques even in very early pregnancy. There is a marked decrease in the amount of blood loss when the other techniques are supplemented with the use of intravenous oxytocics.

Intra-amniotic injection of hypertonic solutions is a method of inducing abortion that has been popularized in the last ten years. An amniotomy through the wall of the mother's abdomen is done, withdrawing about 250 cc. of amniotic fluid from within the uterus and replacing it with the same amount of 20% sodium chloride solution. 50% glucose may be used should the patient's general condition contraindicate the use of sodium chloride. Regular contractions usually begin within a day. Of course there is no harm in supplementing this method with concentrated oxytocic solutions if contractions do not start within a reasonable period of time.

Hysterotomy is, in a sense, a miniature Caesarean section.

It is usually performed abdominally although it is not impossible vaginally. This is reserved for more advanced pregnancies, is much more major surgery and certainly the indication should justify the means. Perhaps as intra-amniotic injection of hypertonic solution becomes more popular, hysterotomy will seldom be used with the exception of those cases in which a permanent tubal sterilization should be performed. Since abdominal surgery is required for the sterilization both procedures can be accomplished through the same incision.

Hysterectomy or removal of the uterus may be preferable in selected individuals. In certain cases such as cancer of the cervix, one can accomplish the abortion and cure the patient at the same time. Hysterectomy may be performed when there are non-related conditions such as fibroids for which the patient would be requiring future surgery under any circumstances. In certain cases, for Roman Catholic patients, hysterectomy has been ruled by their church as an accepted method of abortion when the indication was the abnormality of the uterus and the primary object of the treatment is the diseased organ. The fact that an early pregnancy was terminated has been considered coincidental.

Complications

As noted earlier the word therapeutic means curative. It is important that one evaluate the potential complications of induced abortion, because the treatment could be worse than the disease. Too often a hasty abortion is performed without thoroughly considering all the factors. One forgets too often a classical statement made by Dr. Mengert ". . . there will always be among us surgically minded enthusiasts who operate with more facility than they cerebrate." [34]

The most frequent complications of induced abortion are:

---

[34] Mengert, W. F., "Trends in Obstetrics and Gynecology", *Ob. & Gyn.* 20:923, 1962.

hemorrhage, infection, guilt (grief) or aggravation of the emotional problem, perforation of the uterus, anesthetic complications, and death. With modern medicine it is usually possible to cope with hemorrhage, infection and perforation of the uterus. Anesthetic problems are quite rare and certainly no more frequent than would occur should the patient go to term and receive anesthesia at the time of delivery.

It is very difficult to evaluate the reported mortality rates for induced abortion. The maternal mortality rate in the United States is now less than one per three thousand live births so that having a baby is becoming a relatively safe experience. It was somewhat different 40 years ago when one expected to lose one out of every three hundred mothers. It is not possible to obtain comparable figures for mortality rates with induced abortion.[35] Most of the large series were not performed in this country and not accomplished under the same ideal medical conditions to which we are accustomed. It is probably safe to say that the so-called danger of induced abortion in the United States is almost exclusively limited to those done under illegal situations. The death rate in Chile for abortion has been reported as one in two hundred.[36] Spivak in his report of 262 cases in Toronto, listed 27 patients with morbidity and one patient died.[37] One must remember that many of these patients had major surgery. These people are frequently very sick patients because it is their illness that is the indication for the induced abortion.[38] They are not good anesthetic risks and do poorly at surgery. It would be interesting to see the morbidity and mortality rate of a large series of induced abortions done strictly for psychiatric reasons performed in

[35] Loth, M. F. and Hesseltine, H. C., "Therapeutic Abortion at the Chicago Lying-in Hospital", *Am. J. Ob. & Gyn.* 72:304, 1956.

[36] Greenhill, J. P., *op. cit.*

[37] Spivak, M. M., *op. cit.*

[38] Moore, J. G. and Randall, J. H., *op. cit.;* and Tietze, C., *op. cit.*

hospitals in the United States that are approved by the Joint Commission on Accreditation of Hospitals and using standard acceptable medical and surgical techniques.

The psychiatric consequences must be evaluated and compared to the emotional problems which might have resulted if the abortion were not performed. What about the psychiatric complications of induced abortion? How great really is the risk of death of the average pregnant patient with an emotional problem? It has been known for some time that suicide in pregnancy is very rare.[39] Guilt feelings and psychosis do occasionally follow induced abortion and Barno has reported what various authors have to say concerning this. Others have stated that they have found nothing to suggest that the psychological problems of adjustment following induced abortion were permanent in nature.[40] Simon [41] who reviewed various studies noted that in one series 11% of the patients who had abortions strongly regretted it and 14% had mild regrets, but true post-abortion depression was comparatively infrequent. On the other hand, in a large group of women (who were apparently less of a problem psychiatrically speaking since they were refused abortion), about one-half had serious emotional problems for a year or so before their final adjustment and 25% had serious psychologic symptoms which were still present sometime after the delivery of their unwanted babies.

CONCLUSION

In conclusion it can be stated that there are some clear-cut non-psychiatric medical indications for induced abortion to preserve the health of the mothers but they are

[39] Barno, A., *op. cit.;* and Sim, M., "Abortion and the Psychiatrist", *British Medical Journal,* July 20, 1963, p. 145.

[40] Kretzschmar, R. M. and Norris, A. S., *op. cit.*

[41] Simon, A., "Psychiatric Indication for Therapeutic Abortion and Sterilization", *Clinical Ob. & Gyn,* 7:67, 1964.

becoming quite rare. When determining if an abortion should be performed, the patient's total environment, actual or reasonably foreseeable, should be considered. Raising a child may be more strain on a cardiac patient's heart than the actual stress of delivery. Today, the most frequent medical indications are psychiatric. It is also very clear that psychiatric indications are being used to justify many abortions which perhaps have some psychiatric aspects but are essentially socioeconomic problems. There is yet much to be learned concerning the genetic indications for induced abortions.

We have available a variety of methods of accomplishing an induced abortion. With the latest medical advances they are probably as safe as carrying a pregnancy to term and delivering a full-term baby. Morbidity and mortality when the operation is performed under ideal conditions are probably uncommon.

Chapter 9

PSYCHIATRIC INDICATIONS FOR THERAPEUTIC ABORTION AND STERILIZATION

SUMMARY

The purpose of this paper is to review some current opinions about psychiatric indications for abortion and sterilization. Further, an attempt is made to ascertain the reasons for the great diversity of opinions among psychiatrists about the psychiatric indications for abortion. It is noted that there is not universal agreement as to what mental conditions deteriorate with pregnancy. Some believe abortion is as traumatic for certain emotionally disturbed women as carrying the pregnancy to term. Thus there is need for more empirical data to establish with greater accuracy the situation where abortion will be truly therapeutic.

The nature and value of the foetus also is subject to different opinions that in turn affect the decision about abortion. Three positions are discussed:

1) The foetus has the value of a human being from the moment of conception.
2) The foetus is just an organ of the mother till some arbitrary time.
3) The foetus is a potential human life at the moment of conception but of increasing value throughout pregnancy.

Sterilization is quite a different ethical matter. If contraception is morally acceptable, then sterilization just represents one method. It is the most effective but also the least reversible method and therefore must never be taken lightly. Psychiatric indications for sterilization are discussed. Sterilization is considered to be a method of contraception.

MERVILLE O. VINCENT, M.D., C.M., F.R.C.P. *Dr. Vincent has served on the staff of the Homewood Sanitarium in Guelph, Ontario, (Canada's largest private and psychiatric institution) as assistant medical superintendent since 1962. He is a graduate of the Dalhousie University School of Medicine in Nova Scotia, received training in psychiatry and internal medicine at the University of Michigan, and holds certification in both fields. He is a Fellow of the Royal College of Physicians of Canada. In addition to his professional responsibilities, Dr. Vincent is a frequent contributor to a wide variety of journals and magazines.*

PSYCHIATRIC INDICATIONS FOR THERAPEUTIC ABORTION AND STERILIZATION

by M. O. Vincent *

INTRODUCTION

The title is deceptively brief and simplistic. It, however, covers a host of medical, moral and legal problems. The frightened, depressed, pregnant woman evokes an emotional response within me that makes me wish I were an avant-garde liberal who could carry out abortion "on request." In the relative calm of my study I find a more conservative me. I hope I am guilty of conservatism, not old-fogeyism. Sir William Osler clarified the difference. . . . "Conservatism and old-fogeyism are totally different things. The motto of the one is . . . 'prove all things and hold fast that which is

---

* This paper represents a personal search by me. There is nothing esoteric or abstract in the situation of a psychiatrist with his patient trying to determine if a pregnancy should be interrupted. Therefore the editors have kindly permitted me to write in the first person, that for a moment you may sit where I sit, and feel with, and for me.

good.' And of the other, 'prove nothing, but hold fast that which is old'." [1]

The title also suggests a consensus where I find only diversity. A well known English psychiatrist concluded in an article on Abortion. . . . "A study of 213 patients with puerperal psychosis showed that the condition carries a good prognosis and is virtually unpredictable.

—Instability in pregnancy does not contribute materially to the incidence of puerperal psychosis.

—Suicide is less of a risk in pregnant women than in non-pregnant women.

—Unmarried mothers are relatively immune from puerperal psychosis.

—Abortion, even if therapeutic, may in itself produce a psychosis.

—There are no psychiatric grounds for the termination of pregnancy.

Pressure may be brought to bear on the psychiatrist to recommend termination. He may be told the patient is threatening suicide or be regaled with the dreadful social consequences. The answer is still not to recommend termination, which may indeed be harmful, but to nurse the patient through her unstable phase." [2]

Another English psychiatrist favors abortion on request, while admitting strict psychiatric indications are few. In effect he said this would amount to. . . . "The extension of birth control into the first three months of pregnancy." His position is based on "a fundamental condition of pregnancy that the woman carry a wanted child. When the child will not be wanted by the woman, the pregnancy has to end in abortion." He further states . . . "A Cambridge study showed that 90% of terminations are asked for on grounds of psy-

---

[1] *Applied Therapeutics*, Volume 9, No. 6, June 1967, page 504.

[2] Sim, Myre, *British Medical Journal*, Volume 2, Page 148, July 20, 1963.

chological distress. Yet we must know that only a few psychiatric conditions are worsened by pregnancy. . . . Our response then is not dictated by psychiatric conditions, for these are rare. Our response is a response to the appeal of a woman anguished at the thought of an experience distasteful to her; and so we find medical, psychiatric or social rationalizations to circumvent the law and bring her relief." [3]

In favour of aborting unwed mothers, one psychiatrist stated, "I have yet to see a case in which an unwanted pregnancy has not resulted in psychological damage to the mother, the child or both. Frequently, the damage is major and untreatable." [4]

A woman psychiatrist stated. . . . "Pregnancy should be terminated when a woman is desperate enough to seek it, no matter what the reasons! Too many have died because moralistic clergymen and the mercenary underworld have driven them into the hands of unskilled individuals." [5]

In a report on attitudes of California psychiatrists toward abortion by Rosenberg & Silver in 1965, it was concluded that . . . "The most striking feature of the answers was the lack of unanimity in the attitudes and practices of psychiatrists in a matter which is *assumed* to have scientific criteria and legal validity." [6] (italics mine) Again they note. . . . "The extreme range of opinion represented among the psychiatrists is a far cry from the scientific objectivity that one hopes would apply to determinations affecting the life and health of patients. The range was from those who essentially never recommend therapeutic abortion

---

[3] *Psychiatric News*, June 1968, page 19, Pub: American Psychiatric Association.

[4] Crawley, Ralph M., Laidlaw, R. W., "Psychiatric Opinion Regarding Abortion: Preliminary Report of a Survey". *American Journal of Psychiatry*, 124–4; October 1967, Page 148.

[5] Crawley, Ralph M., Laidlaw, R. W. *Ibid.*, Page 148.

[6] Rosenburg, A. J., Silver, E., *California Medicine*, Vol. 102, P. 408, June 1965.

to those who seem always to do so, from those who regard pregnancy as definitely increasing the incidence of mental illness to those who feel that pregnancy represents virtually no additional stress." [7]

A recent survey showed 44.5% of U.S. physicians and 39.2% of Canadian physicians favored abortion where there was "substantial risk to maternal emotional health." [8]

A similar survey of members of the American Psychiatric Association showed 88.8% of U.S. members and 86.1% of their Canadian members favoured abortion. . . . "when there is significant risk that the mental or emotional health of the mother might be jeopardized." [9]

Such are the varied opinions. Nonetheless the trend is toward more and more therapeutic abortions on psychiatric grounds and few on other medical grounds. This is well documented throughout the Western world.[10,11,12,13,14,15]

Nor are psychiatrists alone in their diversity. Official announcements of Christian bodies show similar range. On the one hand the Roman Catholic Church regards the foetus as a life and new being from the moment of conception. Destruction of the embryo is a killing, therefore, direct destruction of the embryo is a sin. A few exceptions to this

---

[7] Rosenberg, A. J., Silver, E., *Ibid.*, Page 410.

[8] *Modern Medicine of Canada*, May 1967, Page 54.

[9] Crawley, Ralph M., Laidlaw, R. W., *Ibid.*, Page 147.

[10] Shipps, H. P., in *Religion & Birth Control*, ed. John Monsma, New York: Doubleday & Company, Inc., 1963, p. 62.

[11] Calderdone, M. S. (Editor), "Abortion in the U.S.", New York: Hoeber & Harper, 1958.

[12] Davidson, M., *Medical Ethics: A Guide to Students and Practitioners*, London: Lloyd-Luke, 1957.

[13] Baird, Dugald, "Sterilization & Therapeutic Abortion in Aberdeen", *British Journal of Psychiatry*, Vol. 113: p. 705, July 1967.

[14] Bolter, S., "The Psychiatrist's Role in Therapeutic Abortion: The Unwitting Accomplice", *American Journal of Psychiatry*, Vol. 119: p. 312, 1962.

[15] "The Terrible Choice: The Abortion Dilemma", Based on proceedings of the First International Conference on Abortion, Sept. 6–8, 1967. Bantam Books, 1968.

blanket statement come under the principle of "double effect." [16]

On the other extreme, the American Baptist Convention is reported to have recently come out in favor of "abortion on request prior to the 13th week of pregnancy." [17]

I have heard unofficial rumors that some denominations believe both abortion and birth control should be made one hundred years retroactive for denominations other than their own.

THREE POSITIONS

The most significant factor in all this diversity is the question of the nature of the foetus. Different conclusions about the nature and value of the foetus lead to different attitudes towards and indications for abortion.

Basically I note three positions. The first is that the foetus is a new life, a human life, therefore ethical decisions relate to the foetus as a human being. The second position represents the other extreme, that the foetus is only an organ of the mother, until some critical point such as 28 weeks or at actual delivery. The third position is a middle position, one that seems uncomfortable regarding the foetus as just an appendage of the mother, but one that is not prepared to regard it as a new being, and hence tends to refer to the foetus as potential life or primitive life.

Proponents of each position may be moral and concerned about the value and quality of life. Christians and non-Christians are found in all three positions. That is, the abortion issue does not necessarily boil down to a battle between morality and immorality of Christians and non-Christians.

Most Protestant psychiatrists, though differing about the foetus, can concur with the following twelve propositions.

---

[16] Fletcher, Joseph, *Morals & Medicine*, Boston: Beacon Press, 4th printing, 1967, pp. 148–156.

[17] *Christianity Today*, June 21, 1968, p. 40.

These propositions would be generally held by all those with a liberal view regarding indications for abortion. I think on these points we would be in agreement with most Planned Parenthood Societies or the Abortion Law Reform Association in Great Britain.

We favor . . .

(1) The promotion of health and prevention of disease.
(2) Physical and mental health for all existing members of the family.
(3) Family planning and the right of individuals to have only children they want.
(4) The child's right to "wanting" parents.
(5) Appropriate measures to strengthen family life.
(6) The preservation of a new life once it exists.
(7) The ideal that all children should be physically and emotionally healthy and that society has a need to prevent, insofar as possible, the birth of predictably defective persons.
(8) Minimizing the misfortunes that follow rape and incest.
(9) Efforts to resolve the problems of the unmarried, pregnant girl.
(10) Action to reduce poverty and social problems.
(11) All appropriate means of restricting criminal abortions.
(12) Controlling excessive population expansion.

The question now becomes, to what extent can we utilize therapeutic abortion to attain these goals? The answer is dependent primarily on one's attitude toward the foetus. I shall seek to summarize each of the three positions, enlarging upon my own view particularly, realizing that nobody's opinions are any better than his facts. In all of this discussion I am avoiding the concept of the soul and am not entering into any debate about its presence at the time of conception or any subsequent time. I believe in the soul, but I have never seen it. My impression is that the theologians are not too certain about when the soul enters the human or whether it is the very life of the being from its beginning. Therefore, in this discussion I find it useful to talk only about life, not about the soul.

The Foetus a Human Life

The foetus is a new human life. This is the position which I regard as being the most logically consistent at the present stage of medical and scientific knowledge. It is generally accepted that one of the most basic functions of the physician is to preserve human life. This is an ethical position which provides the background for most medical activities. Believing that the fertilized ovum has life, I believe that the physician looking after a pregnant woman is responsible for two lives. The International Code of Medical Ethics, adopted by the World Medical Association, Geneva, Switzerland, in 1948 stated in part. . . . "1) The health of my patient will be my first consideration and 2) I will maintain the utmost respect for human life, from the time of *conception*; even under threat, that I will not use my medical knowledge contrary to the laws of humanity." [18]

The sanctity of life is generally accepted by physicians, but our uncertainty arises at the definition of "human" life. This position is concisely stated by an obstetrician. . . . "Physiologically there can be no doubt but that the fertilized ovum has life, with ability to grow and develop into a recognizable human person. There is no other event in human development which reasonably could be postulated to represent the onset of life. Implantation in the uterus occurs at one week; all organ systems are initiated by four weeks; detectable foetal motion occurs at 18–20 weeks; and the foetus is capable of extra-uterine life at about 28 weeks. There are important milestones in foetal development, but, as stated, none can be postulated as the incipient point of

---

[18] *Medical Ethics: The Christian View*, Edited by Edmunds, V., Scorer, C. G., London: Tyndale Press, 2nd edition, 1966, page 136.

foetal existence." [19] Conception is the great divide between non-life and life. Implantation, placentation and birth changes the form of nutrition, but not the character of the embryo.

The Church of England stated at the Lambeth Conference of 1930 that "abortion aims at the destruction of life which has already come into being. This is contrary to the law of God and of man." [20] While the Church of England does not now speak with the same clarity on this issue, I know of no scientific evidence that has been developed since 1930 that proves that a life is not being destroyed.

Until the nineteenth century, most Christians equated life with quickening of the foetus. This view was shared by Thomas Aquinas. However, since the nineteenth century the Roman Catholic Church has equated conception with the beginning of a new human person.[21]

A Jesuit recently described by analogy the reason for his assumption that if there was any possibility that the foetus is a human life, then it should be treated as if it is in fact a human life. The analogy states that it is immoral to fire a machine-gun through a closed door if one knows someone is standing on the other side of the door. One is deliberately taking a life. If one is certain there is no one behind that door, it is not immoral, at least in the sense of taking a life, to shoot through the door. If, however, one does not know whether or not there is someone behind the door, it is immoral to shoot. The onus is on the man with the gun, to make certain first that there is no person behind the door.[22] The application of the analogy is obvious. In view of the

---

[19] Maxwell, Gordon, in "Religion & Birth Control", ed. John Monsma, New York: Doubleday and Company, Inc., 1963, p. 72.

[20] *Report of the 1930 Committee on Marriage & Sex*, Lambeth Conference (1867–1948) London, p. 199.

[21] Marshall, John, *Medicine & Morals*, New York: Hawthorn Books, 1960.

[22] Wickham, The Reverend Doctor John, S. J., personal verbal communication, March 31, 1967.

sanctity of life, the onus is upon those who would assert that the foetus is not human life to clearly document their position. If it can be clearly documented, I will accept it with a sense of relief. However, I have not seen such documentation to date.

What direction have scientific advances of the 20th century given in this regard? The developments in Genetics and Embryology point increasingly clearly to the fact that a new creature, a human creature comes into existence at conception. There is a discrepancy between the increasing uniqueness and value being placed on the fertilized ovum by science and the devaluation of the fertilized ovum by society in general and the medical, theological and legal professions in particular. A biologist while not discussing abortion but rather the genetic basis of life made these pertinent remarks. . . . "All of human life gains its biological origin with the formation of the fertilized egg. This fertilized egg appears to lack individuality, as we think of it, because of its simplicity of structure, but within it resides an enormous mass of information—the information which will be expressed in due time as a man's intelligence, his health, his general personality, his sex, and his superficial appearance. This information it is now known, is coded in his genes. The genes in turn are molecules of a nucleic acid—DNA or Deoxyribonucleic Acid." [23] Again he states . . . "The discovery of the molecular basis of hereditary is one of the great triumphs of 20th-century science. In the long run it is far more important and far more dramatic than space travel or atomic energy. It has given us the knowledge of the physical and chemical basis of life itself." [24]

In the past, many have found comfort in the concept of viability. The situation being that if the foetus was not via-

[23] Carlson, E. A., "The Ever Increasing Importance of Genetics to Medicine & Man", *Queen's Medical Review*, Kingston, Ontario, 1960–61 Annual, p. 23.

[24] Carlson, E. A., *Ibid.*, p. 24.

ble outside the uterus then it was not a new person, in fact abortion was usually defined in terms of viability. One dictionary defines abortion as . . . "the expulsion of a human foetus before it is viable." [25]

Two other definitions by gynaecologists indicate this also. . . . "Abortion may be defined as an interruption of pregnancy before independent viability of the foetus, and viability is generally considered to occur after about 26–28 weeks of foetal existence." [26]

Another definition from a textbook . . . "Abortion concerns the termination of pregnancy before the foetus has developed sufficiently to survive extra-uterine existence. This includes essentially all pregnancies of less than 28 weeks of gestation and all foetuses of 34 ounces or less in weight, although rare exceptions occur." [27]

The concept of viability had some validity in previous times due to our ignorance. Presently it does not appear to me to be a useful or helpful concept. First of all, a newborn baby at any time after 28 weeks is viable only if the appropriate environment is provided by more mature members of the human race. Therefore there is a sense in which no newborn is viable and able to survive independently outside the uterus. Furthermore, even within the old concept of viability, it is a fact that many infants who were not viable in previous ages are viable with present medical care. I believe the age of viability will be continually pushed back and anticipate that test-tube fertilizations and test-tube or incubator babies may well be a possibility within my life time. If this happens, viability will have gone back to fertilization.

I am committed to the sanctity of life from an ethical

---

[25] *American College Dictionary*, New York: Random House, 1955.

[26] Kearns, Paul R., in *Religion & Birth Control*, ed. John Monsma, New York: Doubleday & Company, Inc., 1963, p. 54.

[27] Maxwell, Gordon E. in *Religion & Birth Control*, Editor: John Monsma, New York: Doubleday and Company, Inc., 1963, p. 68.

religious viewpoint. Further, I believe that scientific evidence at this time suggests that life begins at the time of conception. Therefore I see abortion as taking a life. I have wondered what scientific evidence in the future might possibly change my position. I can envision a finding which at present seems improbable along these lines, that as early as 12 weeks of gestation a foetus could be surgically removed from the uterus and remain viable, eventually starting to kindergarten. As a second part of this experiment, fertilization might take place in the test tube and the embryo developed until 10 weeks and then invariably cease to develop and "die". If both of these experiments were repeated frequently under the best of scientific conditions it might be reasonable to conclude that somewhere between 10 weeks and 12 weeks, a "life substance" reaches the foetus from the mother, truly creating new life and viability at that time. Even if this "life substance" were discovered and eventually injected into our test-tube embryo, it would seem to me to indicate that prior to ten weeks, something was missing that was necessary to make this embryo a new life.

Within this framework of the foetus as a human life, the psychiatric indications for abortion are few if any. The Roman Catholic position is that there are no psychiatric indications for abortion. Suicide and permanent mental deterioration if pregnancy is allowed to continue, are the only truly psychiatric states for which a recommendation for taking the life of the foetus might be made. However, there is continual controversy in the literature regarding the likelihood of suicide. "Pregnancy rarely causes suicide." [28] Most psychiatrists who regard the foetus as a life would take the position that the suicide should be prevented not by abortion but by psychiatric hospitalization and appropriate treat-

---

[28] Niswander, K. R., et al. "Changing Attitudes toward Therapeutic Abortion", *Journal of the American Medical Association*, Vol. 196:13, June 27, 1966, p. 1143.

ment for the depression. Several studies have shown no suicides occurring among women who have been denied therapeutic abortion.[29] Further a variety of studies have indicated that not only is suicide, but attempted suicide, extremely uncommon during pregnancy.[30] Observations in New York City and Northern California suggest that proportionately fewer pregnant women commit suicide than those who are not pregnant.[31]

Permanent psychiatric deterioration of any psychiatric condition because of pregnancy is not well documented. There is debate in psychiatric literature as to whether there is more likelihood of precipitating a psychosis in the mother or deterioration of her mental state by carrying the pregnancy to term or by carrying out a therapeutic abortion.

Janson in Scandinavia, studying therapeutic abortion for psychiatric reasons, came to the paradoxical conclusion that in those women in whom legal abortion can best be justified on psychiatric grounds, one is most likely to get adverse reactions to the procedure. He concluded that. . . . "Legal abortion stands as a fairly ineffective psychiatric therapeutic means. Women who are psychically vulnerable risk a deterioration in their condition, through an unwelcomed pregnancy whatever course is adopted." [32] Hook came to the same conclusion.[33]

I believe that a woman has a right to bear only children that she wishes. I do not believe that this gives her a general

[29] Ekblad, M., "The Relation of the Legal-Abortion Clientele to the Illegal-Abortion Clientele and the Risk of Suicide". *Acta Psychiatric et Neurol*, Scandinavia (Suppl), 1955, p. 94.

[30] Sainsubry, T., *Suicide in London*, London: Chapman & Hall, 1955.

[31] Rosenberg, A. J., Silver, E., "Suicide-Psychiatrist & Therapeutic Abortion", *California Medicine*, June 1965, p. 409.

[32] Janson, B., *Acta Psychiatric et Neurol*, Scandinavia (Suppl), 41, 1965, p. 87.

[33] Hook, K., "Refused Abortion: A follow-up study of 249 women whose applications were refused by the National Board of Health in Sweden", *Acta Psychiatric et Neurol*, Scandinavia (Suppl), 1963, p. 168.

right to take the life of an unborn child. I believe it indicates that she should conduct herself responsibly, then bear the child whose life she either willed or permitted by taking part in the child's conception. It seems to me that this kind of personal responsibility for behavior and consequences is essential to civilization. In view of this, I personally would be open to the consideration of abortion in clear-cut cases of incest or rape where the pregnant woman has had no voluntary part in the child's conception. I personally would not feel that one could lay down an absolute law here. There might be situations in which such a pregnancy should be carried to term and other situations where the individual should not be compelled by society to suffer the consequences of another's sin. This would be a matter of conscience and would have to be determined situationally and painfully. I am concerned that this may be solving a conflict of interests at the expense of a third party (the human foetus), an innocent person.

The Foetus Just an Organ of Mother

The foetus is only an organ of the mother, thus abortion is not taking a life. The physician would look at the foetus in the same way that he would look at a gallbladder, weigh the "pro's" and "con's" and decide if the advantages of removal outweighed those of leaving it alone. The basic assumption is that the woman has a right not to bear a child she does not want, even if she is pregnant. To people of this position, to speak of the "rights of the foetus" is as inappropriate as speaking of the "rights of the appendix to continue its existence in the abdomen." A biologist states it thus:

> "Clearly, the humanly significant thing that is contributed to the zygote by the parents is the information that 'tells' the fertilized egg how to develop into a human being. This information is in the form of a

chemical tape called DNA. . . . The question is: Is
this information precious? . . . . People who worry
about the moral danger of abortion do so because they
think of the foetus as a human being, hence equate
foeticide with murder. Whether the foetus is or is not
a human being is a matter of definition, not fact; and
we can define any way we wish. In terms of the
human problem involved, it would be unwise to define
the foetus as human (hence tactically unwise to ever
refer to the foetus as 'an unborn child')." [34]

Stating the position briefly, "The foetus lives a life dependent on the mother, thus he has absolutely no 'rights'
except those granted to him by his host." [35] Joseph Fletcher
denies that the right to life claimed for the foetus is
valid. . . . "because a foetus is not a moral or personal
being since it lacks freedom, self-determination, rationality,
ability to chose either means or ends, and knowledge of its
circumstances." [36]

If the above characteristics indicate that a being does
not have the "right to life," then I think that these characteristics could apply in the same fashion to a one-day old
baby or a delirious adult in a hospital ward, for each "lacks
freedom, self determination, rationality, the ability to choose
either means or ends, and knowledge of its circumstances."
Fletcher indicates that the embryo before birth is a portion
of the mother and that common sense and a humane perspective would indicate that a part may be sacrificed for the
sake of the whole. I have indicated above that while the
foetus is a part of the mother, I do not believe that it can
be dismissed as nothing more than a part of the mother.

Those who do not regard the foetus as anything more than
an organ of the mother need not concern themselves about
the welfare of the foetus and can proceed with an abortion

---

[34] Hardin, G., "Abortion or Compulsory Pregnancy?". *Journal of
Marriage and the Family*, Vol. 30, No. 2, May 1968, p. 250.

[35] Stern, S. G., M.D., "The Issue of Legalized Abortion". *Canadian
Medical Association Journal*, Vol. 88, April 27, 1963, p. 899.

[36] Fletcher, *op. cit.*, p. 152.

wherever it may benefit the physical, emotional and social welfare of the mother or any members of the mother's family. In brief, those accepting this position would feel free to abort on request. They would make certain that this action would not have a detrimental emotional or physical effect on the pregnant person. They would also feel free to abort any foetus with an above-average likelihood of congenital abnormality.

If I were certain that the foetus is not a human life, I would find myself in the position of granting abortions on request, for if we are not dealing with a human life, this is the most reasonable position.

Foetus as Potential Life

This appears to be the most common position among medical people today. However, I believe that most of the criteria for distinguishing potential life from actual life are extremely arbitrary. Other terms such as primitive life, unconscious life, insensate life are used to convey the thought that the foetus is not just an organ of the mother, but at the same time somehow is not really life. In this position, it is a purely arbitrary decision as to what point life is said to begin, whether it is at birth, 28 weeks, quickening, etc.

That this position gets into obvious difficulty the more advanced the pregnancy, is indicated in the *Time* essay on abortion which stated *re* the Swedish situation ... "Bureaucratic papershuffling often holds up legal operations until the 24th week—producing live babies that sometimes cry for hours before dying." [37]

The position that the foetus is a potential life is probably the position of the majority of North American psychiatrists. The exact indications would vary a great deal from

---

[37] *Time Magazine*, Essay, "The Desperate Dilemma of Abortion", Oct. 13, 1967, p. 31.

psychiatrist to psychiatrist in this broad group, some being very close to the first position that I have taken and others being very close to the position of "abortion on request." If the woman is emotionally upset about being pregnant, this alone would be sufficient indication for abortion for many psychiatrists holding this view. Certainly they would be prepared to recommend abortion if there were any danger of suicide, if there were past or present psychosis, or concern about future psychosis.

Frequently accepted reasons would be psychosis of the husband, the probability of congenital disease, illegitimacy, divorce after conception, pregnancy consequent to adultery, narcotic addiction, an unwanted pregnancy, socioeconomic reasons. The difficult decisions faced by this group were pointed out by Dr. Hoenig . . . "It is often pointed out that it is always very difficult to assess whether the continuation of a pregnancy is liable to adversely affect the mother suffering from a personality disorder or from an abnormal psychogenic development, to what degree and whether permanently or not, no one with any experience in the matter will doubt the truth of that. When it is further pointed out that there is very little evidence or exact knowledge on this problem, this has to be admitted." [38]

New legislation in Britain and North America tends to reflect this middle position. The British Medical Association Committee on Therapeutic Abortion sought to give guidelines for the termination of pregnancy before the new British laws went into effect in April of 1968. In referring to the situation where the pregnancy "has not yet progressed to the state where the foetus is capable of an independent existence," they state . . . "There are few medical conditions which comprise automatic indications for termination of pregnancy. The decision of whether or not to terminate a

[38] Hoenig, J., Correspondence, *British Medical Journal*, Vol. 2, Nov. 2, 1963, p. 1126.

pregnancy must be taken in the light of the circumstances of the particular case—for example, the duration of the pregnancy, whether or not it is in the interest of the physical or mental health of the mother to allow the pregnancy to continue, or whether or not there is risk of serious foetal abnormality. In determining whether or not termination is in the interests of the health of the mother, account should be taken of her total environment both actual or reasonably foreseeable." [39]

Under psychiatric indications, they note that there is considerable variation of opinion. They see reactive depression as being the number one indication. Anxiety state or hysterical reaction and endogenous depression rarely justifies abortion, nor all cases of mental deficiency or schizophrenia. They note the risk of depression and guilt following abortion. They conclude . . . "The task of a psychiatrist in giving his opinion on termination is exceptionally difficult. He is usually confronted by a patient whom he has never seen before, with very limited time in which to make up his mind. The patient may be exaggerating her distress in the hope of obtaining an opinion in favor of termination, or putting moral pressure on the psychiatrist by threatening or attempting suicide, or deliberately making light of symptoms in the belief that the decision to terminate has already been taken. . . . By weighing up all these considerations, the effect of mounting pressures of the pregnancy and the mental health of the mother can be evaluated and a decision as to termination arrived at." [40]

An editorial comment in the Canadian Medical Association Journal regarding these guidelines for psychiatrists noted . . . "The guidance offered is faltering indeed and the burden of the decision is thrust, though with under-

---

[39] "Indications for Termination of Pregnancy", Report by the British Medical Association Committee on Therapeutic Abortion, British Medical Journal, January 20, 1968, p. 171.

[40] Ibid. Br. Medical Journal, p. 175.

standing of his predicament, upon the psychiatrist. The choice of psychiatrist will therefore continue to be a governing factor in securing permission to perform a therapeutic abortion." [41]

It is interesting to note that recently modified laws are avoiding both extreme views and are thus providing medicine with the position in which it is most difficult to make the existential choice. However, the legislation will be permissive, so that each physician and each involved individual will have to arrive at his own moral position in this matter. Do-it-yourself abortion pills may in the future add further weight to the matter of personal decision.

PSYCHIATRIC INDICATIONS FOR STERILIZATION

You will think me as broad-minded about sterilization as I am narrow-minded about abortion. I have indicated elsewhere in this book the moral acceptability, if not the moral imperative, for conception control.[42] Sterilization is usually a permanent form of contraception. In many minds the moral implications of abortion and sterilization are considered to be similar. They are, in fact, entirely different. The latter prevents the formation of new life and the former destroys new life. I concur with Joseph Fletcher's statement regarding Oral Contraceptives. . . . "These actually are not contraceptives, since they do not prevent the meeting of sperm and an ovum. They are sterilizers, temporarily suspending ovulation or the production of any ova at all. . . . There is no longer a practical difference between contraception and sterilization." [43] In this sense it is perhaps unfortunate that the subjects of abortion and sterilization should be grouped together in this paper.

I favor sterilization of any male or female on request

[41] "Therapeutic Abortion", Editorial, *Canadian Medical Association Journal*, Vol. 98, March 9, 1968, p. 513.

[42] Vincent, M. O., Chapter 12, this volume.

[43] Fletcher, *op. cit.*, p. XV.

after convincing myself that it is a rational and informed decision by the person involved. In married couples the decision must be also mutually agreeable. I would, of course, recommend it only if I felt it would not do psychological harm to the individual.

I favor encouraging sterilization by the medical profession for couples where further children are inadvisable on medical, psychiatric or socioeconomic grounds, and who seem unable to successfully utilize other contraceptive devices.

I would recommend voluntary sterilization of all mental defectives, both because of the possibility of genetic transmission and the conviction that mental defectives, in general, make inferior parents.

Sterilization should be encouraged for persons with major mental illnesses where medical opinion is that additional pregnancies or children would be a further stress. This has value not only for the couple involved, but it has eugenic value for the offspring. Representative of this thinking was a paper presented at the American Psychiatric Association in Boston this year which stated in part. . . . "One out of every two children born to a mother diagnosed as schizophrenic will likely become afflicted with a serious psychosocial disability which will cause intense distress to the child and his family, as well as tax the patience and material resources of the community. Not only are the children born to a schizophrenic in danger, but the marital union is likely to be destroyed and the extended family shattered by the volcanic eruptions of psychosis and the tense uncertainty between cataclysms. Motherhood for the schizophrenic can be a disaster, one which she frequently fears and more often knows little how to avoid." [44]

Rogler & Hollingshead in their book, *Trapped: Families*

---

[44] Murphy, M., Chayet, N. L., "Pregnancy in the Schizophrenic: A Challenge to Preventive Psychiatry". Read at the 124th meeting of the American Psychiatric Association, Boston, Massachusetts, May 13–17, 1968. Authors' manuscript, p. 1.

and Schizophrenia note. . . . "Our findings indicate that the impact of the disabled wife, with a galaxy of disturbing symptoms, on the nuclear and extended family, is pervasive and disruptive. Her symptoms corrode the marital union, her children are trapped in a disorganized family milieu, and the extended family is fragmented." [45] This type of evidence means that mental health workers must be concerned about the prevention of pregnancy in the mentally ill in the interest of the offspring. Voluntary sterilization for eugenic reasons is indicated. The basis of this position is the likelihood of serious mental or physical disease being transmitted to the offspring according to reasonable predictions of genetics and medicine. Is it too far-fetched to suggest that here we "make ourselves eunuchs for the Kingdom of Heaven's sake"? This is consistent with the suggestion of Victor A. McKusick, M.D., where he stated, "In this era of population explosion, however, a strong case can be made for urging prohibition on procreation by persons who are demonstrated to be carrying bad genes. . . . The persons carrying bad genes I refer to are: 1) those with a dominantly inherited disorder, 2) two parents who are both heterozygous for an autosomal recessive disorder as demonstrated by the birth of an affected child (or, in the future, specific tests perhaps), and 3) females shown to be carriers of particular X-linked recessive traits. In all these situations, it can be argued, adoption should be urged as a substitute for procreation. The advice may, of course, not be taken. The physician can be very convincing, however, and much depends on how he states the risk: for example, 'There are three chances out of four that the child will be normal' may carry a different connotation than 'There is a 25 percent risk of the child being affected.' " [46]

---

[45] Rogler, L. H., Hollingshead, A. B., "Trapped: Families & Schizophrenia." New York: Wiley, 1965.

[46] McKusick, Victor A., M.D., "Genetics in the Practice of Medicine", *Annals of the Royal College of Physicians & Surgeons of Canada*, July, 1968.

I also favor sterilization as a measure of population control if it is on a voluntary basis. Such is the case in India today.

Though there are still "gray" areas of debate concerning many psychiatric disorders with respect to the relative significance of heredity and environment, present and future genetic research will increasingly make this decision more accurate. I believe we should actively encourage sterilization wherever there is sufficient evidence that heredity plays a major role in transmitting an illness that is in the family. This would apply clearly to such conditions as Huntington's Chorea, Phenylketonuria and some types of mental deficiency. It would appear to apply also, but to a lesser degree, to families with a strong history of schizophrenia or manic-depressive illness.

One cannot conclude without mentioning the problem of compulsory sterilization. This is quite a different matter. It has been observed by many that there is no "right" less regulated than the right to have a child. There are those who feel that we should have to pass an examination to get a license to have a child, since parenthood is at least as important as driving a car. However, there is of course a great difference between legislation that is permissive and legislation that is mandatory. Others feel the having of children is an individual right with which no legislative body should interfere. They believe that no one has the right to compel another to be sterilized, that this is a breach of personal integrity. We are faced with the difficult decision of weighing the definite advantages that could come to society as a whole against the interference with the integrity and freedom of the individual. Some oppose compulsory sterilization because it can be misused as it was in Germany in the 1930's. Others favour it because of the right of the next generation to be born healthy. Some say that we do not have the right to take away, even from mental defectives, their natural right to their procreative faculties. Yet we do not hesitate to institutionalize such people for life. We have to ask ourselves, what is the difference between compulsory segregation and compulsory sterilization? In fact, compulsory segregation quite frequently results in taking away the natural right of the defective to use their procreative faculties.

Having tried to give some definitive answers to certain ethical problems today, I will close on a humble note, admitting that I have not personally arrived at a satisfactory conclusion concerning compulsory sterilization. I am greatly concerned by any legislation which takes away such a vital human freedom, and interferes with the integrity of the individual, and feel that in this area as much as possible, we should seek solutions at the level of voluntary remedies.

POST-SYMPOSIUM CONCLUSIONS

The symposium brought some change in my thinking. I would like to share it. I arrived at the consultation firmly convinced of the sanctity of human life and that a new life was created at the moment of conception. I found it necessary to admit that the latter point was not as certain as the former. Scripture never speaks to this point directly. By inference, Psalms 51 and 139 suggest the foetus has value, but this may be a developing value even as the foetus itself develops. Exodus 21:22 to 25 indicates that the foetus has value, but not equivalent to a "living person". This is more impressive than the Psalms (51 and 139) as the context is dealing with abortion produced by trauma. I came to see that perhaps "human life" as such need not come into existence at a single moment in time. I was impressed by Dr. Kantzer's thesis that the body and soul come into their full value by a process. I became convinced that this position was possible without defining man functionally.

Clearly also people interpret the scientific data of the fertilized egg differently. I still believe that fertilization is the one logical point of origin of new life. But this does not establish the value of the new life and does not prove that this new life is of equal value to a fully developed body and soul.

In essence then, I find I have moved from position number 1 to the conservative pole within position number 3. That is, the foetus has great and developing value, but is less than a human being. It will be sacrificed only for weighty reasons. I find it hard to know how to "weigh" these reasons, but weigh them I must. Every pregnant woman threatened by deteriorating mental health or suicide because of her pregnancy deserves psychiatric care; some deserve abortions. There will be no easy decisions with this group of patients. Within this framework, most pregnancies that are the result of rape or incest should be terminated. When serious foetal abnormality is a certainty early in pregnancy termination will usually be indicated. The more difficult decisions will concern the foetus who has a greater-than-average likelihood of abnormality, but better than fifty percent chance of normality.

In an imperfect world, we are sometimes presented with alternatives we would rather not have. Neither alternative is what perfect love would choose. However, awareness of God's love and forgiveness enables us to live and enter into decision-making even without the choices we would have preferred, but didn't have.

Chapter 10

THE INTRAUTERINE
CONTRACEPTIVE DEVICE

SUMMARY

The IUD, because it is inexpensive, and because of the
simplicity of application, would seem to have a large potential as an aid in family planning especially for the lower
socio-economic segment of the population. The experience
from its use in relation to efficiency and to complications
has been described. The question of the IUD as a possible
cause of early abortion is discussed.

Some of the moral issues related to the use of the IUD
are examined. The problems caused by the population explosion are presented. Planning in reproduction is imperative in our world today and guidelines are suggested in this
direction.

ROSS L. WILLOWS, M.D., F.R.C.S.(C), F.I.C.S., F.A.C.O.G.
Dr. Willows is head of the Department of Obstetrics and Gynecology at St. Boniface General Hospital in Winnipeg, Manitoba, Canada, an Associate Professor of Obstetrics and Gynecology at the University of Manitoba and engages, also, in private practice. He graduated with a B.A. from the University of Saskatchewan and was granted his M.D. in the University of Manitoba. After post-doctoral training at Western Reserve University Hospital at Cleveland, he qualified as a specialist and earned his Fellowship in the Royal College of Surgeons of Canada.

THE INTRAUTERINE CONTRACEPTIVE DEVICE

by Ross L. Willows

The intrauterine device (IUD) has been under examination by the medical profession for several decades. Initially it took the form of the "wish bone" or "collar-stud" pessary fashioned from metal and was used for a variety of gynaecological conditions other than contraception. In 1928, Gräfenberg reported his results of prevention of conception by the use of a metal ring inserted into the uterine cavity. The final results were disappointing and this method was almost completely abandoned. In 1959 there was revived interest in the method by reports of use of different materials and designs. Presently a moulded plastic device is in use and is prepared in three basic forms—the loop, the coil and the bow.

MODE OF ACTION

The method by which the IUD prevents pregnancy is not clearly demonstrated. The device seems to exercise a different action in different experimental animals. It is probable that it may act at different levels to achieve its effect. In sub-human primates the main but not the only mechanism would seem to be acceleration of the ova through the tube. In women with the device in place there is a lower incidence of tubal pregnancies which is incompatible with increased action in the tube. The device does not obstruct the passage of sperm into the tube. The cavity of the uterus is enlarged and the walls normally lying against each other are separated. This could interfere with the normal mechanism of nidation. It has not been demonstrated that fertilized ova are aborted from the uterus; however, this remains a theoretical possibility.

CONTRAINDICATIONS FOR USE OF THE IUD

The absolute contraindications are:

a) Acute pelvic inflammatory disease. When treatment has progressed to the stage where pregnancy may be supported an IUD could be safely inserted.

b) Pregnancy proven or suspected. The optimal time of insertion is immediately after a menstrual period. However, if the only opportunity that presents itself occurs in the latter half of the cycle, it would not be wise to postpone insertions. The device need not necessarily disturb an implanted pregnancy.

The presence of irregular bleeding calls for investigation of the cause of the bleeding. At insertion of the IUD it is a proper concern that all methods available to rule out pelvic pathology be used and more particularly cancer of the reproductive tract.

EFFECTIVENESS OF THE IUD

In a review of available reports it may be stated that

after one year, 3 out of 4 patients will be receiving satisfactory protection from pregnancy. Of the 25% no longer
using the IUD 2% will have experienced an unwanted pregnancy, 7% will experience a spontaneous expulsion of the device and the remainder will require removal because of side
effects. This is slightly lower effectiveness in protection
against the unwanted pregnancy than oral contraceptives
but superior to the reported experience with the diaphragm
or condom. Further study of the various factors involved
could lead to better success with the method.

ADVANTAGES OF THE IUD

The advantages of the use of an IUD are not in its efficiency as much as in its application. This method holds great
promise for those who have only sufficient motivation to
make one visit to a physician. It may be that one opportunity for counselling in family planning is all that is available to them. The method must be commended for its
simplicity. It is not related to coitus and is more acceptable
by this fact than mechanical methods that are related to
coitus. The materials involved are inexpensive. It may be
used indefinitely. Removal of the device permits normal
childbearing to be resumed. In those areas of the world
where overpopulation is becoming most acute this method
may well contribute a great deal in changing the pattern
to a reasonable growth rate.

DISADVANTAGES OF THE IUD

A number of factors must be considered in a discussion
of disadvantages. The insertion of the device requires
trained personnel, ideally physicians, however, paramedical
technicians can be satisfactorily trained. There is a significant expulsion rate (7%) which usually occurs early after
insertion. This may be detected by the patient after self
examination. Routinely she should be checked by the physician at six weeks after insertion. Bleeding and pain may be

experienced to such a degree that removal is necessary. This depends on the judgement of the physician and the tolerance of the patient. The incidence of pelvic infection is slightly increased. In rare instances perforation of the uterus occurs and the IUD is found free in the peritoneal cavity. Dr. Roger Scott has surveyed the specialists in the U.S.A. and Canada and found 10 cases where death occurred and 561 separate cases of critical illness. On further examination of these cases where death occurred he rejected 4 as doubtful and 2 as conjectural, leaving 4 deaths where infection was the chief complication. Despite the presence of complications as listed, the dangers are not as serious as those encountered in crossing a busy thoroughfare, riding in a motor car or the alternative of an undesired pregnancy. The insertion and use of these devices are not known or suspected as a cause of cancer.

THE MORAL PROBLEM

A proper orientation toward the moral problem in the use of the IUD requires us to examine the problem that uncontrolled reproduction has brought to the world. This problem is the population explosion.

Up to the beginning of this century population growth was slow. This slow progress depended on a number of conditions. There was a high infant mortality comparable to that now existing in many developing countries where up to 50% of infants do not live to the age of one year. Famine would periodically take its toll. Added to these were the ravages of war. Life expectancy was about 40 years of age.

Medical science has made the largest contribution to the population increase by reason of increased salvage of the newborn. The life expectancy both by preserving for maturity large numbers of newborn infants and extending the life span in general has been greatly increased. Food production has greatly increased. It has not increased sufficiently to meet the needs of those who starve in the developing countries nor is it able to keep pace with the millions of new mouths who need to be fed each year. We cannot rely on war to reduce our populations in the future. However, the tensions of overpopulation may lead to war.

A MORAL RESPONSIBILITY TO PROVIDE A SOLUTION TO THE POPULATION EXPLOSION

It would appear that the moral rightness of saving the lives of the newborn and feeding the hungry cannot be challenged. Yet these contributions have led to the dilemma of the population explosion. There is a responsibility which lies upon those who have removed the barriers to survival and development of the individual to provide means of maintaining a balance within society of the optimum population suitable to his environment. Knowledge and self control have not proved to be adequate. One of the methods that contributes towards a solution is the intrauterine device.

MORAL ARGUMENTS AGAINST THE IUD

Some have put forward the theoretical possibility that the IUD permits fertilization of the ovum and that the presence of this foreign body leads to abortion. The studies of women with an IUD in place have demonstrated:

1) Ovulation does take place. This has been established by endometrial biopsies, pregnandiol excretion levels, observation of corpora lutea at laparotomy and the presence of the typical basal body temperature curve.
2) The Fallopian tubes are not blocked to sperm.
3) The Fallopian tubes are not blocked to ova.
4) Implantation does not occur, as evidenced by the absence of a prolonged cycle or the presence of decidual tissue or products of conception.

Washings of the Fallopian tubes at laparotomy have yielded the following results; of 92 women with an IUD in place 11 ova were recovered and one was found to be fertilized. Of 161 women without devices 12 ova were recovered and 4 were fertilized. The series are too small to reach any significant conclusions.

Abortions have been demonstrated at 2 and 3 months of gestation with the IUD in place. These, however, do not occur in a greater incidence than might occur spontaneously in the same number of pregnancies occurring in the absence of an IUD.

MORAL PROBLEMS FOR A SOCIETY

The growth of population increasingly becomes the concern of large groups of people living together. Their leaders must engage in planning for the future. The matter of population planning has not been given the attention it has deserved because it has become involved in the controversy of morals and mores within the society. The IUD, in spite of its shortcomings, has a role to play until better methods are devised and should be used to assist the struggling societies to achieve population stability.

MORAL PROBLEMS FOR THE INDIVIDUAL

When a man and wife conclude that they should have no more children, and there are many just reasons for this decision, their next question is the choice of the right method. Is the IUD right for them? If the choice is the IUD and the uterus accepts this device, the couple is protected according to the rated efficiency that experience has demonstrated for this method. The timing in the passage of the ovum has been altered slightly or the shape of the uterine cavity has been somewhat changed. When the device is removed the woman may again become pregnant. On the basis of this knowledge and in the purity of her own motives she would be right to adopt the use of the IUD.

SECTION 3

CONSIDERATIONS
OF MEDICAL ETHICS

Chapter 11

CONTRACEPTIVES AND THE SINGLE PERSON

SUMMARY

Orville K. Walters, Professor of Health Science and Lecturer in Psychiatry at the University of Illinois, examines five ethical stances the physician may adopt in deciding whether to prescribe contraceptives for the unmarried girl. Three of the options are not articulated premises. Situation ethics and the historic Christian position are sanctioned by Church spokesmen and so are considered at greater length. Four basic criteria of Christian ethical decision cited as being applicable to the problem: Scripture, reason, tradition and experience. Situation ethics is found to be inadequate on seven counts.

ORVILLE S. WALTERS, M.D., Ph.D. *The author is Professor of Health Science and Lecturer in Psychiatry at the University of Illinois at Urbana. He holds the M.D. degree from St. Louis University and the Ph.D. in Physiology from the University of Kansas. He was ordained to the ministry of the Free Methodist Church while serving as President of Central College. Trained in Psychiatry at the Menninger School, Dr. Walters is certified to practice by the American Board of Psychiatry and Neurology. His articles have been published by professional journals, the* CMS Journal, Christianity Today, *the* Christian Century *and* Religion in Life.

CONTRACEPTIVES AND THE SINGLE PERSON

by Orville S. Walters

The development of effective oral contraceptives and the committing of these drugs to the medical profession as legal distributors have involved the physician deeply in the complexities of sexual ethics. In the case of Protestants, the point of greatest tension is likely to be whether contraceptive medications will be prescribed for the unmarried girl. The physician may come to this decision with one of several possible attitudes: 1) the broadly permissive; 2) the neutralist; 3) reluctant sanction; 4) the situationist; 5) the historic Christian position. In the paragraphs to follow, these attitudes will be examined in turn, especially as each relates to the prescribing of contraceptives for the unmarried.

THE BROADLY PERMISSIVE

Freud prepared the way for the Kinsey report, according to Lionel Trilling, but in all the years of his activity, Freud never had the authority that the Kinsey report achieved in a few weeks. Trilling commented upon the permissive influence of the report,[1] while Reinhold Niebuhr described the premarital promiscuity that Kinsey advocated as "moral anarchism".[2] In the same vein, one might say that Kinsey prepared the way for the Playboy Philosophy and many of the expressions of sexual permissiveness in today's world. This attitude and the demands that grow out of it are bound to involve the physician.

The physician who prescribes contraceptives for the unmarried girl out of a broadly permissive attitude that accepts the New Morality must, in so doing, weigh the time-honored medical maxim, "to do no harm." He must recognize that

> . . . Fornication is more than an isolated, pleasurable exercise of the sexual organs; it is the expression of an attitude of mind in which God, other persons, and the self are all involved.[3]

The storm of responsible criticism that descended upon Kinsey, and the contemporary reaction of sober protest against the Playboy Philosophy, reflect not merely a residuum of moral conservatism, but a substantial body of conviction that such an ethical code is damaging to human personality in ways that are beyond the ability of any social science to quantitate.

> Aside from the question of decency and morality, promiscuity is bad because it is harmful to the young

---

[1] Trilling, Lionel, "The Kinsey Report," in *An Analysis of the Kinsey Report on Sexual Behavior in the Human Male and Female.* New York: Dutton & Company, 1954, p. 213.

[2] Niebuhr, Reinhold, "Kinsey and the Moral Problem of Man's Sexual Life," *Ibid.*, p. 213.

[3] Bailey, Derrick S., *The Mystery of Love and Marriage.* New York: Harper & Brothers, 1952, p. 53.

woman. It works against her interests. Human nature
being what it is, the demonstration that a course of
action is harmful is more likely to be effective than the
argument that it is indecent or immoral.[4]

The case for chastity is by no means argued solely on
religious grounds.[5,6] A university psychiatrist finds that
"most of the sexual problems of students who consult psychiatrists today . . . arise when the student is contemplating or participating in premarital sexual activities." [7]
Another psychiatrist asks the question, "Why, in a time of
greater sexual freedom, do sexual problems continue to
abound, with sexual inadequacy apparently becoming more
pervasive?" [8] A symposium on premarital coition concludes,

> Girls and boys of this generation need help in detecting
> and rejecting . . . the . . . subtly persuasive, fraud-
> ulent national propaganda of the new sexual morality.
> . . . Four thousand years of Judeo-Christian wisdom
> cannot be dismissed lightly. There are still valid and
> urgent reasons for saving sex for the right time, place,
> and person, within the sanctions of a concerned so-
> ciety.[9]

THE NEUTRALIST

In assuming this position, the physician may deny that
any ethical choice is involved in his prescribing. He may
declare, instead, that the crucial decision to use or not to
use contraceptives belongs entirely to the unmarried person
who makes the request.

[4] Levin, Max, *Vassar and the Non-Virgins*. Baltimore: Williams
and Wilkins, 1966, p. 4.

[5] Calderone, Mary S., "The Case for Chastity," in *Sex in America*.
New York: Bantam Books, 1964, p. 140.

[6] Levin, Max, "The Physician and the Sexual Revolution," *New
England Journal of Medicine*, 273:1366, December 16, 1965.

[7] Halleck, S. L., "Sexual Problems of College Students," *Medical
Aspects of Human Sexuality*, May, 1968.

[8] Shainess, Natalie, "The Problem of Sex Today," *Amer. J. Psy-
chiat.* 124:8, 1968.

[9] Sanders, Mervyn S., "What are the Psychological Effects of Premarital Intercourse?", in *Medical Aspects in Human Sexuality*, April,
1968.

The idea that the physician can remain neutral in this or any similar situation is illusory. In every moment of the physician-patient relationship there is communication, verbal or non-verbal, that is bound to disclose the physician's own philosophy of life and his ethical stance. If the doctor's response serves, however subtly, to favor the patient's decision to use, his claim of neutrality is abrogated. The act of complying with the request of an unmarried girl for contraceptive medication is not simply transferring to her the ethical decision to use or not to use, but is active participation in the decision.

A request for contraceptive medication from an unmarried girl is virtually a declaration of intent to participate in extramarital coition.[10] For the physician to renounce any complicity in the patient's moral decision by implying, "It's her decision, not mine," is to disregard the considerable professional authority inherent in the physician's vocation. The physician is charged by custom and by law with being the keeper of potent medications, to be released when he considers them contributory to the welfare or the improvement of his patients. Therefore, every prescription signifies the selection of whatever is best suited to resolve the patient's presenting problem. The patient's acceptance of a prescription implies confidence in the physician's concern and in his competence to make a wise choice for the patient.

The ancient system by which the doctor earns his livelihood from the patient's fee is based upon his willingness to accept responsibility for the patient's health. The only time a physician can properly disclaim responsibility is when the patient fails to follow the regimen prescribed. The physician is paid to make choices for his patients and cannot avoid responsibility for the course he recommends.

---

[10] Prescriptions given immediately preceding marriage and those given for the treatment of recognized menstrual disorders, are specifically excepted in this discussion.

RELUCTANT SANCTION

While objecting that premarital sex is a bad thing, the physician may be convinced that it is unpreventable and therefore may prescribe contraceptives in an acceptance of the inevitable. He may say, "If I don't prescribe, she'll get the pills anyway," which implies that it is futile for him to take a positive stand in favor of chastity.

This viewpoint seriously underestimates the strength of the physician's moral influence and authority with his patients. In a way utterly unique in human relationships, the patient turns himself over to the physician, submitting to violation of his most personal intimacy and, at times, literally placing his life in the hands of his physician. The patient's confidence is based primarily upon his attribution of scientific knowledge and skill to the doctor, but it also carries a strong component of faith in the physician's integrity and respect for his opinion.

For the doctor to consider his patient's moral decision as predetermined and beyond the reach of his influence is to segment the person and to abdicate responsibility for providing assistance and guidance in any except the physical or emotional dimension. The doctor who begins by trying to deter his patient, then grants her request, is likely to vitiate by his acquiescence whatever positive value his initial reluctance may have had. A strong position against premarital coition, buttressed by an unwillingness to compromise on grounds of expediency, may provide needed moral strength and support to the patient.

Another form of the "reluctant" position recognizes that premarital sex is bad but contends that an illegitimate pregnancy is worse. The physician's dilemma may be compounded by the patient who has a history of one illegitimate pregnancy and who comes seeking to avoid another. The doctor may be convinced that in granting the request for contraceptives, he is choosing the lesser of two evils.

In weighing the alternatives, the physician must realize that he is balancing a real decision against a contingency —an act by another person that may or may not take place. By refusing, and by throwing the weight of his professional authority behind continence as a wise choice, the doctor may help to avert the contingent act, illicit coition. Granting the request, even though it may seem the lesser of two evils, carries implied sanction of the anticipated illicit sexual activity, no matter how much reluctance may be expressed initially. In thus prescribing contraceptives, it is difficult for the doctor to avoid being identified as an accessory before the fact, that is, as a person who assists, counsels or encourages another to commit an act, even though he is absent at the time the act is committed.

THE SITUATIONIST

The ethical decision confronting the physician who is asked to prescribe contraceptives for the single girl has been greatly complicated by the proclamation of the new morality. Unlike the preceding positions, none of which necessarily has a Christian context, situationism asserts that its roots lie securely in the classical tradition of Western Christian morals,[11] with agape as its sole criterion. However, since the system declares freedom from rules, laws and principles, it has been described by one of its critics as a non-Christian nonsystem of nonethics.[12]

Ramsey, using terms coined by Frankena, subdivides Christian ethics based upon agape into *act-agapism,* in which the law of love is to be applied directly and separately in each case, and *rule-agapism,* which decides what we ought to do by determining which *rules of action* embody love. He takes sharp exception to the *exclusive* act-agapism set forth by Fletcher, contending that there can be no social ethics unless there are some rules of practices required by

[11] Fletcher, Joseph, *Situation Ethics.* Philadelphia: Westminster Press, 1966, p. 13.
[12] *Ibid.,* p. 11.

agape.[13] Moreover, he demonstrates that act-responsibility can be established only by arbitrarily rejecting rule-responsibility.[14]

The physician who is endeavoring to practice his vocation as a Christian is under some constraint to evaluate the claims of situation ethics, which has arisen largely within the church. The situationist asserts that, since rules and laws may be superseded by the individual circumstances of any situation, premarital sex is at times constructive rather than wrong. From this viewpoint, the encouragement of extramarital coition might conceivably be a potential benefaction, however remote the contingency. The crucial elements for a decision lie within the situation, since act-agapism dictates that "even the most revered principles may be thrown aside if they conflict in any concrete case with love." [15]

Fletcher maintains that "situational factors are so primary that we may even say 'circumstances alter rules and principles' ".[16] The notion that there are immutable laws of heaven is idolatrous and a demonic pretension.[17] "For the situationist there are no rules—none at all".[18] Love will not share its authority with any other laws, either natural or supernatural.[19] "Whether any form of sex (hetero, homo, or auto) is good or evil depends on whether love is fully served".[20]

Situation Ethics Examined

The response of other ethicists to the new morality has been prompt and vigorous. The following paragraphs sum-

---

[13] Ramsey, Paul, *Deeds and Rules in Christian Ethics.* New York: Charles Scribner's Sons, 1967, p. 8

[14] *Ibid.,* p. 15.

[15] Fletcher, *op. cit.,* p. 33.

[16] *Ibid.,* p. 29.

[17] *Ibid.,* p. 31.

[18] *Ibid.,* p. 55.

[19] *Ibid.,* p. 85.

[20] *Ibid.,* p. 139.

marize the criticisms of some who have made careful evaluation of the situation ethics viewpoint.

Situation ethics devaluates history and tradition

Gardner cites as a major inadequacy in Fletcher's thought "his tendency to view the self as making its moral decisions in an ahistorical present".[21] Because it is a revolt against traditional moral standards in favor of unstructured freedom, he believes situationism will prove to be a transitory form of ethics.[22]

> The self cannot understand its own identity as a social being apart from its memory of past experiences and past relationships . . . neither can any acting subject understand its neighbors . . . apart from their history which is rooted in their past experiences and action. Knowledge of the past is prerequisite for interpreting the meaning and time, both for the present and the future of human relationships.[23]

Bennett calls attention to the Christian wisdom that the church and the Christian citizen bring to the context. Christian teaching concerning man and his relationship to God, freedom and sin cannot be derived from the situation.[24]

Kennedy approves Chesterton's definition of tradition as

> giving votes to the most obscure of all classes, our ancestors. Tradition asks us not to neglect a good man's opinion, even if he is our father. . . . We will have the dead at our councils.[25]

Even Bishop Robinson acknowledges that "we could not but flounder" without the cumulative experience of the

---

[21] Gardner, E. Clinton, "Responsibility in Freedom," in *Storm Over Ethics*. United Church Press: Bethany Press, 1967, p. 64.

[22] *Ibid.*, p. 38.

[23] *Ibid.*, p. 64.

[24] Bennett, John C., "Principles and the Context," in *Storm Over Ethics, op. cit.*, p. 16.

[25] Kennedy, Gerald, "The Nature of Heresy," in *Storm Over Ethics, op. cit.*, p. 136.

race as a "bank of experience which gives us our working
rules of 'right' and 'wrong' ".[26]

Ramsey summarizes the situationist neglect of consensus:

> Instead of salutary reference to the community's think-
> ing on ethical questions, and to its deposit of ethos, the
> stress falls upon the fact that "every man is his own
> casuist when the decision-making chips are down." [27]

Situationism depreciates principles and laws

Bennett believes that "a contextual ethic completely
separated from universal or broadly based normative considerations is not really viable".[28] He insists that the most
absolutist contextualist is sure to make use of bootlegged
principles.[29] Gardner emphasizes the need for greater attention to the regularities, the constancies, and the struc-
tured character of moral relationships.

> I see an indispensable place for law—including prin-
> ciples and rules—in ethical analysis . . . the very
> possibility of meaning in any moral situation depends
> upon its relatedness to a generalized pattern of values
> and/or duties in terms of which a single choice be-
> comes intelligible. . . . Used in the service of love, law
> fills a need for direction in ethical reflection.[30]

Gleason insists that God has given man "a natural
light of intelligence by which he may know what is to be
done and what is to be avoided in the moral sphere. This
natural law is itself a participation in the eternal law, which
exists in God himself." Situational ethics relies upon "the
subjective, immanent light of the individual" rather than
"the law of nature or the law of the decalogue." Thus the
written law of God, communicated to man through divinely

---

[26] Robinson, John. A. T., *Honest to God*. Philadelphia: Westminster Press, 1963, pp. 119–120.

[27] *Op. cit.*, p. 151.

[28] *Op. cit.*, p. 9.

[29] *Ibid.*, p. 2.

[30] *Op. cit.*, pp. 53, 55, 49.

appointed authority, is relegated to a position of secondary importance.[31]

Smith criticizes situationism because it establishes the base for the methodological model upon the exceptional case.

> Although the method of situation ethics is introduced with deference to the place of principles in the decision-making process, every case cited by Fletcher as illustrative of the situational approach demonstrates abandonment of generally accepted moral maxims.[32]

Situational ethics neglects social considerations

The question is raised by Ramsey:

> We must ask whether there are any *societal* rules that embody the highest general responsibility and which are the most followship-producing rules for *society as a whole,* or whether this is a matter of 'situational' acts only . . .[33]

The Quaker report recognized the same point:

> However private an act it is never without its impact on society, and we must never behave as though society—which includes our other friends—did not exist.[34]

Gardner also cites the antinomy between the competing claims of single individuals and those of the community. These cannot be settled responsibly, he insists, unless the dialectical relationship between the two sets of claims is understood.[35]

The new morality overrates human rationality

Bishop Robinson believes that agape should determine

---

[31] Gleason, Robert W., "Situational Morality," in *Storm Over Ethics, op. cit.,* pp. 118, 125, 126.

[32] Smith, Harmon L., "When Love Becomes Excarnate," in *Storm Over Ethics, op. cit.,* p. 103.

[33] Ramsey, *op. cit.,* p. 6.

[34] *Ibid.,* p. 20.

[35] *Op. cit.,* p. 55.

conduct at any moment of decision, unencumbered by prior commitments of any sort.

> Love alone, because, as it were, it has a built-in moral compass, enabling it to 'home' intuitively upon the deepest need of the other, can allow itself to be directed completely by the situation.[36]

Similarly Fletcher asserts that the situationist must be prepared to set aside or to compromise the ethical maxims of his community and its heritage *"in the situation* if love seems better served by doing so."* He follows a moral law or violates it, according to love's need.[37]

The expectation that extemporaneous decisions can be rationally and correctly made by situational intuition in the face of "nearly ungovernable emotions" [38] or "physiologically induced illusion" [39] is unrealistic if not naïve, Reinhold Niebuhr has recognized that

> . . . The natural passions which exist side by side— with the capacity of rationality . . . are always subject to the corruption of man's spiritual pretension, to human sin.[40]

Streeter wrote,

> When passion is the arbiter, my own case is always recognized to be exceptional. . . . When Aphrodite whispers in my ear . . . if any exception is admitted, my case is certain to be the one.[41]

Niebuhr questions whether reason is ever sufficiently powerful "to achieve, or even to approximate, a complete

---

[36] *Op. cit.*, p. 115.

[37] Op. cit., p. 26.

[38] Wynn, John C., "Churches and Churchmen: Study of Meaning and Non-meaning," in *Sex, Family and Society in Theological Focus.* New York: Association Press, 1966, p. 27.

[39] Thielecke, Helmut, *The Ethics of Sex.* New York: Harper & Row, 1964, p. 201.

[40] Niebuhr, Reinhold, *An Interpretation of Christian Ethics.* New York: Meridian Books, 1956, p. 114.

[41] Lunn, Arnold and Lean, Garth, *The New Morality.* London: Blandford Press, 1964, p. 77.

harmony between what is demanded for the self and what is granted to the other" since the force of egoistic impulse is so powerful.

> If it is defeated on a lower or more obvious level, it will express itself in more subtle forms. If it is defeated by social impulse it insinuates itself into the social impulse, so that a man's devotion to his community always means the expression of a transferred egoism as well as of altruism.[42]

The situationist over-simplification of moral decision is apparent when the fact of original sin is faced. Man as he is (his existence) is in standing conflict with man as he was created (his essence). Sin tends to corrupt his judgments and to bias his choices.

> Plainly, the waywardness of the human heart works against any *ethos*, customs, or laws that are generally good for all, and not only against 'the traditional code'.[43]

Situation ethics is an accommodation to contemporary culture

In a chapter titled "Some Presuppositions," Fletcher appropriates William James' definition of the *right* as "only the expedient in our way of thinking".[44] This acceptance of the expedient contrasts sharply with Ramsey's view of Christian ethics as "the Christian life lived in rational reflection".[45] Fletcher's incorporation of pragmatism leads naturally to relativism. "As the strategy is pragmatic, the tactics are relativistic." [46] This he acknowledges to be a conformation to today's philosophic temper. "Situationism . . . is the crystal precipitated in Christian

[42] Niebuhr, Reinhold, *Moral Man and Immoral Society*. New York: Charles Scribner's Sons, 1932, pp. 29, 40.

[43] Ramsey, *op. cit.*, p. 20.

[44] *Op. cit.*, p. 41.

[45] *Op. cit.*, p. 209.

[46] *Op. cit.*, p. 43.

ethics by our era's pragmatism and relativism".[47] The consequences to Christian faith are candidly acknowledged:

> The shift to relativism carries contemporary Christians away from code ethics, away from stern ironbound do's and don'ts, away from prescribed conduct and legalistic morality.[48]

In partial support of this "shift away from the rules of rationality," Fletcher cites "acceptance of unconscious and motivational dynamics as the foundation of human behavior." [49] This concession to an irrational and threatening unconscious stratum of human nature on the basis of psychodynamic representations is not justified by the facts. As I have shown in a recent review,[50] the acceptance of such a conclusion is more an affirmation of faith in a sectarian dogma than a conclusion supported by solid scientific evidence.

Situationism makes an absolute of love

Fletcher recognizes that relativism means being relative to something. "In Christian situationism the ultimate criterion is 'agapeic love' ".[51] However, he contends, situationism does not absolutize the relative; instead, it "relativizes the absolute." Fitch disagrees sharply, pronouncing situationism "absolutist" in its "marvelous contempt for the inherited body of laws, commandments, principles and rules—which teach us the discriminations of love and of justice".[52]

Gardner deprecates Fletcher's "love monism," his substitution of love for justice, prudence, and all other virtues.

---

[47] *Ibid.*, p. 147.
[48] *Ibid.*, p. 45.
[49] *Ibid.*, p. 44.
[50] Walters, Orville S., "Theology and Changing Concepts of the Unconscious," *Religion in Life*, XXXVII, p. 112, 1968.
[51] *Op. cit.*, p. 45.
[52] Fitch, Robert E., "The Protestant Sickness," *Religion in Life*, XXXV, 498, 1966.

. . . There is need for love and for justice in the life of the community, and the latter cannot be reduced to the former without falsifying the antithetical as well as the complementary character of the relationship between these two values.[53]

Fletcher's claim that "love and justice are the same" [54] is also rejected by Sellers. He grants that love is a "higher" virtue than justice, "if by that grant we do not understand ourselves to be signing away the complementary self-standingness of justice".[55]

Situationism emphasizes action and intent to the neglect of content

Objective value theory is rejected.

There *are* no values at all; there are only things which *happen* to be valued by persons. . . . It gains its value only because it happens to help persons. . . . Situation ethics . . . does not ask . . . what *is* love, but how to *do* the most loving thing possible.[56]

Smith asks, "But how does a person know that he is doing the loving thing in the situation? What judges decision and action?" He concludes,

This mark of existentialism, the reduction of the criteria for moral judgment to sincerity and integrity . . . does not provide any clear ground for distinguishing between acts which are good and those which are bad.[57]

Gleason's comment is similar:

The action that follows upon a good intention should also be conformed to all the divine and natural laws that are involved in the particular situation.[58]

---

[53] *Op. cit.,* p. 56.
[54] *Op. cit.,* p. 87.
[55] Sellers, James, "Mr. Ramsey and the New Morality," *Religion in Life,* XXXVII, 282, 1968.
[56] Fletcher, *op. cit.,* pp. 58, 59, 52.
[57] *Op. cit.,* p. 100.
[58] *Ibid., p.* 127.

Gardner calls the greatest weakness of *Situation Ethics* "its failure to deal seriously with the need for clarification of the substantive content and meaning of moral choices".[59]

The new morality is thus vulnerable to attack on a broad front and is likely to precipitate more problems than it solves for the physician who seeks a defensible ethical position. Gardner declares that the situationists have gone to "the brink of antinomianism".[60] Ramsey charges that Fletcher's ethics cannot be distinguished from antinomianism, anomianism or existential situationalism.[61]

THE HISTORIC CHRISTIAN POSITION

The Christian sexual tradition has its roots in the strict code of the Old Testament which proscribed extramarital sexual activities on moral and religious grounds.[62] This code was in effect ratified by Jesus as he upheld respect for the commandments. In enunciating the new commandment emphasizing love, he did not abrogate the old. Even as he focused down upon the inner motive, he did not lessen the gravity of the offense of adultery and fornication.[63]

Paul continued this essential emphasis as he bracketed immorality and adultery with the basic sin of idolatry [64] and described sexual sins as opposed to the activity of the spirit.[65] The emphasis upon chastity that has characterized Christian sexual ethics is thus deeply rooted in biblical teaching.

> However imperfectly they grasped them, however ineffectually they put them into practice, Christians recognized from the first that certain sexual truths

---

[59] *Ibid.*, p. 40.

[60] *Ibid.*, p. 48.

[61] *Op. cit.*, p. 152.

[62] *Sex and the Church*. St. Louis, Mo.: Concordia Publishing House, 1961, Ch. 2.

[63] Mark 7:21.

[64] I. Cor. 6:9-10.

[65] Galatians 5:19.

belonged to the Gospel—the spiritual equality of man and woman in the sight of God, the high theological significance of marriage, the impartial application of the rule of chastity to both sexes.[66]

Recent Attacks on Christian Sexual Ethics

Christian sexual ethics have often been subject to such attacks from without as that of Russell.[67] However, the past few years have brought multiple assaults upon traditional codes from within the church in the name of Christian love. Typical of this defiance of traditional morality are the statements of Williams, "Where there is healing there is Christ, whatever the church may say about fornication" [68] and of Cox, "We must avoid giving a simple yes or no answer to the question of premarital chastity".[69]

Cole acknowledges that part of the ferocity of the contemporary attack upon moral standards is "certainly traceable to rationalization, the attempt to justify behavior that violates those standards," although he recognizes some sincere conviction that a new set of norms is needed.[70]

Situationist rationalization tends to base its rejection of traditional morality upon one of three assertions:

Christian morality must be modified because it is so widely rejected today

"The supranaturalist ethic . . . is a position that men honour much more in the breach than in the observance." Bishop Robinson is undoubtedly partly correct in his statement that "the sanctions of Sinai have lost their terrors,

[66] Bailey, Sherwin, *Sexual Ethics*. New York: Macmillan, 1963, p. 19.

[67] Demant, V. A., *Christian Sex Ethics*. New York: Harper & Row, 1963, p. 10.

[68] Williams, H. A., "Theology and Self-Awareness," in *Soundings*. Cambridge: Cambridge University Press, 1962, p. 82.

[69] Cox, Harvey, "Evangelical Ethics and the Ideal of Chasity," in *Witness to a Generation*. Indianapolis; Bobbs-Merrill, 1966, p. 151.

[70] Cole, William G., *Sex in Christianity and Psychoanalysis*. New York: Oxford University Press, 1955, p. 285.

and people no longer accept the authority of Jesus even as a great moral teacher".[71] Lunn and Lean offer a sharp riposte:

> The clear implication is that God's laws have something in common with a political programme and should be restated when they are felt no longer to command the support of a majority.[72]

There is no such thing as a Christian ethic

"Bishop Robinson rightly says that 'there is no one ethical system that can claim to be Christian, but I am inclined to say that *any* ethical system is unchristian or at least sub-Christian' ".[73]

Robinson deprecates a supranaturalistic ethic that stands for objective moral values and he denies that Jesus' commands were universal principles.[74] Burnaby calls in question even the possibility of deriving norms from the teachings of Jesus:

> . . . an infallible Christ can be of no avail to us, unless we are sure both of what he said and of what he meant by it . . .[75]

These comments, like much situationist quibbling, ignores the overarching fact of Christian ethics, that "the ultimate context of every moral situation is that of the divine will," involving creation, judgment and reconciliation, which provides the ultimate framework of meaning for all human decision-making. Even though man was created free, his autonomy is circumscribed by God's sovereignty as Creator and judge. Chastening and wrath are an inescapable aspect of divine sovereignty when man rebels in pride and self-

---

[71] *Op. cit.*, p. 109.

[72] *Op. cit.*, p. 74.

[73] Fletcher, *op. cit.*, p. 12.

[74] *Honest to God, op. cit.*, p. 113.

[75] Burnaby, John, "Conduct and Faith," in *God, Sex and War.* Philadelphia: Westminster Press, 1963, p. 108.

centeredness. Even Jesus' ethic cannot be properly understood except in the light of the Old Testament conception
of God, man and the world.[76]

> Although Jesus summarized the whole duty of man in
> the twofold love commandment, he spoke of many
> other virtues even more frequently than he spoke of
> love; and he emphasized the abiding need for "the law
> and the prophets" to safeguard morality from hy-
> pocrisy and sentimentality.[77]

Christian standards of sexual morality are too restrictive

"There is a vast body of modern opinion which holds that
the Christian standard in sexual relations . . . is unnatural
and impossible to observe for men and women in general".[78]
Lunn and Lean point out that even in pagan Greece, "Plato
could argue that the ideal of continence did not necessarily
ask too much of human nature." The New Moralists, they
comment, "appear to think it more compassionate to condone
sin than to convince people that, in Christ, can be found the
power to conquer it".[79]

Acceptance of Niebuhr's view that "the ethical demands
made by Jesus are incapable of fulfillment in the present
existence of man" [80] surrenders not only the ideals relating
to adultery and fornication, but also the very capacity to
confer unearned and undeserved love, that is, agapism in
any form.

Freud examined the Christian ideal, "Thou shalt love
thy neighbor as thyself" and concluded that it is "unpsy-
chological".[81]

If he is a stranger to me and if he cannot attract me by

---

[76] Gardner, E. Clinton, *loc. cit.*, p. 58.

[77] *Ibid.*, p. 62.

[78] Demant, V. A., *op. cit.*, p. 10.

[79] *Op. cit.*, pp. 97, 101.

[80] *An Interpretation of Christian Ethics*, op. cit., p. 59.

[81] Freud, Sigmund, "Civilization and Its Discontents," in *Standard
Edition, Complete Works*, XXI, 143.

any worth of his own or any significance that he may already have acquired for my emotional life, it will be hard for me to love him. Indeed, I should be wrong to do so.[82]

Freud's judgment concerning the difficulty of giving undeserved love was accurate as far as unregenerate man is concerned. It is only by the intervention of divine grace that we are able to become the channels by which agape is bestowed upon the unlovable.

Examination of the context is not a peculiar virtue of the new morality. Christians have always had to examine the circumstances of the situation in making some ethical decisions, since biblical and churchly tradition have never provided specific guidance for changing cultures and conditions. It is said quite correctly that we are all in some sense "situationists." The possibility of divergent conclusions where no specific guidance exists is well illustrated by the difference between Catholic and Protestant attitudes toward contraception in marriage.

CONCLUSION

To avoid errant tendencies in the derivation of ethical decisions, Protestantism has drawn guidance from three principal sources: scripture, reason and tradition. John Wesley was responsible for renewing an emphasis upon a fourth element, experience, in which he included an awareness of the Holy Spirit moving upon the human spirit. Although he was an early practitioner of the empirical in religion, Wesley was well aware of the perils of subjectivism, and sought always to maintain a consistent balance among all four elements.

Fletcher is eager to identify situationism with personalism, to emphasize that people are at the center of concern. He describes God as "personal" and refers to the *imago Dei*

---

[82] *Ibid.*, p. 109.

that man bears.[83] These are ancient propositions, learned from a scripture that has always been personalistic in its emphasis. What is new about situationism is the process of selectivity by which the wisdom of both Word and church are subordinated to man's unlimited and unguided volition.

Situationists plead for an empirical ethic, "a morality of involvement and discovery," but reject the safeguards provided by scripture and the church against subjectivism and rationalization. "The Word of the Lord is there—yet not as proposition".[84] The right is reserved to abandon entirely the guidance of the church as "establishment-mindedness." Agape is pried out of its scriptural context, and left alone to cope with the caprice of specious logic and self-deception.

The "miracle drugs" produced by the synthetic manipulations of biochemistry have revolutionized modern medicine. Yet each one has its hazards, and its introduction must be accompanied by a recital of the qualifications and limitations that have been learned by experience. These warnings are joined to those general principles governing bodily function that the physician has learned in his study of physiology, anatomy and pathology.

It would be possible for an eager young physician to rebel against an "authoritarian" pharmacology, "liberate" himself from a "legalistic" Food and Drug code, and set out to administer medications to his patients without benefit of the accumulated wisdom of scientific medicine. Recent medical history makes it easy to imagine the consequences. The same danger of uncontrolled, capricious choice in moral and ethical matters ensues if the Christian heritage of divine and human wisdom is reduced to an obsolescent appurtenance.

---

[83] *Op. cit.*, p. 51.
[84] Robinson, John A. T., *Christian Morals Today*. Philadelphia: Westminster Press, 1964, pp. 37, 38.

Chapter 12

MORAL CONSIDERATIONS IN CONTRACEPTION: A CHRISTIAN VIEW OF CONTRACEPTION WITHIN MARRIAGE

SUMMARY

Contraception in Christian marriage is not wrong but has very significant, positive value. In this paper the position is expounded firmly for the benefit of all Christians who may have lingering doubts about this matter. Scriptural, medical and psychological support is marshalled in defense of the arguments presented.

MERVILLE O. VINCENT, M.D., C.M., F.R.C.P. (C) *Dr. Vincent has served on the staff of the Homewood Sanitarium in Guelph, Ontario (Canada's lagrest private psychiatric institution) since 1960, and as Assistant Medical Superintendent since 1962. He is a graduate of the Dalhousie University School of Medicine in Nova Scotia, received training in Psychiatry and Internal Medicine at the University of Michigan, and holds certification in both fields. He is a Fellow of the Royal College of Physicians of Canada. In addition to his professional responsibilities, Dr. Vincent is a frequent contributor to a wide variety of journals and magazines.*

MORAL CONSIDERATIONS IN CONTRACEPTION

by M. O. Vincent

A Christian Viewpoint on Contraception Within Marriage

This topic is "pregnant" with possibilities for disagreement. Therefore it is important to define contraception immediately as "any conscious activity aimed at preventing fertilization". It follows that abortion by any means is not being considered.

The Christian ethic is rooted in Scripture. Moral imperatives and principles are noted from which we deductively make specific applications to contemporary situations. Ethical decisions are motivated by love for God and our fellow men, guided by the Holy Spirit and considered judgment. There is no specific text in the Scripture to settle the contraception issue for us. The overall Scriptural view of the nature of God, man, marriage and sexual intercourse leads, however, to the view that we have a right to conception control.

THE RIGHT TO CONCEPTION CONTROL

The Nature of God

God is the Creator and Sustainer of mankind. God created us male and female. He designed us physically so that sex relations were a possibility. He designed us emotionally with sexual desire that makes sexual relationship a probability. He planted a desire in me that causes me to be aroused by the human female, but not by a female spider or female rhinoceros. This is undoubtedly a mystery for the male rhinoceros, but for this design and desire, I give God thanks. God saw that each thing he created was good: sex is of God; therefore, sex is good.

God in his sustaining love has revealed for our guidance something of the nature of man, marriage and sex, because he is concerned about our well-being.

The Nature of Man

Man is a creation of God. God gave him reason, judgment, a sense of responsibility and a will. Therefore, man is not governed just by instinct. Man can direct many affairs in his own life; he has value and freedom to use God's gifts according to his own condition and circumstances. God gave man dominion over the earth, and when man the creature fell, God even gave his son to be man and to redeem man. The reconciled man therefore seeks God's will, so that he may exercise his dominion responsibly, for God made man responsible to him. To subdue and have dominion over nature in a manner demonstrating both love to God and our fellow man is a Christian principle apparent throughout Scripture, even from the first chapter of Genesis.

We read. . . . "And God blessed them, and God said to them, be fruitful and multiply". It is to be noted that "to be fruitful and multiply" was given by God more as a blessing than a commandment and certainly as a blessing, not a

curse. Even if this verse is understood as being a commandment for the 20th century, it is to be noted that God did not
say by what factor we were to multiply, whether it be one,
two or ten. If the human race ceased to be fruitful and to
multiply, it would disappear in one generation.

The Nature of Marriage

Marriage is an institution ordained by God. Scripture
indicates several functions of marriage.

Companionship and mutual aid

We do not read in Scripture that woman was created primarily for the propagation of the species but rather
(Genesis 2:18) "because it was not good for man to be
alone". God's plan provided for a companion who would
satisfy the unfulfilled yearning of man's heart. Woman was
created for mutual fellowship and companionship. Man was
to be a social creature and his wife was to be one with whom
he might share love, trust, devotion and responsibility. She
was to respond to his nature with understanding and love
in a reciprocal relationship. A similar emphasis on a loving
relationship is found in Ephesians (5:22–23) where the
marriage relationship is described as analogous to the relationship between Christ and the Church. This loving companionship, if not the prime scriptural purpose of marriage,
is at least as important as the procreative function.

Procreation

Obviously marriage has a procreative function. This is, by
God's design, related to intercourse. No where does Scripture
restrict sex relations to the sole purpose of procreation.

Health of Society

In fact, one function of the sexual relationship in marriage
that Paul allows might be called a "moral prophylaxis"

(I Corinthians 7:9), that is, marriage prevents sexual irregularities in society.

The Nature of Sexual Intercourse

I believe that sexual intercourse is intimately involved with the two major purposes of marriage, namely companionship and procreation. Its relation to procreation is obvious. However, intercourse has an important unitive function in marriage. We are biological creatures by God's design and biologically intercourse decreases tension. But it involves much more than biology. It involves all the personality, and at its highest level it is a medium of deep communication, physically, psychologically and spiritually.

There is communication of concepts and feelings that defy complete verbal expression, the communication of love, commitment of the whole of life, security and interdependence. "God made marriage for sex and sex for marriage. God made sex one of the means for continuously uniting a man and his wife in the deepest and most realistic way, a unique way in which they are 'known' to each other as they could not otherwise know each other, in the fullest expression of mutual love unlike any other demonstration. The 'one flesh' concept is basic and dominant in the Bible's teaching on marriage" (Genesis 2:24; Exodus 21:10; Leviticus 18; Deuteronomy 24:5; Matthew 19:5–6; Mark 10: 6–8; I Corinthians 7:2–6; Ephesians 5:31).[1] "The mystery is this: By sexual contact, I learn that by myself I am, and I must always be, a fragment; only my partner enables me to gain my own completeness." [2]

Four additional points regarding intercourse and Scripture are to be noted:

1) Scriptural sequence is that marriage precedes inter-

---

[1] Oscar E. Feucht, *Sex and the Church*, Concordia Publishing House, St. Louis, Mo. 1961, p. 218.

[2] Otto Piper, *The Christian Interpretation of Sex*, Charles Scribner's Sons, New York: 1955, p. 61.

course. Therefore, fornication, adultery and prostitution with or without contraceptives are not a Christian option.

2) No where does Scripture say specifically that intercourse must always be for the purpose of procreation.

3) Sharing and meeting one another's sexual needs is so important that Paul advises against prolonged abstinence (I Corinthians 7:3–5) and implies frequent sexual relations as the norm in marriage without any mention of procreation.

4) No where does Scripture say that a couple may not engage in sexual intercourse primarily for mutual pleasure and satisfaction. God established a physical attraction between the sexes. This is not wrong and in the marriage relationship, as the Song of Solomon stresses, sex is a sensuous delight and it is to have its normal, healthy role in providing fulfillment and joy for both partners. It is not something to be shunned but to be praised.

I believe Scripture teaches that sexual union has functions other than procreation. If this is so, under certain conditions conception may be hindered while the other functions are filled. I believe the case is clear that the Christian has a right to conception control.

THE NECESSITY OF CONCEPTION CONTROL

I believe that most families have some necessity for contraception, both for their individual needs and for the needs of society. Whenever an additional child would be a significant emotional, physical or economic burden to either a wife or a husband, the couple has the necessity to consider before God the advisability of having such a child, whether this is the tenth child or the first.

Contraception is essential in that it is the only means of preventing people, even Christians, from having unwanted children. Nothing is more detrimental to a child than to be unwanted. In this day and age, it is irresponsible for Christians to have unwanted children. Scripture emphasizes the concept of responsible parenthood (I Timothy 5:8). We should not bring more children into the world than we can nurture spiritually, financially, emotionally and educationally.

Turning to society as a whole, we are confronted by the population explosion. In treating disease, we physicians have taken seriously God's command to subdue nature and have drastically decreased the death rate. As a result the population is outstripping food supply and economic development. Faced with this acute problem, should we not make as great an effort to prevent new life as to prolong existing life? I believe our Christian concern for our neighbor compels us not only to think seriously about the limitation and size of our own family, but should involve us in worldwide educational plans that seek to help people to see the wisdom of voluntarily limiting the size of their families. I believe our Christian concern for our neighbor demands our involvement in this area at this time in history. "In 1920 the world population was less than two billion. By 1960 it was almost three billion. If present rates of growth continue, it will be seven and one-half billion by the end of the century." [3]

THE FAMILY'S DECISION

Having established the morality of contraception in some situations, we come to the point of the couple who says, "Should we have children, how many, and how far apart?" There is no law that can tell a couple how many children they should have or how they should be spaced. This decision is in the arena of Christian liberty. Christians know that

---

[3] *Expanding Populace in a Contracting World*, M. H. Merrill, J.A.M.A., August 22, 1966.

their lives, even their sexual lives, belong to God; therefore, they will act in love rather than selfishness. They will observe the times and circumstances in which they are living and through reason and the guidance of the Holy Spirit, will seek to make responsible decisions. No one can dictate the answer for another. How this freedom is used can properly be judged only by God, not man.

Some of the factors which have to be weighed in arriving at a decision are:

1) Can all of the needs of the children be met with the addition of another child? This involves physical, emotional, spiritual, economic and educational needs. (Proverbs 22:6)

2) Will another child affect the emotional or physical well-being of the mother and even of the father?

3) Over-production of children may be as sinful as selfish avoidance of parenthood.

4) Economic reasons for contraception are not necessarily selfish. "But if any provide not for his own, and especially for those of his own house, he hath denied the faith, and is worse than an infidel." (I Timothy 5:8)

5) What is the likelihood of genetically transmitted illness?

6) Some couples don't like children. They would make poor parents. I believe they have a right to marital companionship without children.

THE METHOD

If the motive for contraception is proper, is the method used of ethical significance? I heartily concur with the statement of the Augustana Synod of the Lutheran Church which stated, "The means which a married pair uses to determine the number and the spacing of the births of their children are a matter for them to decide with their own consciences, on the basis of competent medical advice and in a sense of accountability to God. So long as it causes no harm to those involved either immediately or over an extended period, none of the methods for controlling the number and spacing of the births of children has any special moral merit or demerit. It is the spirit in which the means is used, rather than whether it is 'natural' or "artificial,' which defines its 'rightness' or 'wrongness'. 'Whatever you do, do all to the glory of God' (I Corinthians 10:31) is a principle pertinent to the use of the God-given reproductive power." [4]

To deal with specific methods lies outside the purpose of this paper, except to comment briefly on three methods. Abstinence is undoubtedly the most effective contraceptive means. However, it defeats the whole purpose of sexual in-intercourse in marriage and unless it is completely satisfactory to both husband and wife, it would be considered immoral, as indicated in the 7th chapter of I Corinthians.

Coitus interruptus (withdrawal prior to ejaculation) is in general an unsatisfactory means of contraception both because it tends to be psychologically frustrating for husband and wife, and secondly because it is a rather unreliable method.

There are two major objections to rhythm. First is the fact that it too is frequently ineffective; and secondly, it interferes with the naturalness and spontaneity of the sexual act, in that it rules out sex relations around the time of ovulation. This is often the time of increased sexual desire in the female.

Finally, sterilization is a method of contraception. *Seen in this light, the moral principles bearing on sterilization are the same as those for other methods of contraception.*

---

[4] *Social Pronouncements of the Augustana Lutheran Church and Its Conferences*, 1937–1956 Ed. "The Commission on Morals & Social Problems of the Church" Rock Island: 1956, pp. 23, 24.

The significant difference is that it is the most permanent form of contraception and therefore cannot be entered into lightly. Therefore, when any couple come to a personal conclusion that it is mandatory that they have no more children, they might reasonably come to the conclusion that one of them should be sterilized. Whether it is to be the husband or the wife is again a matter for the individual consideration of the marital partners after careful weighing of the facts, which should include competent medical opinion.

Chapter 13

THERAPEUTIC ABORTION AND STERILIZATION AS ETHICAL PROBLEMS

SUMMARY

The seeming indecisiveness of applied Christian ethics is examined, and shown to be inevitable when a broad attack is made on a complex problem, rather than some simplistic "rule of thumb" approach. First, the factors which fix ethical decisions are explained, and how they interplay. They include beliefs and acquired knowledge, and their effects upon behavior, both individual and social. The questions of absolute versus situational ethics, of the wide spread of knowledge today, of the place of law and laws and of the meaning of a professional relationship are all debated. There is also discussion of the process of social and individual decision making, illustrated by the recent British legislation on abortion. This includes the problem of when life begins as seen from a medical standpoint. Ideas which help in problem solving include life potential, measuring the effects of social measures, and moral law applied so as to fit the detailed situation. Bad laws make problems, as does a lack of laws. The recognition that social factors contribute to the need for abortion makes problems. Reasons are given for solving these by keeping the health of the mother or the foetus as the deciding factor.

DUNCAN W. VERE, M.B., M.D., F.R.C.P. *Doctor Vere is now the Head of the Therapeutic Section in the Department of Pharmacology and Therapeutics of the London Hospital Medical College and is also a recognized teacher in medicine of London University. He graduated in medicine (1952) from the London Hospital Medical College. He subsequently earned another doctoral degree in his field of clinical therapeutics (1964) and became a Fellow of the Royal College of Physicians in 1968. His research work is concerned with clinical trials, the nephrotic syndrome and in the efficiency of systems of prescribing drugs. He has had an interest in medical ethics. He frequently speaks and writes on that subject in England.*

THERAPEUTIC ABORTION AND STERILIZATION AS ETHICAL PROBLEMS

by Duncan W. Vere

To say that something is unethical should be a strong argument, but in today's discussions it often seems weak. Why? This may be illustrated with reference to sterilization and abortion. Both, whether in their primary or colloquial sense, share with other ablations a sense of destruction and evil, of vitiation of plan or purpose, and failure of intent. To me, both are always wrongs, justifiable only when balanced against greater wrongs which they are aimed to avert. The alternatives are not right *or* wrong but rather more or less wrong—the old problem of a "tragic choice." (This is worth saying at the start for many press the idea that abortion will become so accepted as to seem the ordinary, "natural" and right conduct in difficult situations.) But to say that sterilization and abortion are always evils does not strike everyone as so evidently true as it seems to me. Why? Because my view is based on presuppositions which all do not share. The chief presupposition is the Jewish-Christian idea that life and its ordinary development are begun and maintained by God, so that life destruction or diversion should be decided in His interests (though these do not conflict with a true human interest), not in subservience to part-foolish human whims and desires. A humanist presupposition, that man's decisions are self-sufficient, might lead to a contrasting outcome.

So a search must be made for the determinants of ethical decision. One has just been noted, the presuppositions or bases of ethics. We should not be beguiled by the common notion that if two ethical viewpoints lead to the same practical outcome their differences are unimportant. A Muslim and a professor of public health may both eschew pork, but for reasons which differ.

Ethical differences are determined not only by variations in knowledge of a presupposed kind, but also by knowledge about those people who are the subjects of ethical decision.

Ethical decisions are also determined along a second, quite different dimension, which runs from the individual, through the family or group to society and out to humanity as a whole. There is much confusion between individual and social aspects of the same subject. They are freely mixed even in dictionary definitions. Sometimes the word means the opinions of one person, sometimes the generally agreed views of a society—a sort of average concept.

In a leading article, the British Medical Journal declared, "Medical ethics are the collective conscience of the profession." [1] Well and good, provided it be remembered that there are individual ethics as well. Even Kant seems to have allowed an ambiguity here. He said, "There is but one cate-

---

[1] *British Medical Journal*, "Ethics and Abortion", Leading Article, April 6, 1968, pp. 2, 3.

gorical imperative. Act only on that maxim whereby thou canst at the same time will that it should become a universal law." [2] But this very "universal" would have different outcomes for the individual and for the group, who may at times properly want something different; it annihilates itself in the enactment. For example, it may be morally desirable and beneficial in some wars to have both militants and conscientious objectors! It can even be right to hope that only a minority will follow your course of action. The individual is always supposed to obey his conscience, but society's consensus resists being overridden by one man's conscience. So there is conflict and confusion.

The doctor is torn between his own personal ethics, the duty to use free judgment to help a patient, the worthy but sometimes impracticable codes of his professional society, and the pressurized demands of the public "conscience." Lesser problems which stem from this differential include the fact that individual and collective ethics change at different rates, are best discussed by differently qualified people, and interest different sorts of people. Individual ethics is studied by the practitioner of a profession. Collective ethics bemuse the politician, administrator, sociologist and fund trustee. These problems were well argued from a humanist viewpoint by Dubos [3] and Leake.[4]

A most informative letter showed the variegation of collective ethics on the abortion issue.[5,6] Of one hundred senior

2 Kant, Immanuel, *Fundamental Principles of Morals*. Trans. A. D. Lindsay, p. 421.

3 Dubos, R., "Individual Morality and Statistical Morality". In colloquium. *Annals of Internal Medicine* 67, Supplement 7, p. 57.

4 Leake, C. D., "Technical Triumphs and Moral Muddles". In colloqium. *Annals of Internal Medicine* 67, Supplement 7, p. 43.

5 Howells, J. G., "Legalising Abortion". *Lancet*, 1, 728 (April 1st).

6 Detailed reference will be made to recent British discussions on abortion. Much of this has been overshadowed by the recently enacted laws which permit a widening of the grounds for therapeutic abortion. Because many of the issues now at stake seem to be ethical models of wide validity and importance, they are detailed here and not from thoughtless parochialism.

psychiatrists, 24 held that abortion (at an appropriate stage of pregnancy) should be available on demand, 56 wanted the medical situation, including social factors, to be evaluated before decision, 16 wanted only therapeutic abortion for real or threatened maternal disease and 4 held other views. This sort of survey is most commendable, for it shows not only the voting average, as it were, of a group but also the scatter about that average. If, as in this case, the numbers in the wings of the distribution nearly equal those in the center we should ask whether two distinct viewpoints or societies are emerging rather than random scatter about one central value. This could be important in determining legislation, but enough has been said to show how ethical decision making is determined by different individual and collective outlooks.

We are now in a position to set out our two main determinants as the rows and columns of a four-fold table giving four headings for discussion (Fig. 1).

A COLLECTIVE BASIS OF ETHICS

Most agree that western society is moving away from a Christian basis, whether in Sweden, Britain or the United States.[7,8,9,10] It is hard to decide towards which ethics opinion has moved. This tends to undermine official codes of ethics for these require a strong collective basis to have authority.[11]

In a desperate attempt to gain authority and stifle insis-

---

[7] Giertz, G. B., "Ethical Problems in Medical Procedures in Sweden", *Ethics in Medical Progress*, (CIBA Symposium) ed. G.E.W. Wolstenholme and M. O'Connor, London: J. and A. Churchill, 1966, p. 140.

[8] Leake, *op. cit.*

[9] Gelfand, M. *Philosophy and Ethics of Medicine*, London: E. and S. Livingstone, 1968 (especially pages 37–38, 121–125).

[10] Ormrod, Sir Roger, "Medical Ethics", *British Medical Journal*, 2, April 6, 1968, p. 7.

[11] Ferguson, R. S., "Ethics and Abortion", (Letter) *British Medical Journal*, 2, April 20, 1968, p. 173.

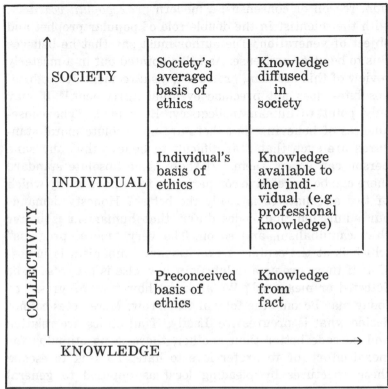

Fig. 1. To show how ethical decisions are determined by
factors which are distributed along two dimensions
but interact.

tent doubts about the validity of the new systems of ethics,
attempts have been made to derive them from a scientific
basis.[12,13,14] The new systems seem to have in common a
rejection of all absolute or permanent ethical principles.[15]
These are replaced by relativism based on human observa-

[12] Glass, B., *Science and Ethical Values*. Chapel Hill: University
of North Carolina Press, 1965.

[13] Leake, *op. cit.*

[14] Huxley, Sir Julian, *The Humanist Frame*. London: Allen and
Unwin.

[15] Dubos, *op. cit.*

tion, reason or consensus; a modern *"vox populi, vox dei"*; with the scientist in the double role of popular prophet and object of veneration. The author must say that he believes this to be utter nonsense. As Lillie pointed out in a masterly review of this problem, protracted disagreement over ethical absolutes does not preclude eventual agreement.[16] It may only point to human inadequacy. He added, "The consequences of believing that there are no absolute moral standards are such that it is difficult to believe that any sane person can accept them." If there is no absolute standard there can be no relative comparisons, for who is to say which of two alternatives is really the better? Honesty demands our admission that codes differ, that humanism is better than cannibalism, and so on. The very "moral progress" which is at the center of evolutionary humanism is impossible if there are no absolutes, for how else is progress to be detected or measured? We all know how the "progress" of today may become the folly of tomorrow. Mere votes cannot decide what is progressive. Lastly, if all ethics are relative and no code better than another, there is no stimulus for moral effort, or to prefer love to hate. To seek to escape these strictures by pleading local as opposed to general standards is to be open to questions of how their boundaries are determined, or why there should not be coalescence of the good to reconstitute the universal and the absolute. Lillie also contends that ethical relativists are right to think that ordinary moral rules are not the ultimate, absolute principles which distinguish right from wrong, but are rather their application to particular circumstances.

Space has been spent on this because many, in the Church as well as out of it, are rushing after the new relativism in an almost Gadarene fashion. They seem not to notice where their premises lead. This is a major determinant of the new

---

[16] Lillie, W., *An Introduction to Ethics*. London: Methuen, 1955, p. 105.

attitudes to abortion and sterilization, which become increasingly biological and materialist for these reasons. It will be shown below that, though there are absolutes relevant to this matter, they may not be those which are routinely invoked.

COLLECTIVE KNOWLEDGE ABOUT PEOPLE WHO ARE SUBJECTS OF ETHICAL DECISION.

This determinant has greatly affected sexual ethics because there has been a quite explosive diffusion of knowledge about sexuality in our society.[17] It is not that methods to procure abortion or sterilization have greatly improved, or that the need for either has grown. In fact the therapeutic need has diminished because of striking advances in other treatments and in contraception. The demand should be falling to quite low levels, but rises because popular ethics and knowledge of the subject have changed.[18] It is trite to say that the knowledge explosion which is determining attitudes to abortion is distorted and incomplete. Technical know-how is not matched by spiritual understanding. Few know or ask what life is really for or about.[19] Most know that abortion is available—few know when to ask for it or how to avoid the necessity.

On the credit side, however, there is growing social anger at hypocritical manipulations of law so as to favor wealthy candidates for abortion.[20,21]

The nature of socially determined decisions.

The way in which social decisions are made is of the

[17] Lederberg, J., "A Geneticist looks at Contraception and Abortion". In colloquium. *Annals of Internal Medicine* 67, Supplement 7, p. 27.

[18] Cogan, N. M., "A Medical Social Worker Looks at the New Abortion Law", *British Medical Journal*, 2, April 27, 1968, p. 235.

[19] Hemphill, R. E., "The Abortion Bill", *Lancet* 1, February 11, 1967, p. 324.

[20] Jenkins, Alice, *Law for the Rich*. London: Gollancz, 1960.

[21] Lederberg, *op. cit.*

greatest importance. The author has never seen reliable opinion poll data plotted out on graph paper, and really has no idea of what their shape might be for the abortion issue. However, it could be expected that in many situations, like, for example, the treatment of elderly people, or the fate of the foetus, things would distribute themselves so that there are some cases, say to the left, where nearly everyone would agree that a doctor should not intervene. There are others, to the right, where nearly all would agree that he should, and many in the middle where opinions differ and the "don't know" deciders are numerous. If such data could be taken and plotted out, with the proportion of definite decisions, one way or the other, as ordinates and the proportion of known factors favoring action as abscissae, there would probably be a U-shaped curve. We ought to do this in every difficult issue, and apply extant statistical tests suited to its analysis. It might improve our decisions about the individual. Be that as it may, the abortion problem has these qualities.[22,23]

Most will agree that there is not a great ethical problem in destroying ova or spermatozoa. Nature itself does this all the time on a grand scale. Most would at present agree that infanticide, even of the deformed and imbecile, is wrong. Between the two lies the valley of indecision, marked by a gradual, not sudden development, with inflexions at conception, implantation, full embryogenesis, birth and incipient sentience. At one end are two cells, at the other a person, and whatever anyone may say to the contrary, there is no sharp point on the curve which gives a fully satisfactory divide between impersonality and personality. Many theologians have proposed birth, or quickening, or full embryo-

---

[22] Popkes, B., "Ethical problems arising from Advances in Medicine". *Report of Second International Congress of Christian Physicians*. ed. Connell, A. M. and Lindeboder, G. A., The Hague: A. J. Oranje, p. 17.

[23] Gelfand, *op. cit.*

genesis, or conception, as the dividing line. It might be asked why they did not pick the development of the foetal circulation,[24] since they also argue that life is in the blood! The very multiplicity of "sharp lines" shows that none has the sharpness that its proponents would wish. And it is with such data that society has to reach its decisions, to draw its lines and define its goals.

The author is well aware of the risks of his argument. It opens the door to pressure for infanticide [25] and weakens legislation, and legalistic argument. But if it is the truth, why can't people face it? Is Christianity so weak that it has to be supported by legalism? Surely what we must learn to do is to apply Christian principle to these shifting sands, not pretend that they do not shift. There are sound arguments against infanticide without invoking pseudo-biological reasons. They are shifting, and the U-shaped curve has moved perceptibly to the left.[26] That is why there is now a new abortion law in England.

The former Archbishop of Canterbury has set down some most helpful ideas on how to tackle this sort of problem. He argued that, bearing in mind the ethical dubiety of life destruction in general and the difficulty of fixing points in foetal development in particular, it is best to start with what is known, (i.e. move towards the center from both directions along our curve) till the limit of knowledge is reached. Then, and only then, will ethical responsibility have been satisfied, for no one can be expected to know what he cannot know. He argued as follows:

"All will agree that from the moment of birth, the child born is a person, with all the rights of a person.

---

[24] Vere, D. W., "Why the Preservation of Life?", *Ethical Responsibility in Medicine.* ed. V. Edmunds and C. G. Scorer, Edinburgh and London: Livingstone, 1967.

[25] Lederberg, *op. cit.*

[26] Dubos, *op. cit.*

> "All will be able to agree that from the moment of conception to the moment of birth the direct responsibility for the embryo belongs wholly and exclusively to the mother.
>
> "There will not be agreement as to any particular moment of time at which the human embryo becomes possessed of individual rights to a continuance of its life under (almost) all circumstances." [27]

Dr. Fisher then showed that, within these limits, the deciding point should be theologically not biologically determined. Of the mother he wrote, ". . . responsibility belongs to her motherhood, and for it she is answerable to God. But in its discharge she rightly . . . needs the advice of her doctor. The doctor must never advise an abortion for nonmedical reasons, or for reasons of social or personal convenience. But society may properly give advice through an Abortion Law as to what consideration, other than purely medical . . . he may take into account in advising the mother how to fulfill her obligations. . . ." [28] This wise guidance shows how theological principles can be properly used without pressing legalistic, but unreal, dividing lines. The crux is that the foetus, as the Yorkshireman said, is "neither nought nor summat." In the next section we discuss again the limits which should apply to society's pressures upon the individual.

THE INDIVIDUAL DOCTOR'S KNOWLEDGE ABOUT PEOPLE WHO ARE SUBJECTS OF ETHICAL DECISION

The doctor's position is unique. The patient enters a professional relationship with him to gain his knowledge, and morally sincere practical help.

---

[27] Fisher, Lord, *In the Service of Medicine, 49*, London: April, 1967, p. 2.
[28] *Ibid.*

Problems of professional relationship in abortion

What is the nature of this professional help? Is it only to be therapeutic, concerned with health, or are there wider possibilities? Mr. Justice Brandeis defined a profession in 1933. The definition (Addendum I) does not specify the nature of the work done, only that it should be in the client's interest.[29]

There is certainly confusion over the professional implications of the new British law, which will be discussed where it has relevance to our subject. Many distinguished writers insist that it should deal only with questions of health and disease. Sir Dugald Baird wrote, "What the Act does is to make clear beyond doubt that termination of pregnancy is legal, and that the decision to terminate or not should be left, as far as possible, to the clinical judgment of the doctor concerned, and that in reaching their decision doctors may take into account the effect of the patient's total environment on her health." [30] Nothing could be clearer than these three points stated in that way. Similarly, the memorandum from the Medical Defence Union stated (of Section 1 (2) of the new Act, see Addendum II), "It is this provision which may have given rise to the belief that the act makes abortion lawful 'on social grounds.' This is a misconception. It is the risk to the physical or mental health of the woman or of her existing children which is the determining factor. Certainly the practitioner may take environmental factors into account. He may have regard to those factors which exist and those which may be reasonably anticipated, *but the test is whether there is risk to health.*" [31] This is also close to the desired interpretation of

---

[29] Brandeis, Mr. Justice, "Business or Profession", Boston: 1933.

[30] Baird, Sir Dugald, "Ethics and Abortion" (Letter) *British Medical Journal 2*, April 20, 1968, p. 173.

[31] Medical Defence Union, "The Abortion Act, 1967". *British Medical Journal 1*, March 23, 1968, p. 761.

the British Medical Association [32] and the Royal College of Obstetricians and Gynecologists. [33]

Be that as it may, many read the Act (Addendum II) in another way. [34] Some feel that, whatever its intent, in practice it will assimilate to abortion on demand, or to governmental control of medical standards. [35,36]

Ethics are certainly demanding great semantic skill. Sir Roger Ormrod argued persuasively that the term "therapeutic" has become stretched beyond the limit to cover what are really social actions of a medical nature. [37] The author does not approve Ormrod's argument, which seems to agree that change must and should proceed in the direction which he indicates as if this were a *fait accompli*, an inevitable social development.

Ormrod set out to prove that, as the demands of society upon them broaden, doctors have the alternative of agreeing with society or abdication. They must either extend their wonted professional range outside what are the normal meanings of health and disease, or the state will do the new work for them. He added, "It is inconceivable that the profession could tolerate a situation in which it is told to undertake procedures of this kind by any other person or persons." Yet the only alternative, it seems, is to do what the main professional societies have found to be unprofes-

---

[32] British Medical Association, *British Medical Journal* (Supplement *2*), 1967, p. 66.

[33] Royal College of Obstetricians and Gynecologists, "Legalized Abortion, Report by the Council". *British Medical Journal*, *2*, April 2, 1966, p. 850.

[34] Dunwoody, I., "Abortion on Social Grounds" (Question in House of Commons) *Lancet*, *1*, April 20, 1968, p. 857.

[35] Sim, M., "G.M.C. and Abortion Act". *British Medical Journal*, *2*, May 4, 1968, p. 298.

[36] Goodhart, C. B., "Abortion Regulations". *British Medical Journal*, *2*, May 4, 1968, p. 298.

[37] Ormrod, *op. cit.*

sional. This is no alternative in fact,[38] but a wholly un-natural and horrible pressure.

The medical profession succeeded in enlarging its social activity into public health, but this lacked the ethical constraints in abortion, and the practitioners of public health, invaluable as their work has been, ceased to be clinicians, transferring allegiance from the individual to society.[39] Some clinical researchers similarly widen contributions to society whilst reducing their professional contact with individuals. But none of these is a true precedent for a public abortion service. Many no doubt hope that these objections will wilt in the dry winds of a new opinion. The dilemma was well stated in a leading article in the *British Medical Journal*, "The principle at issue is fundamental if doctors are to preserve their right to call themselves professional men." [40] Unfortunately, it is difficult to insist that the term "profession" shall not embrace this new kind of relationship with people. The modern answer to the problem is to stop stretching the word "therapeutic" and start stretching the word "profession". We assume, on no very secure ground, that health is the main determinant of the definition of "the medical profession." But a few years ago barbers were debating whether to include health among their professional pursuits, a warning not to stake issues of right and wrong upon the definition of a word. There are deeper answers. Ormrod's assessment is nearly right. There are two main, equally distasteful choices before the profession. But there is a third, to attempt to change the ethical pressures of society.

Lastly, one or two detailed points may be made in com-

---

[38] McLaren, H. C., "Indications for Termination of Pregnancy". *British Medical Journal*, 1, February 19, 1968, p. 376.

[39] Gelfand, *op. cit.*

[40] "Ethics and Abortion", *British Medical Journal 2*, April 6, 1968, p. 3.

ment. It is futile to try to force an antithesis between "clinical" and "social" indications. Social factors clearly contribute to the clinical case. Provided that health, not social factors, remain the *chief determinant*, our ethical position stands. Note carefully that we are considering a situation where all agree that it is largely the interests of individuals, not society, that are at stake. So the pressure of the majority should not decide the matter for these individuals. There is another more difficult situation where individuals are asked to suffer for the good of society, but that is not the case here. Many think that the abortion decision is always made by the doctor.[41] It is often made effectively by the patient, who tries doctors *seriatim* till she succeeds. The new British law is officially interpreted to mean that a doctor who refuses to abort on conscientious grounds "should take all necessary steps to enable her to receive advice from a doctor who is untroubled by conscientious objections." [42] This seems an unhappy wording, which will make many feel that the official reaction is somewhat hypocritical and has scant regard for conscientious objection. It seems as if the doctor must help indirectly to procure that to which he objects, and is at risk should he fail.

One hopes that the real intention of this clause was that the doctor, having advised against abortion, asks the patient whether she is determined to have another opinion. If she is, he will refer her to a colleague whose judgment is known to be unbiased, but one hopes not devoid of all conscientious objections!

The impact upon those near to the candidate for abortion

The next problem is to see how the professional relationship affects people other than the mother. It is conventional to draw a legal line at the mother and deny direct responsi-

---

[41] Ormrod, *op. cit.*
[42] *British Medical Journal*, 1, March 23, 1968, p. 761.

bility to others.[43] However, to affect someone is to incur responsibility towards them, and it would indeed be odd to ignore effects upon society in the very case where a social measure is in view.[44] The husband and family are obviously part of the doctor's direct responsibility. Less direct, but very important, is the effect of his action on social attitudes. Doctors are now very much high priests of society, and recent opinion and law making have been much affected by them. The problem was well discussed by Daube [45] who drew attention to its many ingredients—the uncertainty of the professional relationship, the risks of legal action against parents or doctors for negligence in failing to abort for some serious complaint, the impossibility of arguing usefulness to society as a criterion, the effects of the clamour about overpopulation upon regard for the individual, and the risk of doctors becoming the instruments of government. His solution was that the doctor must at all times have shown himself to be constructive. This is very fair, but puts him at the mercy of society's current view of constructiveness.

Legalized abortion has been pressed as a way to stop criminal abortion. There is substantial, though disputed, evidence that it may not, possibly because those who look for a secret answer will not seek a public one.[46]

It is always difficult to decide when to apply a social measure to try to correct an individual evil.[47] The sins of a feckless parent will always be visited in some ways on her unwanted child. Our decision is how and when this should happen, by making social provision for the child or by aborting it. Abortion is claimed to be the responsible way out, but

---

[43] Daube, *op. cit.*

[44] Hemphill, *op. cit.*

[45] *Op. cit.*

[46] Huldt, Lars, "Outcome of Pregnancy when Legal Abortion is Readily Available". *Lancet, 1,* March 2, 1968, p. 761.

[47] Hemphill, *op. cit.*

must responsibility necessarily be shown by refusing to share responsibility for a child's development?

Frequently it is found to be the father, not the mother, who is rejecting the child.[48] The only provision regarding the spouse in the interpretation of the British Act is that his wishes should always be known, but that they should be set aside if opposed to an abortion on which mother and doctor are agreed. To disregard the spouse is theologically unacceptable, whatever the legal position may be.

The importance of potential life

By this is meant that, in ethical decisions, attention must not only be paid to the patient's *actual* powers, but also to his *possible* recovery or development. This has been argued elsewhere [49] in connection with the preservation of adult life. The same idea applies to the foetus, which of course has more potential than any other stage of human development. Many writers neglect this aspect, concentrating upon the actual, slight development of the foetus as a reason for regarding it as destructible at will. Medawar asked why we do not treat the foetus according to "traditional wisdom". "We don't baptize miscarriages; we don't in fact hold funeral services for them. I think that over matters like this (changing standards) we should revert to a traditional and common-sense morality that does in fact make a distinction between the foetus—particularly the early foetus—and the newborn child." [50] It seems that the point which is overlooked here is at least the potential of the foetus.[51] People don't baptize miscarriages because they *are* not persons nor ever could be, since they are dead for

---

[48] Cogan, *op. cit.*

[49] Vere, *op. cit.*

[50] Medawar, Sir Peter, "Discussion in Colloquium", *Annals of Internal Medicine, 67,* Supplement 7, 1967, p. 66.

[51] Others would, of course, take issue with Medawar on the ground that the foetus is already a person on theological grounds, a view which, to the author at least, is unproven.

natural reasons, not because of human intervention, and have not become persons. But, had they not been abnormal, they *could* have become persons. From the moment it is mixed and put in the oven, a woman will refer to a sticky mass of ingredients as "my cake." If it burns no one can eat it. But if it is not spoiled it still may become a cake. With an eye to its potential she calls it her cake before it is such in fact.

To ignore potential is to detract from the real value of a foetus. The author believes that to uphold potential is valid, but it demands a reappraisal of many long-held views. It has been said that the doctor has no professional relationship to a foetus. You could argue, on similar grounds, that he also has no relationship to an unconscious subject, but in fact he saves him, bearing his potential recovery in mind. We would submit, in agreement with Gelfand [52] and Daube [53] that the doctor, though he cannot have a professional relationship with the foetus, has professional responsibility for its potential life, similar to that which he has for an unconscious or demented adult.

A similar problem arises with sterilization, where an over-hasty operation may deprive a woman of her potential capacity of motherhood, should she remarry, for example. It is the irreversibility of a thorough sterilization procedure, and of foetal destruction, which makes these decisions so grave. The work of Thompson and Baird,[54] though intended very properly to reassure the profession about sterilization, only showed that the procedure was very satisfactory to those referred for it, and selected first with great care. There is no proof that the operation does not destroy worthwhile potential at times over a wider setting.

---

[52] *Op. cit.*
[53] *Op. cit.*
[54] Thompson, B., Baird, Sir Dugald, "Follow-up of 186 sterilized women", *Lancet*, *1*, May 11, 1968, p. 1023.

The need to find facts

Much of our discussion of abortion and sterilization has been theoretical. But knowledge can be a good determinant only when it is knowledge of fact. Until we know the outcome of changed laws in society we cannot say within the limits of certainty, what is right and what is wrong. There is, of course, a difficulty here. Overpressed, this view leads directly to rejection of all ethical premises, and a Pearsean attitude of "try everything and see." Such utter pragmatism is anti-Christian, and for this reason many Christians have shied away from fact-finding exercises. But an idea overpressed to one extreme is as bad if pushed to the other. No one can deny that, having decided from theological premises that a course of action is properly begun, its ethical evaluation is not thereby completed, but must wait for appraisal of the outcome. Good intentions succeed in good effects. For this reason it is best that new laws should operate for a limited time, and proper measurement of other outcomes be part of their provisions.

The proper influence of law upon the doctor's decision

There is only one aspect of law which is relevant here, its ethical impact. Some believe that the new British law will effectively hamstring ethical discussion, since a breach of the ethical code will come to be definable only when a criminal charge has been successfully proven. To have kept within the blunt outlines of the law may now be held to justify an act which formerly would have incurred severe professional discipline.[55] It has been stated by responsible legal authority that precise desirable indications for abortion cannot be legislated.[56]

---

[55] General Medical Council, *British Medical Journal*, 2, April 20, 1968, p. 185.

[56] "Memorandum of the Joint Committee of the New Society and the British Academy of Forensic Sciences". The Solicitors' Law Stationery Society, London: Oyez House, Breams Buildings, 1967.

Society's laws must not become the determinants of ethical decision.[57] The very need for law can be a springboard for humanistic materialism,[58] for law enforcement can only be effectively based on objective criteria.[59] It incurs the dilemma that in opening a way for reasonable cases it opens to ethically objectionable cases as well. It is only possible to refine this situation if ethical objections are allowed in cases where there is no breach of the legal code. Laws provide limiting lines required to protect the individual and society from each others' destructive acts. They delimit, but do not prescribe conduct. They are relative, and only remotely derived from the absolute ideas of right and wrong in the moral law. The abortion laws should in fact be needed relatively seldom,[60] but their opportunity readily granted where other measures fail to solve a serious medical problem. The proper relationship of laws and ethics is well illustrated by Christ's words, "For your hardness of heart Moses allowed you to divorce your wives, but from the beginning it was not so. And I say to you whoever divorces his wife, except for unchastity, and marries another commits adultery." (Matthew 19:8,9)

THE INDIVIDUAL'S BASIS OF ETHICS

We can only discuss a Christian basis here; this can contribute to the sum of collective ethics but will never become wholly accepted by this present world.

First, the Christian will want to look for an ethical basis in the creation ordinances, though many never get further than that. Two ordinances seem relevant, the value of hu-

---

[57] The distinction between *law* and *laws* is crucial here. We must not confuse the *moral* law, the principle of law (necessary for sinful man) and society's *laws* which are their faulty human expression.

[58] Browne, R. T. D. and Sturdy, D. C. "Integrity of the Profession", *British Medical Journal, 2,* May 25, 1968, p. 489.

[59] Lederberg, *op. cit.*

[60] Daube, *op. cit.*

man life, amplified in Genesis 9, and discussed fully in two recent books.[61,62] The other is the commandment to "have dominion over every living thing that moves upon the earth" (Gen. 1:28). It is this second ordinance that may have surprising relevance to abortion and sterilization, and to which we particularly wish to attract attention. Christian men have sometimes had difficulty in seeing that it is godly to subdue nature in proper ways. But they are often in blank astonishment when they find *that nature extends within themselves*. We have scarcely begun to think out how we should gain dominion over this little bit of nature that is within us. Yet it conforms to the same laws that govern the rest of the biosphere. Is it to remain unsubdued? Are godless men to teach us ways to subdue it in man's interest, when we could teach them better ways to subdue it in God's interest? The other ordinance, to fill the earth, must also be reappraised wherever the earth is locally overfilled. When will the Church wake to coherent action in these tremendous ethical opportunities and responsibilities?

The Christian would next turn to Mosaic law. Many have pointed out that Exodus 21 gives a mandate for regarding foetal life as less valuable than the mother's. Few point out that the passage establishes that the foetus *has* a value.

Next, the Christian will turn to our Lord's ethical teaching. Reading accounts of the abortion problem will show that men who make no claim to be Christians often produce cogent, reasoned accounts of their views which lead to simple, practical solutions. But Christians often seem to present the paradox—sometimes within one article—of claiming some superior revelation from God, presenting a mass of carefully compiled fact and opinion, followed by a blurred

---

[61] Murray, J., *Principles of Conduct*. London: Tyndale Press, 1957.
[62] Beattie, J., "Therapeutic Procedures and the Sanctity of Life", in *Ethical Responsibility in Medicine*, ed. V. Edmunds and E. G. Scorer, London: Livingstone, 1967, p. 72.

picture of what should be done. To people looking for a lead
this is bewildering. However, a little reflection will show two
sound reasons for the contrast. First, the problems are often
too complex for simple, legalistic classification. It's rather
like the feeling you would get were a child to come to say,
"I borrowed this doll from Jenny, and I'm not sure whether
she knows, but her mummy said I mustn't, and now I've
broken it. What should I do?" There is no simple *and* honest
solution to that problem. The second reason is that many
people want us to go on in the Old Testament system and
social code, or at least in the parts of it which can still be
fitted to life. But Jesus' ethical teaching is more relevant,
and more difficult, as for example in Matthew 19.

Most people have no difficulty in following a linear
relationship between two variables in algebra. This is like
"Thou shalt not kill." It is simple, directly applicable, and
enough for prosaic minds. But fewer can follow the inferences implicit in a second order differential equation. This
is more sophisticated, and harder to apply. Yet, once
grasped, it solves the obscure problem. Jesus really taught
three ethical premises—trust in God, justice (or equality
of worth, if not ability, amongst men), and love, or disinterested care for all. The opposite of justice is "iniquity,"
or inequality of judgment. These principles are far harder
to apply directly. They really mean that a certain kind of
character will make a man behave in a certain kind of way.
But their relevance to abortion is not far to seek. To panic
in face of an enlarging family and a shrinking bank balance
is not to trust. To contract a family fecklessly is not to love.
To say that the foetus has zero value and the mother who
conceived it total value, or to say that, in a mortal clash
between the interests of mother and foetus the mother must
be allowed to suffer in the interests of God-given life, both
seem plain "iniquity," or inequality. Mother and foetus both
have value, but the ratio between them varies. Our task is to

strike a conscientious and disinterested balance between them in the light of all the information available to us. No rule, or law or code or catch phrase can cover the case. Abortion solves the thing only after the event. Contraception is better, being an *a priori* solution. Self-control is the highest order of preventive, but is possible only where there is strong, right motivation.

There are no direct mandates, so some people do nothing. But a lack of mandate need not inhibit action. There are no mandates for laparotomy or anesthesia. There are for healing. The problem is then how we apportion the values which strike the true balance. It is here that the clash comes and it depends on bases of ethics directly. Those whose basis is largely or exclusively biological or scientific strike it well over to the mother's side. Those whose basis includes an idea of God as the Giver of biological facts give the foetus more potential value, and therefore find a simple solution more evasive. It is easy to agree that white cat is white; you can argue for a long time whether a grey cat is more white or more black. Also, the Christian is not always very good at considering the rights of society, at rendering his own things to Caesar.

Lastly, the Christian would look to apostolic teaching. Here there emerges the idea of action aimed to fulfil as nearly as possible an ideal of family life. There is an absolute, permanent basis of ethics, not in the shape of casuistrical rules but rather a permanent ethical target, a motive to maximize love. Knowledge increases, social relationships change, but love remains—constructive, obedient to God, disinterested towards man. This is not "situational ethics" because its mainsprings are independent of the situation, residing in the moral Law of God. But the local outworking will differ depending upon the situation. It may be a loving thing today to refuse an abortion to A, to grant it to B. On another occasion this may be reversed, but the motive and aim are independent of the situation. It is odd to hear at times vociferous Christian opposition to abortion in England and support for it in India, without there being agreement on the central matters of motive and aim. Life is to be subdued in love and in God's interest. The local methods are secondary to the principle. Matthew Arnold wrote, "But there remains the question: what righteousness really is. The method and secret and sweet reasonableness of Jesus." [63]

Someone will object at once to what has been said. These Christian ethics are impractical. Most do not accept them. Many Christians seem incapable of keeping them. You have got to have detailed laws to preserve society.

This is a true and very important objection, though my brief was to write of ethics and not of laws. Laws there must be, but let them be framed so as to accord with and support the best available ethical knowledge. Our need to be ruled by laws must never be allowed to obscure the ethical teaching which transcends them. For the Christian at least this should always remain his goal, and he will wish to demonstrate its outstanding virtue to others. Christ constantly transmuted legal into ethical discussion with the Pharisees. This was not to deny the value of laws, but to state their true meaning. The conduct of a true love is always within the limits of true laws. But in a society where all do not truly love, laws are needed which curb the untrue without restricting the true. For these reasons, abortion laws cannot prescribe detailed reasons for abortion. They can and should proscribe abortion with ill intent. They may permit abortion with good intent, but the individual's conscience must then decide what is good in freedom from social pressures. These pressures at present center upon interference with life for reasons of social convenience rather than health. It

---

[63] Arnold, Matthew, *Literature and Dogma*, Chapter 12, Para. 2.

is this which we have opposed by a Christian view of life, holding that the law can become too permissive in this matter. Further intensive study continues to be a vital necessity.

ADDENDUM I

The Peculiar Characteristics of a Profession
(Brandeis, 1933)

First. A profession is an occupation for which the necessary preliminary training is intellectual in character, involving knowledge and to some extent learning, as distinguished from mere skill.

Second. It is an occupation which is pursued largely for others and not merely for oneself.

Third. It is an occupation in which the amount of financial return is not the accepted measure of success.

ADDENDUM II

The following is an excerpt from Abortion Act 1967 (United Kingdom): An Act to amend and clarify the law relating to termination of pregnancy by registered medical practitioners.

1. (1) Subject to the provisions of this section, a person shall not be guilty of an offence under the law relating to abortion when a pregnancy is terminated by a registered medical practitioner if two registered medical practitioners are of the opinion, formed in good faith—
    (a) that the continuance of the pregnancy would involve risk to the life of the pregnant woman, or of injury to the physical or mental health of the pregnant woman or any existing children of her family, greater than if the pregnancy were terminated; or
    (b) that there is a substantial risk that if the child were born it would suffer from such physical or

mental abnormalities as to be seriously handicapped.

(2) In determining whether the continuance of a pregnancy would involve such risk of injury to health as is
mentioned in paragraph (a) of subsection (1) of this
section, account may be taken of the pregnant woman's
actual or reasonably foreseeable environment.

2. (1). Subject to subsection (2) of this section, no person
shall be under any duty, whether by contract or by any
statutory or other legal requirement, to participate in
any treatment authorised by this Act to which he has a
conscientious objection:

Provided that in any legal proceedings the burden of
proof of conscientious objection shall rest on the person
claiming to rely on it.

Chapter 14

MALE STERILIZATION— MEDICAL, THEOLOGICAL, SOCIAL AND PERSONAL ASPECTS

SUMMARY

Tensions arising from the confrontation of conservatism in some physicians with a radical approach to medical progress in others are analyzed, especially as they apply to male sterilization. A brief description of medical facts related to the operation is given, and the possible indications for the procedure are outlined. Three different types of pressure, theological, social and personal, resulting from application of medical knowledge in this area, are discussed. The author concludes that great caution must be exercised in recommending male sterilization, but that there definitely are situations in which this measure is advisable, either for the individual family or as a means of population control. Even though the operation unhappily deprives the body of a normal endowment, Christ's own approach of upholding the authority of the moral law (as in Matthew 19: 3–9) while accepting that compassion must influence our actions is cited as an example of conduct to be emulated by the physician and the non-medical layman.

C. GORDON SCORER, M.B., M.D., F.R.C.S. (E), F.R.C.S. (Edin.). *Dr. Scorer is a consultant urologist at the Hillingdon Hospital in London. He graduated in medicine from Cambridge University and the London Hospital, after which he pursued postgraduate education in surgery. He earned an additional doctoral degree in his field and later qualified as a Fellow, both in the Royal College of Surgeons of England and the Royal College of Surgeons of Edinburgh. He served as a surgeon with the Royal Navy from 1941 to 1946 in the Eastern Mediterranean and South India. He has contributed often to professional journals. He is co-editor of the book,* Medical Ethics—A Christian Approach. *Dr. Scorer is the immediate past Chairman of the Christian Medical Fellowship of Great Britain.*

MALE STERILIZATION—MEDICAL, THEOLOGICAL, SOCIAL AND PERSONAL ASPECTS

by C. Gordon Scorer

GENERAL CONSIDERATIONS

Every advance in our power to control man, either his mind or his body, demands of us a corresponding increase in wisdom and exercise of restraint in the use of that power. We learn how to do something to the human body before we have decided whether or not it is right to do it. We press forward in an uncharted sea hoping, if possible, to avoid damage to the welfare of our patients and the esteem of our profession. It is the long-term effects of a proposed new treatment which are the most difficult to assess.

It is right that we should be cautious in making radical changes, for he who touches man touches a living soul, a being created in the image of God. A Christian doctor is bound to be especially sensitive at these growing points. In Anglo-American medicine we have been profoundly influenced in the past by Christian concepts, but today many of our colleagues no longer feel any loyalty to Christian traditions. In addition, we are presented with such totally new possibilities of altering the human body that quick and easy decision cannot reasonably be made.

There are two extremes of approach to new ideas. The conservatives resist all change even of long out-dated attitudes. They try to fit a 16th century understanding to a mid-20th century world and can see no reason to re-align their position. The radicals—an increasingly large number—appear to be ready to do anything to man if it will afford him some sort of temporary physical benefit. They throw down the old landmarks and carve out new highways before they have paid due attention to the sensitivity of man's nature or gained appreciation of the later results of their actions.

In former centuries and at certain junctures Christians have tended towards conservatism. For example, in the name of the Church they resisted the practice of surgery because it was considered wrong to shed blood. Some resisted the practice of anatomy because it was wrong for man to desecrate the body which God had created. Some resisted the introduction of anaesthetics because it was considered wrong to reduce the pain of childbirth and to deprive a woman of her conscious will as a person. Rearguard actions have been fought and lost, sometimes ignominiously, to the forces of new endeavor. History has frequently shown Christians to be unnecessarily fearful about the new technical advance, but justified in their ethical demands that all man-centered operations should be safeguarded by respect for man as a living person who has his own unassailable dignity, responsibility and rights. Medical inventiveness and expertise has now reached a new highwater mark, encroaching into the very secret places of life itself. What is the Christian's attitude to the current efforts to control man's procreation?

In the case of male sterilization we have a problem different in kind from some recent spectacular advances, but it carries with it an ethical concern which is none the less real. Here is a trivial operation, the technique and effects of which have probably been known for centuries. Here is a procedure of universal applicability and no danger, though morbidity in unskilled hands is not negligible. It is striking that it is only in the last two or three decades that it has come into prominence as a recommended surgical operation all over the world. This is presumably because of the current necessity to control some rapidly expanding populations, and it is also a reflection of a changed climate of opinion in regard to sexual ethics. Let us look a little more closely at the facts about the operation before discussing the ethical and other problems.

THE OPERATION AND ITS INCIDENCE

It is estimated that about 100,000 people undergo voluntary sterilization every year in America. The operation is not notifiable and therefore figures are approximate but the proportion of vasectomies is said to be rising.[1] Both America and Canada have organizations supported by voluntary contributions to foster the growth of voluntary sterilization. Britain, too, has such an organization known as the Simon Population Trust. Accurate figures for the number of sterilizations carried out in the United Kingdom are not available, but there are over 2,000 vasectomies a year now and the number is probably rising rapidly.

In India it is stated that between 1955 and 1965 over a million people were sterilized and about 68% of these were men. Since 1966, when the campaign for birth control was intensified, it is estimated that 4 million men have volunteered for sterilization.[2] Other countries such as Pakistan,

---

[1] Blacker, C. P., Jackson, L. N. 1966 *Lancet*, *i*, 971.
[2] Times, London, June 4th 1968.

Korea and Taiwan are developing sterilization policies. It appears, therefore, that family limitation by division of the vasa efferentia is being done much more frequently now than it was 10, 5 or even 2 years ago.

The operation is a simple one which can be performed without hospital admission or general anaesthesia. It requires a careful and precise technique and leads to a minimum of complications provided it is done expertly. It is recommended that 1 cm. of each vas deferens is removed from the scrotum and the ends ligated with an unabsorbable suture after turning each end backward on itself.[3] Sexual intercourse after the operation may lead to conception unless a period of three months has elapsed and it should only be practiced without contraception when two or more successive counts have proved the complete absence of active motile sperms.

Restoration of the lumen of the vas can be carried out by re-anastomosis. Results of the operation cannot be predicted with certainty but in the most experienced hands sperm will re-appear in the ejaculate in 60% or more.[4]

The sexual effects of the operation were investigated by Gamble (1950)[5] when he reviewed 50 cases between three months and six years after the operation. Of these, 23 had the operation performed because they had as many children as they wanted, 19 because of the wife's ill health or the danger to her of another pregnancy and 8 because of the husband's poor health. Many aspects were studied but, briefly, all the men said that their wives were satisfied (and often released from the fear of pregnancy) and only 3 of the men had some reason for dissatisfaction. In summary it was considered that problems arose only in those who were psychologically ill-suited for the operation. This means,

    [3] Hanley, H. G. 1968 *Lancet, ii,* 207.
    [4] Hanley, H. G. *loc. cit.* Phadke, G. M. 1964 *Maharashtra Medical Journal,* Poona, *11,* 227.
    [5] Garrison, P. L., Gamble, C. J. 1950 J.A.M.A. *144,* 293.

of course, that selection of patients for operation is of paramount importance and careful discussion of the issues involved with both husband and wife is essential.

Having said this it may be pointed out that there is some evidence [6] that the results of the operation are not always as satisfactory as is supposed even when a very careful selection of cases is made. Granted sexual desire and performance are usually unchanged, or may be enhanced, the long term psychological effects cannot be dismissed as negligible even though they are often attributed to society's unjustifiable suspicion of the procedure.

POSSIBLE INDICATIONS

Possible indications for the operation are fivefold—eugenic, socio-economic, convenience, prophylactic and racial.

Eugenic Indications

Eugenic indications suggest themselves when there is a probability that the offspring will have a serious mental or physical abnormality. Is it right that we should allow such children to be conceived if we can prevent it? Is it right that such deformities of mind or body should continue unchecked from generation to generation? In the case of mental defectives some would argue that compulsion may at times be appropriate. The grounds advanced are that we use legislative authority to isolate those who may spread dangerous infectious disease—why not, therefore, limit the powers of those who can launch into society a child who can only be a burden to it?

Socio-economic Reasons

Socio-economic reasons are raised in relation to problem

---

[6] Ziegler, F. J., Rodgers, D. A., Knegsman, S. A. 1966 *Psychosomatic Medicine, 28,* 50. Ferber, A. S., Tretze, C., Lewit, S. 1967 *Psychosomatic Medicine, 29,* 354. Rodgers, D. A., Ziegler, F. J., Levy, N. 1967 *Psychosomatic Medicine, 29,* 367.

families, that is, to those families in which there are already too many children to be brought up by an overworked mother with inadequate resources. In this group we place the poor of both hemispheres and many lands. This is the group that chiefly gives rise to the population explosion. Too many children are being born into a world of squalor, semi-starvation and hopeless prospect. The urgency of the situation needs no comment.

Reasons of Convenience

Reasons of convenience present the opposite problem. A married couple, usually affluent and educated, at the age of 25 or so have had two or three children and want no more. Why, they say, should we accept the uncertainty and inconvenience of contraception for the next quarter of a century when a minor operation can give permanent security?

Prophylactic Indications

Prophylactic indications are sometimes confused with and called "therapeutic". This is a misnomer, for vas ligation never *cured* any disease. A truly prophylactic approach is suggested almost solely for the wife's sake because further pregnancy would endanger her health. This is an alternative to prophylactic sterilization in women—the somatic indications for which have become less, and psychological much more, frequent in recent years. One observation is pertinent here—and it is heard with increasing frequency. If it is desirable to prevent conception—why, hitherto, has the woman been the one who has to accept surgical intervention? If man is the responsible head of the family is it not as much, if not more, his concern that his wife's health not be imperiled or that no unwanted or deformed child arrive in the world? It is not merely a matter of chivalry but of common sense that he should submit to what is in fact a much less serious operation of sterilization—if such be indicated.

Racial Indications

Racial indications—to mention it is to condemn it. Just as castration of males by a conquering power has been carried out on its enemies in some dark eras of history, so vasectomy by crushing has also been done to prevent a subjugated people from breeding. It has no interest for the medical practitioner, although a colleague of mine has had to attempt the restoration of some done during the late world war.

CURRENT PRESSURES AND THEIR PROBLEMS

Male sterilization is a particularly interesting subject because it brings into focus three strong influences which are at the present time being exerted on mankind. First, we are beginning to perfect delicate and powerful techniques for altering a normal man whether by surgery or by drugs or by mind-conditioning. We are learning ways of controlling him with remarkable precision. Second, we have the terrifying prospect of gross over-population of some parts of the earth with the probable consequence of famine, anarchy and even genocide. It is influencing the political outlook of many nations. It is a menacing specter to anyone who looks more than ten years ahead. Third, we are moving towards a society in which sexual intercourse is being deliberately advocated and advertised as a right which every man may claim for himself with scant regard, or none, to his associated responsibilities. The effects in the break-up of family life and social stability are far reaching.

Each of these three pressures, so different in kind, is directly or indirectly the result of the application of medical knowledge. They are *our* concern as physicians. They can be classified under three heads. The theological: How much do we interfere with man whom we believe to be created in the image of God? The social: What is our attitude to society with its hitherto unrestrained freedom to procreate? And the personal: How do we regard the current revolution in sexual ethics? A few points can be considered under each of these heads.

A THEOLOGICAL FRONTIER

Present indications for carrying out a vasectomy have already been mentioned. When the operation is to forestall the possible serious danger to a mother's health of another pregnancy, or because of the probability of major genetic defect in the infant or, perhaps, because of the urgent need of population control in some communities, careful thought needs to be given so that the right course may be chosen. Yet, it is not unreasonable to pause to consider first the kind of operation it is. It is assumed that the "patient" is a man in good health. By what right does a doctor operate to limit the powers of a normal person? His work is to combat disease. His skill is developed towards cure and alleviation. His thought and training are directed to putting right what is wrong. Now, a controlled degree of medical prophylaxis is acceptable as, for instance, injection to immunize against diphtheria, or vaccination to prevent smallpox. But such actions have no permanent anatomical or physiological effects on the patient. They do, in fact, what nature herself has taught us to do to ward off the invasion of potentially lethal disease. But what is now suggested is surgery, not therapeutic surgery on one who is diseased, but prophylactic surgery on one who is healthy, and this in order to leave permanent or semipermanent anatomical and physiological change. We have crossed a frontier—invisible, perhaps, but none the less real. When a vasectomy is done we operate on a normal person and damage him, even though the effect on bodily health is minimal or none. Ought we to be operating on normal men?

If we accept that it is right to alter the healthy man and destroy a physical endowment, for whatever reason, shall the physician not find it difficult to resist other operations on normal people for equally plausible reasons? Indeed, what argument can be raised against, say, the use of drugs or surgery to alter temperament and thereby achieve a change of character or a docile community. Are we right to tamper with man in this way? Is this not where we say no on the principle that damage to a healthy person is outside the permissible limits of surgical or medical practice? Are we so impoverished of moral and spiritual and intellectual resources that we have to alter the structure of the human body in order to maintain our control of human life and human welfare?

Are we sure that the indications in any particular case are decisively in favor of a procedure that deliberately creates damage? Would not some simple contraceptive method suffice? It seems only right that we should regard the operation with some reserve, if not distaste, and use it only when it is the sole possible means that can be used to prevent a human tragedy.

SOCIAL CONSIDERATIONS

Here we face a different problem which pulls our thinking in the opposite direction. Increase in population in some parts of the world is leading to undernourishment in large communities and will, in a very few years—if it has not done so already—result in potential or actual starvation. Missionaries from the East are urgent in their pleas for action. It is said that there are areas in India in which within five years the starving will be fighting for food. Anarchy, disease and race wars may follow. Here Christian sympathy and Christian advice must be linked with wise statesmanship. We fully support the ideal that no child should be brought into the world unless there is the possibility of adequate nourishment, nurture and security. The long term solution must be education and information for all intending parents; but this takes time. The medical revolution for *saving* life has surged ahead so fast that the newer idea of limitation of family size has fallen a long way behind. It is agreed that sophisticated methods of contraception such as the application of the coil in women, are difficult to apply in rural areas amongst the illiterate or semi-educated and, of course, they are only part of the solution. The policy of encouraging male sterilization offers hope to a hard-pressed government. Vasectomy on a wide scale is considered to be one of the methods of averting calamity (to be used in conjunction with others) and it is a step towards the desired goal.

The criticism of vasectomy is that it is the intelligent and well-to-do who avail themselves of it rather than the ignorant poor who would most benefit. Moreover, it does lead to individual problems amongst a people whose mortality of infants and women is still high and where a man, having had the operation, may well have to forgo the opportunity to re-establish a family. As a temporary expedient done on a voluntary basis by government persuasion it may be that the right thing is being done.

THE PERSONAL

In earlier centuries the main purpose of sexual intercourse was defined as the procreation of children; the mutual care and concern of the partners for each other was given second place. Today the unitive aspect of intercourse is being more and more emphasized, to the extent that there are now those who say that the procreative side should be divorced from it completely. But can the two ever be deliberately separated without doing damage to the personality of man? Can we rightly bow to the modern trend which makes of sexual union a right which any man may claim— or further still—a necessity for his physical and psychological well-being?

The true starting point is that sex union shall always be undertaken with due consideration of its effects. Christian teaching emphasizes restraint and self-discipline arising out of responsibly made decisions. This view keeps intercourse strictly within the marriage relationship and even there sets responsibility before rights, though it does not deny the latter. Man, by the corruption of his own heart, the weakness of his own will or the confusion of his own thinking, may go astray at this point, but it is here that the saving power of the Gospel comes to his aid. God's intentions are for man's lasting good; while the teaching of the Bible never supports repression of natural instinct, it always commends responsible control.

If we relax and accept current moves towards the making of sexual intercourse in itself the supreme human experience to which man has unexceptionable rights, we threaten the institution of marriage and therefore the permanence and security of family life. Marriages are held together by love through self-restraint and the will to be faithful to an agreement, publicly made and voluntarily accepted as binding. In the case of Christians this is often described in terms of, and as a reflection of, God's pledged and unalterable faithfulness to His own people. Sexual intercourse should be the seal of a contract already secure, not an action standing in isolation.

Now vasectomy is a planned permanent separation of the two aspects of sexual intercourse. Naturally the medical profession tends to safeguard its use at the present time and only applies it with caution, but widespread acceptance of the operation would imply that sexual intercourse as such is an end in itself and to be indulged in with only the minimum of limitations that a free society happens to expect.

CONCLUSIONS

It may well be argued that if an operation which deprives the body of a normal endowment is considered unacceptable, why then in certain instances can it be permitted? Would it not be more logical to take an absolute position and forbid it altogether? Such an attitude, however, cannot reasonably be taken in a world where we have to combat evil in so many and various guises. Indeed, we find that Christ Himself understood the kind of dilemma which we face in some of our problems, and while upholding the authority of the moral law yet accepted that compassion must influence the action of those who seek to serve mankind in its need.[7]

The Christian physician is guided by certain great principles which he believes to be God-ordained. These include the life-long security of the marriage contract, the need for children to be wanted and loved and protected, the need for life to be lived in self-discipline and the service of others and, for the physician, his own specific calling to maintain the health and integrity of the body and to resist the destructive forces of disease wherever met.

It is a physician's experience that at times the gross effects of some evil on the woman, the child or the community may be such that family life and health of individuals can be maintained only by the sacrifice of the integrity of the body, in certain instances, by sterilization.

---

[7] Matthew 19:3–9.

SECTION 4

SOCIETAL
REALITIES

Chapter 15

RAPE, INCEST AND MULTIPLE ILLEGITIMACY AS INDICATIONS FOR THERAPEUTIC ABORTION

SUMMARY

After a review of the relevant literature, psychological, genetic and sociological considerations on the issues are introduced, followed by some principles which might guide the Christian making decisions about cases (pregnancies) involving rape, incest, or multiple illegitimacy. The author concludes that abortion *should* be offered to a patient in cases of rape or incestuous pregnancy, but should not be approved (legalized) in cases of multiple illegitimacy. Some of the rationale is set forth on which such conclusions are based. A note of caution about undue liberalization in this area is sounded at the conclusion.

DAVID F. BUSBY, M.D. *Dr. Busby is in the private practice of psychiatry in Niles, Illinois (suburb of Chicago). He is on the senior active staff of the Lutheran General Hospital in Park Ridge, Illinois, and of Forest Hospital, Des Plaines, Illinois. He received his medical degree from the University of Tennessee Medical School in 1949. After two years military service and five years in general practice in Chicago, he returned for psychiatric residency training at Hines Veterans Administration Hospital in suburban Chicago and was certified by the American Board of Psychiatry and Neurology. In addition to medical teaching, he is Professor of Pastoral Psychology at Trinity Evangelical Divinity School, Deerfield, Illinois, and is a frequent lecturer to professional societies and lay audiences both secular and Christian and has several articles published. Dr. Busby and his wife were born in Memphis, Tennessee, and with their five children, now live in Chicago, Illinois.*

RAPE, INCEST AND MULTIPLE ILLEGITIMACY AS INDICATIONS FOR THERAPEUTIC ABORTION

by David F. Busby

INTRODUCTION

The topic, while somewhat sub-specialized, is of practical value, if for no other reason than because the literature concerning it is scant and controversial. Two of the three subjects (incest and multiple illegitimacy) were not even indexed in the vast majority of books and periodicals reviewed in a prolonged search. Enough was found, however, to suggest some premises:

1) A majority of the writers support abortion in pregnancies that are the result of *rape*. A few American states already have legalized abortion for interruption of pregnancies caused by rape.
2) In pregnancy involving *incest* a fair consensus favors offering abortion; authorization, which has existed in Europe for some time, has recently begun in the United States.
3) In a pregnancy within the context of *multiple illegitimacy* no evidence of legal authorization for abortion on such grounds was found, nor could any definitive recommendations be found for such a case.

A REVIEW OF THE LITERATURE

Rape and Incestuous Pregnancy

Some samples of opinions concerning the management of pregnancy that results from rape or incest will indicate the current trend and recommend the status of the law or approved medical practice.

> *Clemmensen:* "In Denmark, which has a population of over four million, legislation about surgical abortion was first passed in 1939. Therapeutic abortion was . . . allowed after certain sexual crimes (ethical indication) or in cases of severe hereditary taint (eugenic indication)." [1]

> *Harvard Conference:* "The countries of Northern Europe—Norway, Denmark, Sweden, and Finland—occupy about the middle ground between restrictive and permissive abortion laws. These four countries permit abortions . . . in cases of rape, forcible or statutory, or incest." [2]

> *Galdston:* "From a biological point of view, unless overwhelming reasons exist, such as incest and rape, I think any abortion is likely to have serious traumatic sequelae." [3]

> *Duvall:* "Incest is another type of sex crime which may result in pregnancy and for which our antiquated laws provide no sanction for abortion. . . . Pregnancy resulting from sexual crime should be a recognized indication for legal abortion. This should include rape . . . and incest." [4]

> *Spivak:* "Many legal bodies, both in the United States and Canada, have drafted proposed changes to liberalize existing archaic therapeutic abortion statutes to bring them closer to modern medical and social concepts and principles. It is felt that a liberalized

---

[1] *Abortion in the United States:* Ed., M. Calderone, M.D. Hoeber-Harper 1958; p. 21.

[2] *The Terrible Choice: The Abortion Dilemma:* Harvard-Kennedy Abortion Conference, 1967, Bantam Book 1968; p. 49.

[3] *Abortion in the U.S.* p. 121.

[4] Duvall, E.: *Sex Ways—in Fact and Faith.* New York: Association Press 1961; p. 220 and 223.

abortion statute, besides making therapeutic abortion voluntary and wholly removed from coercion, should contain the following clauses as reasonable grounds for terminating an existing pregnancy: . . . To permit interruption where impregnation was accomplished through sex crime, proved rape, incest, or in the case of a female mentally incapable through youth or mental retardation to anticipate the potential results of coitus." [5]

Harvard Conference: "The American Medical Association, at its June, 1967, meeting, in effect endorsed the ALI approach. . . . The AMA's new policy position is that it is opposed to induced abortions except when: . . . there is documented medical evidence that continuance of a pregnancy, resulting from legally established statutory or forcible rape or incest may constitute a threat to the mental or physical health of the patient. . . . Three states (California, Colorado, and North Carolina) recently expanded their laws to permit abortions . . . in cases of rape and incest. . . . The Colorado legislation . . . (April, 1967) permits the termination of a pregnancy in an accredited hospital following hospital-board determination that . . . the pregnancy resulted from forcible rape or incest or statutory rape when the girl is under sixteen and the parent or guardian consents to the abortion." [6]

The following quotations suggest some genetic-eugenic and psychiatric factors underlying such recommendations.

Adams and Neel: "Eighteen prospectively ascertained cases of brother x sister and father x daughter matings are described. A series of illegitimate children whose mothers were as nearly matched as possible to the incest mothers for intelligence, age, height, weight, and socioeconomic conditions were used as controls. Six of the children of incest had died or were found to have major defects on follow-up six months after birth date, whereas one of the comparison children was so classified. This is a larger inbreeding effect than

[5] Spivak, M.M. *Therapeutic Abortion, A.J. Ob-Gyn.* 97:316 1967, p. 316.
[6] *The Terrible Choice* pp. 53, 49, and 54.

would be predicted on the basis of published findings from marriages of first cousins." [7]

Kretzschmar and Norris: "Some patients, particularly those that become impregnated as the result of rape or incest may, due to associated acute anxiety reactions, have had an additional psychiatric indication of severe depression and possible suicidal risk. After psychiatric evaluation, it was felt that six patients with either rape or incest as their presenting complaint had a significant enough depressive reaction to diagnose them as potentially suicidal." [8]

The only writer I found speaking out against abortion in incestuous pregnancy was a Catholic contributor to *Christian Century:* [9] I imagine that a prior commitment to a sweeping anti-abortion position perhaps coupled with an idealistic expectation that the good that can come from suffering represents its sufficiently redeeming feature would constitute the primary motivations for those in opposition. One source [10] did recommend omitting incest from abortion legislation, but this is paradoxically to facilitate such indication.

In summary, it would appear that for psychopathologic and genetic-eugenic reasons, offering abortion for incestuous pregnancy is not only permissible but also ethically indicated in current secular literature. It remains for others, such as a Christian symposium, to ascertain if there is any evidence to the contrary.

Multiple Illegitimacy

The question of abortion involving multiple illegitimacy, was most difficult and confusing to research. In the first place, though there is discussion regarding contraception,

---

[7] Adams, M. and Neel, J.: Children of Incest, *Pediatrics* 40:1 1967, p. 61.

[8] Kretzschmar, R. and Norris, B.: Psychiatric implications of Therapeutic Abortion *A. J. OB-Gyn.* 98:368 1967, p. 369.

[9] Novak, *Christian Century* 1967.

[10] *The Terrible Choice* p. 101.

sterilization and other close but tangential issues in such cases, there could not be located a single writer venturing even a tentative opinion, much less a definitive analysis of or firm recommendation concerning abortion in same. Numerous journal articles and several books on the subject of unwed mothers in general and recidivism in particular were reviewed, either in original or in abstract. Included were studies of:

1) The medical and sociologic aspects of unwed mothers (and of the putative father and both their families).[11,12]

2) Personality characteristics of women with repeated illegitimacies.[13]

3) Comments on a hypothetical case of multiple unwanted (though legitimate) pregnancy.[14]

4) The sociological considerations of (legalized) abortion as the "contraception of the poor." [15]

But none refer to therapeutic abortion in illegitimacy *per se.*

Some of the issues involved in attempting to ascertain and evaluate the ethics and morality involved in this question are: 1) The motivations of the mother; 2) The sequelae (of offering such abortion) on a) The individual and b) The community and nation as a whole, both as to morality and as to the population explosion. In this connection some key questions arise. Would the liberalized offering of abortion tend toward undermining the morality of the community by facilitating sexual acting-out in both promiscuous and so-called faithful "steady" relationships? Or is the refusal to liberalize lowering morale and promoting rebellious sexual-

---

[11] Wearing, M. P. et al: A Medical and Sociologic Study of the Unwed Mother *A.J. Ob-Gyn* 97:792 1967.

[12] Vincent, C. E.: *Unmarried Mothers*, Free Press of Glencoe, 1962, pp. 53–184.

[13] Malmquist, C. et al: Personality Characteristics of Women with Repeated Illegitimacies *A.J. Orthopsych.* 1966 p. 476.

[14] *The Terrible Choice*, pp. 24–28.

[15] *Ibid.*, pp. 24 and 59–67.

ity including pregnancy? Many girls report that part of the excitement of sexuality is in the risk of pregnancy and thus refuse contraceptives. In comparing "easy" abortion with available contraceptives it would appear that the latter while cheaper, and safer, are easy to forget to use, i.e., require foresight, whereas "easy" abortion could further encourage such laxity. Levitt says:

> "more knowledge of contraception is more likely to increase the demand for abortion than to decrease it. Once established, a responsible attitude to parenthood will not lightly submit to unplanned, unwanted pregnancy." [16]

Further Sociological Considerations

One large factor involved in considering abortion liberalization is the fact that illegitimate babies represent our country's primary source of adoption and its consequent blessing of many homes. With demand exceeding supply already in most localities, would the community's best interest be served by increasing abortions, thus potentially reducing the supply? Of course this question, in turn, hinges upon a more basic question: would the liberalizing of abortion in fact reduce the adoptive supply or would it tend to shift present illegal abortions to legal and more medically favorable locales, thus decreasing the death rate and perhaps actually increasing the supply? If so, would such be desirable? In that connection, Glass writes:

> "Abortion can scarcely be regarded as an ideal method of birth prevention. But given the defects of present contraceptive techniques and the dubious alternative of clandestine abortion, the provision of a much wider access to legal abortion is by no means an unrealistic policy." [17]

Another sociological dimension involving illegitimacy is

---

[16] *Abortion in Britain: Family Planning Conference,* London: Pitman Publ. 1966; p. 100.

[17] *Ibid.,* p. 65.

the fact that tight abortion laws would seem to keep high both the demand for and the price of illegal abortions, thus resulting in one more instance of discrimination against and oppression of the poor so commonly descried these days as well as in the days of Isaiah (1:17) and James (2:1–10). Some have paradoxically supposed the reverse may be true, namely, that current welfare legislation favors the poor by causing their indiscretions to be rewarded out of the rich's taxes—more children, more support!

ETHICAL CONSIDERATIONS, A CHRISTIAN APPROACH

In conclusion, we turn to the question of the Christian ethical determination. In the absence of specific scriptural or theological guidelines concerning disposition of incestuous and multiple illegitimate pregnancies and those due to rape, it appears to me that the Christian has two basic alternatives: Either 1) Consider all abortion to be unjustifiable murder, or 2) Consider the "evidence"—the general issues and the specific circumstances—and determine for himself what would seem to be "the mind of Christ", the will of God, in these (and all other such) matters. I hold to the latter.

In making decisions about an individual case, the responsible doctor or individual turns to the Scripture for general principles and to the heritage of learning and experience of other Christians, including investigation of the body of writings on Christian ethics which are available. In reviewing the literature, the author has found a number of texts to be particularly helpful in this area of decision-making, among which are: *Christian Personal Ethics*,[18] *The Ethics of Sex*[19] and an appealing treatise entitled, *The Grounds*

[18] Henry, C. F. H.: *Christian Personal Ethics*, Grand Rapids: Eerdmans. (1960).

[19] Thielecke, Helmut: *The Ethics of Sex*, New York: Harper and Row 1964.

of Christian Moral Judgments.[20] (In connection with the last named, it should be pointed out that whereas its main thrust seems to be situationalistic beyond evangelical acceptance, still certain points are made and issues treated in a way that seems both valid and helpful to this author.)

CONCLUSIONS

With full awareness that all generalizations in medicine and even in ethics are dangerous, and that exceptions to any rules laid down about the management of illegitimate pregnancies are likely to be common, the following guidelines are suggested, influenced both by a consensus in the literature studied and by personal clinical experience:

1. Abortion should be offered in cases of pregnancy due to incest. The principal underlying reason for this recommendation is derived primarily from genetic considerations. The birth of offspring with undesirable or frankly abnormal traits is of significant probability. Furthermore, the incestuous act is almost always motivated by an existing psychological abnormality in one or both partners in the mating. Such a psychological defect may, or may not be, transmissible. In any event, the child born in such a relationship usually has disadvantages—even more formidable than those facing a child born as a result of other illicit sexual relationships, even if the child be wanted which would be abnormal. If the mother is the innocent party in such a situation, the psychological trauma she can suffer by bringing the pregnancy to term is a sufficient indication in itself to favor abortion as a solution to the problem.
2. In the case of rape, the psychological trauma to the mother is usually equally overwhelming. Should the victim be married, allowing the pregnancy to go to term would impose undue psychological problems for both the mother and her husband, as well as for the child. It is generally conceded that subjection of

[20] *Soundings: Essays Concerning Christian Understanding:* Ed.: A. R. Vidler, London: Cambridge U. Press 1962. Chap. 9.

the innocent party to such suffering by withholding the opportunity of an abortion is unwarranted.

3. Multiple illegitimacy as a routine indication for abortion should not become part of approved medico-legal practice.

The grounds for this recommendation include the fact that such a pregnancy, while often distressing, does not usually precipitate psychiatric crises.

Furthermore, the child of such a pregnancy has as good a chance to be normal and to be wanted through adoption as any other child in the general population.

The possibility of other indications for abortion coincidentally present in the case of multiple illegitimacy should be considered.

While beyond the specific purview of this paper, it should be noted that provided there is informed consent of the parties concerned, sterilization should be considered for mothers involved in multiple illegitimacy. Each individual case would have to be decided carefully on its own merits.

A word of caution and challenge: With many strident voices being raised proposing and even demanding abortion on simple request (which so easily degenerates into whim or fancy) the need to find and communicate a consensus of reasonable standards is great. For many Protestants, the need may be met through the Affirmation on the Control of Human Reproduction (see Part III) which opposes any devaluation of human life and promotes the realization and practice of the dignity and responsibility of man under God.

Chapter 16

A SOCIOLOGICAL PERSPECTIVE ON ABORTION AND STERILIZATION

SUMMARY

John A. Scanzoni, Associate Professor of Sociology of Indiana University, reports statistical information reflecting attitudes and practices in various countries regarding abortion and sterilization. As a result, he asserts that abortion is practiced as a means of population control by a sizeable proportion of the world's population. The comparative popularity of sterilization and abortion is discussed, with an analysis of possible reasons for the difference.

In the concluding section, Dr. Scanzoni presents duties of Christians as they face social change on these issues, and offers guidelines for couples who are considering abortion and sterilization.

JOHN A. SCANZONI, A.B., Ph.D., *is an Associate Professor of Sociology at Indiana University, Bloomington. He holds the A.B. degree from Wheaton College and the Ph.D. from the University of Oregon. Prior to entering doctoral study, he served in rural areas of the United States with Village Missions. He is engaged in research and writing on the sociology of the family and the sociology of religion. In addition to numerous articles in religious and professional journals, Dr. Scanzoni is the editor of a book,* Readings in Social Problems. *He has also written a book recently released:* Achievement, Society and the Family.

A SOCIOLOGICAL PERSPECTIVE ON ABORTION AND STERILIZATION

by John Scanzoni

INTRODUCTION

The objective of this chapter is twofold: one, to examine the issues of abortion and sterilization from a broad sociological stance; and second, to interpret this perspective from the added dimension provided by Christianity.

Definitions

For the purpose of the discussion in this chapter, abortion means feticide, the termination of pregnancy sometime after an ovum has been fertilized by a sperm. This may be self-induced or done with outside assistance, but it is a deliberate action. Spontaneous abortion (in which expulsion of the embryo from the uterus occurs involuntarily) is not considered.

By sterilization is meant a deliberate action in which the

services of a physician are sought to *prevent* conception surgically through an operation. Most often the surgery is permanent, though not always. This is to be distinguished from involuntary sterilization through illness or injury, or sterilization for purposes explicitly other than for conception control.

ABORTION AS A WORLDWIDE PHENOMENON

The evidence shows that these two types of fertility control do not exist apart from contraception. One cannot really talk about abortion and sterilization without first considering contraception. The reason for this is that in most cultures, families who utilize abortion and sterilization have already tried contraception.[1] If attempts at contraception are successful, then the need for either abortion or sterilization disappears. It is among those families that do not make contraception work *to their own satisfaction* that more radical means are most often brought to bear to reduce fertility.

If contraception fails, abortion tends to be considered next. If contraception fails *repeatedly,* or if abortion is not employed for one reason or other, then sterilization is the next logical step. Considering world cultures as a whole, the incidence of abortion (both recorded and estimated) is higher than that of sterilization. This is because it is the more obvious—it is what comes immediately to mind upon discovery of an unwanted pregnancy. Davis and Blake conclude, "Abortion is widely practiced in pre-industrial societies, being the individual's *principal* means of limiting fertility." [2] They then raise the question as to *why* this

---

[1] Ralph Thomlinson, *Population Dynamics*, (New York: Random House, 1965), p. 201.

[2] Kingsley Davis and Judith Blake, "Social Structure and Fertility: An Analytic Framework," in Ruth L. Coser, ed., *The Family: Its Structure and Functions* (New York: St. Martin's Press, 1964), pp. 655–656.

should be so, given that contraception is less hazardous to health than interference with pregnancy.

They suggest several reasons in answer to their own question. First, "As compared to mechanical and chemical means of contraception, abortion is technically simple." [3] To individuals not accustomed to the intricacies of technologies and logic that members of developed societies take for granted, contraception is extremely complex. Even remembering to take a pill once a day can be extremely difficult. Consequently, many people in underdeveloped societies, and even many disadvantaged as well as advantaged people in developed societies find contraception fails them. Thus, it *ipso facto* becomes much simpler to focus on doing away with the fetus than to try to prevent conception.

A second and related reason stems from the failures themselves. Since conception does not always occur anyway after intercourse even without contraception, there is a tendency on the part of the less informed to view conception either as totally random or else in fatalistic terms.[4] In Latin America, for example, such terms as "Asi es la vida," *such is life;* or "Que será, será," *what will be, will be,* often describe attitudes toward conception. Thus, a casual attitude toward contraception develops in contrast to the deadly serious effort to do away with a fetus once it is discovered. And this deadly serious effort is defined as being almost inevitably successful as compared with the many disappointments they have found in contraception.

A third reason for the popularity of abortion, say Davis-Blake, is that "abortion is not applied at the time of intercourse and does not require cooperation between man and woman. It is a woman's method and can be practiced without the man's knowledge." [5] Since repeated studies have

---

[3] *Ibid.*
[4] *Ibid.*
[5] *Ibid.*

shown that most methods of contraception cannot take place without effective husband-wife communication, and since this type of communication often breaks down, it is evident why contraception itself often fails. Realizing this, the woman is aware that she can always fall back on abortion without having to "bother" to communicate with her husband. Finally, they say, "Although a child may be desired at the time of intercourse, subsequent events may alter this attitude, at which time abortion rather than contraception is a remedy." [6] In other words, the uncertainties of life may lead the couple to deem it necessary to end a formerly desired pregnancy.

Given these four factors: simplicity, certainty, communication, and the vagaries of life, it is no wonder abortion is so universal in developing countries. But even in modern nations, abortion is, according to Thomlinson, "a very effective birth control method and far more widely used than is recognized." [7]

ABORTION IN MODERN SOCIETY

In France for example, it is currently estimated by the U.N. population branch that the number of abortions greatly exceeds the annual number of registered births.[8] Abortion has been legalized by the governments of Japan, the USSR, Communist China, some East European nations, and just this year, Great Britain. Moreover, the Scandinavian nations are extremely permissive toward abortion. Currently in the U.S., seven states plus the District of Columbia permit abortion if the *health* as well as the life of the mother is endangered (Colo., Calif., N.C., Ala., N.J., Ore., N.M.). Colorado's law includes *mental* as well as physical health.[9]

---

[6] *Ibid.*

[7] *Op. cit.*, p. 198.

[8] *Ibid.*, p. 198.

[9] Helen Hennessy, "Abortion Laws Facing Reform Across Nation," NEA newspaper report, April 28, 1968.

In spite of the rigid laws that applied until recently *throughout* the United States, some authorities estimate there are from 700,000 to 2,000,000 abortions annually.[10] In the U.S.,

> "abortions occur more often to married than unmarried women. Among wives, 17 percent of all pregnancies end in induced abortion. And of the women who *do* have abortions, 74 percent report no serious physical or psychological consequences. Most abortions are performed on married women aged 20–34 who already have one or more children, but who have not previously been aborted. The higher the parity, the higher the percentage of pregnancies terminating in abortion." [11]

Kinsey, for example, argues on the basis of his studies that of all girls who become pregnant before marriage, 95 percent of the college educated girls end the pregnancy with induced abortion, and 88 percent of the less educated girls follow the same procedure.[12] Race makes an even greater difference in the incidence of abortion than does education. A recent Public Health Service Study suggested that one reason for the soaring illegitimacy rates among nonwhites (in 1964, it was 97.2 vs. 11.0 for whites) is the fact that nonwhites *do not* resort to abortion to terminate pregnancy.[13] The nonwhites in our society are like much of the population in developing societies in that they do not effectively make use of contraceptive techniques. But unlike people in other cultures, and perhaps due to our strict abortion

---

[10] Thomlinson, *op. cit.*, p. 198.

[11] *Ibid.*, p. 199.

[12] Alfred C. Kinsey, "Illegal Abortion in the United States," in Robert W. Roberts, ed., *The Unwed Mother* (New York: Harper and Row, 1966), p. 197. See also P. H. Gebhard, W. B. Pomeroy, C. V. Christenson, *Pregnancy, Birth and Abortion*, (New York: Harper and Row, 1958).

[13] *Trends in Illegitimacy*, National Center for Health Statistics, Series 21, No. 15, February, 1968, Washington, D. C., U. S. Dept. of Health, Education and Welfare.

laws, they do not utilize abortion either. The consequence is a swelling of illegitimate births among them.

The modern nation which has most dramatically made use of induced abortion as an instrument of public policy is, of course, Japan. A series of laws passed from 1948 to 1952 legalized induced abortion for whatever reason. Takeshita reports that the criteria of "health and finance problems" were so "unspecified and the certified physician is his own screening board, so that the applicant's intention, whatever it may be, is sufficient cause for approval." [14] At the same time, the Japanese government began a systematic program in education in the use of contraceptives. Though abortion was felt necessary to curb the huge population growth of that period, it was thought that feticide would eventually give way to contraception. Surprisingly, however, by 1961, the proportion of the population who resorted to abortion was 41 percent as compared to only 15 percent in 1950. "What is more, induced abortion has been found to be more likely among past users of contraception than among non-users." [15] Like those doing it illegally in the U.S., most women who have abortions are in their thirties or early forties, use contraception regularly, and already have as many or more children than they want. Takeshita argues that in spite of Western criticisms (which are, by the way, far less today than ten years ago) the trend is for Japanese to continue to use contraception, but in the event of failure, to have the fetus removed by artificial means. *The Japanese, in short, see contraception and abortion as complementary methods of birth control.*

The other Asian nation which as part of *official* policy has legalized abortion is mainland China. Their abortion laws are as liberal as those of Japan, and the motivation is the

---

[14] John Y. Takeshita, "Population Control in Japan: A Miracle or Secular Trend," *Marriage and Family Living*, February, 1963 (Vol. 25, No. 1), p. 46.

[15] *Ibid.*, p. 47.

same, viz., to slow a burgeoning population growth. However, the Chinese Medical Association came out in formal statement against government abortion policy.[16] Furthermore, Tien argues that "it is hard to find any prominent Chinese figure in or outside the Communist party who entered a plea for the adoption of mass abortions." [17]

Thus, in spite of legal approval of abortion, there is strong grass-roots sentiment against it—due perhaps to traditional views of family and children. In any event, China's efforts to institutionalize contraception have been largely ineffective, particularly in the region of most rapid growth, viz., the rural areas. What is more, Tien argues that abortion is not likely to be accepted in China as the major form of population control, or even as a complement to contraception, as it is in Japan.[18]

CONDITIONS AFFECTING THE USE OF STERILIZATION

Most students of population both in the U.S. and abroad concur that while abortion generally follows failure of contraception, repeated failures usually lead to sterilization if it is available. Puerto Rico is an example of a society where strong religious sanctions against both contraception and abortion actually lead to an extremely high incidence of sterilization. Puerto Ricans share with other developing peoples a dislike for an inability to use contraceptive techniques effectively.[19] They also tend not to favor abortion, in much the same way as the Chinese. But in addition, Cook argues that Puerto Rican women were so embarrassed by having

---

16 H. Yuan Tien, "Induced Abortion and Population Control in Mainland China," in *Marriage and Family Living, ibid.*, p. 41.

17 *Ibid.*

18 *Ibid.*

19 Reuben Hill, J. Mayone Stycos, Kurt W. Back, *The Family and Population Control*, (Chapel Hill, N. C.: The University of North Carolina Press, 1959), pp. 179–180.

to confess to the priest so often their use of contraceptives that "in increasing numbers they are rolling many little sins, and a constant aggravation, into one big sin by turning to sterilization as a solution to their problem." [20]

Furthermore, knowledge about such operations was totally unknown among the general Puerto Rican population until the church circulated numerous pastoral letters inveighing against it. The result is that in Puerto Rico, the popularity and actual use of sterilization is extraordinarily high. The trend is toward increasing usage, especially among the better educated.[21] The long range trend there seems to be a juxtaposition of contraception and sterilization, in a fashion analogous to the juxtaposition of abortion and contraception in Japan.

A recent nationwide study of fertility in the U. S. provides the most up to date assessment of this behavior in our society. The incidence of sterilization, or contraceptive operations, is not limited to large families. Three quarters of all couples who have had operations have two to four children, which is within the range of children desired by most American families.[22] However, in spite of seemingly modest family size, most couples who experience sterilization already have more children than they want, and report failure to use contraception effectively.[23] In fact, failure of contraception is probably the single most important factor accounting for the decision to sterilize.

Catholics use sterilization far less than Protestants.[24] Not only is it against official church teaching, but Catholics are

---

[20] Thomlinson, *op. cit.*, p. 201.

[21] Hill, *et al.*, *op. cit.*, p. 169.

[22] Pascal K. Whelpton, Arthur A. Campbell, John E. Patterson, *Fertility and Family Planning in the United States* (Princeton, N. J.: Princeton University Press, 1966), pp. 139–140.

[23] *Ibid.*

[24] *Ibid.*, p. 141.

far less apt than Protestants to become anxious about in-
effectual birth control. Since they make less serious attempts at contraception than Protestants, they are less
dismayed by failure. Protestants who fail after "trying
hard" are very likely to consider and to use sterilization.

Concomitantly, the incidence of sterilization is much
greater in the Southern and Western sections of the U.S.,
than anywhere else.[25] This is due primarily to fewer Catholics living in these areas, plus the fact that the Catholic
Church exercises less control over hospitals and doctors in
these areas than it does elsewhere. Sterilization also occurs
more frequently in rural areas than in cities, both because
there are more such areas in the West and South, and also
because there are fewer Catholics.[26]

Sterilization is inversely related to education for two important reasons.[27] First, education contributes to effective
use of birth control techniques. Second, physicians seem
more likely to encourage the more radical step of sterilization among the less-educated, due to their repeated failures
with contraception.[28] Physicians seem more optimistic about
the abilities of the better educated to cope with contraception.

The major reason given by American couples for sterilization is "health of the mother," but since this is defined
so broadly, it often means that the couple do not want or
simply cannot handle another child.[29] Sterilization in the
U.S. is becoming more frequent, but not anywhere near estimates of the increasing incidence of abortion. Abortion is
still more widely favored in the U.S., chiefly because it is
not irreversible. Most often, pregnancy could follow abor-

---

[25] *Ibid.*, p. 143.
[26] *Ibid.*
[27] *Ibid.*, p. 147.
[28] *Ibid.*
[29] *Ibid.*, p. 149.

tion if so desired, while after sterilization this is much less likely.

A CHRISTIAN PERSPECTIVE ON ABORTION AND STERILIZATION

The Christian and the Larger Society

The opposition of the Catholic Church to abortion and sterilization is well known. Pope Pius XI warned of the "grave sin of taking the life of the offspring hidden in the mother's womb," in connection with abortion; and "interference with natural law" in the case of sterilization.[30] Protestant views influenced the very first abortion laws ever passed anywhere, viz., in England in the early 19th century. The idea then was that the soul entered the body at the moment of "quickening of the embryo," that is, the first time the woman felt movement in the uterus, usually around the fourth month.[31] Therefore, in English law, abortion was punishable only after quickening and was eventually made a capital offense.

The prime basis for having laws against abortion is that some feel it constitutes a form of murder. Hardesty, writing in *Eternity* magazine argues that abortion is the "killing of a human being," because a "fertilized ovum (zygote) contains all that is needed to produce a unique person." [32] But her argument is seriously undermined by the research of Hardin, a biologist at the University of California at Santa Barbara. Hardin has done extensive work with DNA, the substance which is at the core of all biological life. He argues, "The early stages of an individual fetus have had very little human effort invested in them; they are of very little worth. . . . The DNA of a zygote (he estimates that 38 percent of *all* zygotes are spontaneously aborted anyway)

---

[30] Thomlinson, *op. cit.*, p. 199.

[31] *Ibid.*, p. 200.

[32] Nancy Hardesty, "Should Anyone Who Wants an Abortion Have One?" in *Eternity*, June, 1967 (Vol. 18, No. 6), pp. 32–34.

is not a human being." [33] So from the standpoint of advanced biological research as to what life is all about, it is evidently impossible to say unequivocally that the fetus is truly human.

Moreover, from the psychological and sociological perspectives, there is nothing "human" at all about the early fetus because it can in no way *interact* meaningfully with other human beings. From the biblical viewpoint, some scholars have marshaled obscure passage to support the idea that the fetus is human; but Hardesty herself admits that the only direct reference to the topic of injured fetuses is found in Exodus 21:22–25.[34] And this passage, she acknowledges, would support the idea that the biblical writer did *not* hold the fetus to be human.[35] The passage reads:

> "When men strive together, and hurt a woman with child, so that there is a miscarriage (so that her fruit depart from her, KJV), and yet no harm follows, the one who hurt her shall be fined, according as the woman's husband shall lay upon him; and he shall pay as the judges determine. If any harm follow, then you shall give life for life, eye for eye, tooth for tooth, hand for hand, foot for foot, burn for burn, wound for wound, stripe for stripe" (RSV).

Therefore, it seems apparent that there is no conclusive argument that the fetus is human. Arguments against abortion on this ground are as uncertain as the arguments against contraception on the ground that the sperm and egg carry the *potential* of human life and should not therefore be destroyed or wasted.

However, even if one could defend the idea that the sixth commandment applied to the fetus, he is then confronted by the fact that this commandment is subject to numerous

---

[33] Garrett Hardin, Ph.D., "Blueprints, DNA, and Abortion: A Scientific and Ethical Analysis," *Medical Opinion and Review*, Vol. 3 (February, 1967), pp. 74–85.

[34] Hardesty, *op. cit.*

[35] *Ibid.*

modifications regarding creatures that are *clearly* human. Some Christians allow the policeman and the soldier to kill, and the state to carry out capital punishment. In short, unless one is a thoroughgoing New Testament pacifist, there are times when it is *permissible* to snuff out human life. The same then would apply to the fetus. The worldwide trend is clearly in the direction of adopting laws that reflect this conviction. Regardless of his own personal beliefs and behavior, the Christian ought not to oppose the liberalizing of laws on sterilization and abortion.

In cases of rape, incest, or disease that might lead to physical and/or mental deformity, the right to abortion cannot be denied. Likewise, the alarming increases in illegitimacy in our own society could be sharply curtailed if abortion and sterilization were readily available. It is not that the Christian condones premarital sex, but unless and until the majority of people adopt a Christian sex ethic, something must be done immediately to relieve the conditions which spawn the cycle of poverty, the ghettoes, and the ensuing misery and urban violence. The same threat of overpopulation among the underprivileged affects not only the U.S., but the whole world. And infinitely more important is the right of the child himself to be a *wanted* child. It is the *rejected* child who in turn often rejects society and brings grief to both it and him.

The Christian Family and Control of Fertility

Having submitted that the Christian should not impose his ethics on society apart from individual regeneration, whether they involve abortion, divorce, alcohol, or whatever, the question then becomes personal: What guidelines govern the Christian's own personal behavior in this realm?

A core issue here is the Christian's view of God's sovereignty and man's responsibility. Some who feel that they should submit to the inscrutable will of God would not even use medicine, since this might be thwarting certain of God's purposes learned only by suffering. Others might use medicine but feel that contraception is an attempt to frustrate God's will, and thus they trust to God to send as many or as few children as He wills. Still others who use contraception but happen to fail once or more often feel that once conception has occurred they should trust God for whatever happens next.

But like the use of medicine or contraception, I am persuaded that the decision to abort or to sterilize is a matter of Christian liberty. In any of these areas, "he who doubts is condemned," as Paul says, because "he does not act from faith" (Rom. 14:23). But in the case of abortion, if the couple is convinced the fetus is not human or if certain conditions warrant its termination, it then becomes legitimate (where legal) as a method of fertility control.

In weighing this kind of decision, there are three basic factors for the Christian family to consider. First, the husband-wife relationship. Will an additional child, if unwanted, be detrimental to that relationship for whatever reason? Second, the personal health of the principal individuals involved, viz., father, mother, and especially the child. Does any child deserve to be brought into the world and not be wanted? This, of course, is a principal argument for contraception, and it applies with equal force to these other forms of birth control. This is also a strong argument for abortions among unmarried girls. Third, what will be the effect on children already in the family? Will an additional child be detrimental to relationships with them, or perhaps hinder their personal development? Moreover, husbands and wives should arrive at this kind of decision *democratically* with each other. They should pray much and consult often with compassionate Christian friends.

In sum, as with the issue of the contraceptive technique of birth control, the Christian family must determine for itself whether an additional child might hinder its corporate and individual task to serve God in the world. On the answer to this question should hinge its decision whether or not to employ abortion or sterilization.

Chapter 17

THE POPULATION EXPLOSION: WORLD AND LOCAL IMPERATIVES

SUMMARY

Donald H. Bouma, Professor of Sociology at Western Michigan University, presents a brief historical and statistical survey of world population problems, with a look at some of the proposed remedies. The major attention is given to population problems affecting North America, and the United States in particular. The growth of population in various socio-economic levels is considered, with emphasis on the negative sociological and personal effects of uncontrolled human fertility. High rates of infant mortality, debilitating illness, juvenile crime and the "battered child syndrome" are seen to correlate with rapid growth of population.

The author concludes with a plea for the support of programs of family planning by all who are concerned for the improvement of society. Because the newer methods of fertility control require the involvement of the physician, it is especially important that he be aware of the problems and helpfully committed to seeking a solution.

DONALD H. BOUMA, A.B., M.A., Ph.D. *Dr. Bouma joined the faculty of Western Michigan University as Associate Professor of Sociology in 1960. He was appointed Professor in 1963 and has since served in that capacity. He holds degrees from Calvin College (A.B.), The University of Michigan (M.A.), and Michigan State University (Ph.D.). He has also taught at Calvin College and Michigan State University. Dr. Bouma has served as President of the Michigan Sociological Society and the Family Service Association.*

With particular research interest in the urban racial crisis, he has written a recently published book, The Dynamics of School Integration.

THE POPULATION EXPLOSION: WORLD AND LOCAL IMPERATIVES

by Donald H. Bouma

INTRODUCTION

The problem of population quantity is a mosaic of complexities involving the whole spectrum of individual and group behavior. Demographic factors are intertwined with a plethora of other factors: transportation, migration, health services, poverty, racial friction, agricultural production, cybernation, religion, industrial changes, world power struggles, employment, education, family problems, housing, malnutrition, disease, mental illness, abortion, and many more.

Ever since Thomas Robert Malthus, the Anglican clergyman, first zeroed in on the problem in 1789, in his classic *Essay on Population,* there has been sporadic attention to the matter of numbers of people. Malthus posited a conflict between man's desire for food and his desire for sex and concluded, without empirical validation, that the food supply expanded arithmetically while the population expanded geometrically. Recently, the problems of one country were succinctly put in this nutshell: the limited fertility of the soil and the unlimited fertility of the people.

Through time the growth of numbers has been viewed as bane or boon, depending on the dominant cultural values of time and place. When viewed as desirable, because of the needs of a growing economy or in terms of military or geographical expansion, positive policies were formulated including direct and indirect subsidies for children and the courting of immigrants. When quantity increases were viewed as undesirable, because of pressures on subsistence or problems of congestion of one sort or another, negative policies were formulated involving birth control, sterilization, abortion and the banning of immigration.

Today the problem of accelerated demographic increase, with negative ramifications both world-wide and local, has high cynosure. While some focus attention on the resultant complications for the collectivity, whether it be the world community or the crowded inner-city, others emphasize the hazards to individual welfare. Here attention will be given to two aspects of each.

THE WORLD PROBLEM

First, there is the population explosion in world perspective. It is difficult to describe in a meaningful way what is happening. One can say that at the turn of the century the world's population will exceed 7½ billion, but what is that supposed to tell me? While I cannot imagine what a billion is, I am daily insensitized to the concept by repeated reference to a multi-billion dollar national debt.

Or one can say that, at the present rate of growth, by the year 2050 there will be only a foot of land left for each person, or that by the year 3050 or so the earth will cave in from the weight of people. While this may or may not be so, it hardly motivates one to go out and do something about it today.

There are several ways of describing what is going on today which may be insightful. It took from the beginning of history to 1830 for the world to get its first billion people. It took from 1830 to 1930 to get the second billion, but only from 1930 to 1960 to get the third billion. By 1966 there had been added another half billion.

The world population is growing at about 2% per year. Had this rate existed from the time of Christ to now, there would be about 20 million people in the place of each person now alive, or 100 people to each square foot on this earth. Each day there is a net gain of 190,000 people in the world, as 330,000 are born and 140,000 die. Roughly the world birth rate is 40 per 1,000, while the death rate is 20 per 1,000. This is the basic ingredient of the population explosion.

It is important to note that the high rate of population growth is not the result of a rising birth rate, but of a markedly declining death rate. The headlong rush toward saturation of the earth with humanity is a consequence of modern science which increasingly defers death. It may be said that the population explosion results from the fact that there has been a vigorous attack by modern science on the outgo (death) segment of the demographic formula, without corresponding attention to the input (births) segment.

Meanwhile, true to the Malthusian theory, world food production has not kept up. In spite of increased efforts in the last decade, world food production is increasing at only 1% per year while world population is increasing at something just over a 2% rate. A leading church official has suggested that the challenge is to set more places around the dinner table of the world rather than reducing the number of guests. Obviously the problem is not only to find room for more place settings, but more food to put on the plates—or fewer guests.

THE AMERICAN PROBLEM

The second social aspect of the population explosion manifests itself in the inner city where the highest birth rates occur in those segments of our communities which are most problem-producing. A foreign student once said, "America is a funny place; all of the big families live in little houses, and the little families live in big houses."

Social Results

Ameliorative programs aimed at the problems of the blighted inner city are vitiated by the steady stream of additions to the problem-prone populace. In one midwestern community of over 200,000 population, studied by the author over the last two decades, the following was found to exist in two census tracts in the inner-city as compared to the city as a whole: perinatal death rate, twice as high; neonatal death rate, twice as high; illegitimate birth rate, 7 times as high; infant death rate, 125% higher; relief load, 10 times as high; tuberculosis rate, 4 times as high; syphilis rate, 10 times as high; gonorrhea rate, 20 times as high; over-all crime rate, 10 times as high. And, importantly, a live birth rate 50% higher than the city rate.

While blighted areas constituted only 15% of the land area in this community, 30% of the people lived there and produced 55% of the adult crime rate, 75% of the juvenile delinquency, and 75% of the multiple-problem families known to social agencies. The community invested $13 in tax dollars for every $1 in taxes received from that area, to say nothing of the charitable dollars invested in the area. One of the four major hospitals in the city indicated that in 1965 close to $60,000 in maternity costs were not collected by it because of the poverty status of the family and its inability to qualify for support from any public program.

Add to all of this the fact that a considerable percentage of the children born in the inner city were unwanted by the parents, and the population explosion takes on a new and close-to-home meaning. The National Academy of Science reports that in any given year 32% of the white and 43% of the non-white couples in the inner city bear unwanted children. It is today a well-documented fact that the proportion of women stating that they have more children than they want rises as one goes down the scale of family income. The lower the income, the higher the proportion of families with unwanted children.

These two sets of facts cry out for public attention; the areas of our communities which produce most of our irritating problems have the highest birth rates, and these same areas have the highest percentage of births of unwanted children. This presents one of those rare situations where the needs of the community and the needs of the individual can be met by the same program—the control of births.

The relationship between high birth rates and poverty, especially generational poverty, is well established. Sociologist Harold Sheppard in his recent monograph, "Effects of Family Planning on Poverty in the United States" (published by the Upjohn Institute of Employment and Community Research, Kalamazoo, Michigan), found that 33% of all families with five children are poor and 43% of all families with six or more children are poor. For every 100 poor persons age 22 through 64 (prime working ages) there are 148 children, in sharp contrast to 79 among the non-poor.

Dr. Sheppard concludes that high birth rates among the poor are not merely a result of poverty, but are a cause of poverty. If the poor have fewer children, those children who are born will have a greater chance of moving out of poverty in their adult lives. In addition, by virtue of having fewer children, many heads of families themselves will move out of poverty.

At the present time it costs something in excess of $7,000 to raise a child to age 17 under the Aid to Dependent Children program, assuming there are no unusual problems. Sheppard estimates that for every $1 spent on family planning there would be a saving of $70 in public money. He figures that savings on reduced public expenditures (for maternal health care, child health care, care of mental retardates, aid to dependent children) and on greater incomes possible if children are spaced, would amount to $700 million, compared with $10 million for family planning.

Too often we think of the problem as one that affects faceless millions many miles and oceans away, but the threat to the well-being of our own communities and our own pocketbooks is a clear and present one. In the past 20 years we have spent more than $40 billion in welfare payments, yet there are more people on welfare today than ever before —and there will be still more tomorrow.

There will be still more tomorrow for many reasons, including the growth factor in our population, the greater awareness on the part of the public of the unmet needs among the poverty group, and the increased knowledge on the part of the poor of various governmental helping programs that are available. Mass media documentaries, particularly the recent and controversial CBS special on the conditions of the poor in four areas of this country, have brought millions of Americans closer to the problem than ever before.

Increasingly effective pressure on the part of the black militant movement and white Action Now groups, dramatized by Resurrection City and the Poor People's March in Washington, has resulted in an acceleration of change in both governmental and voluntary aid programs. Further, these groups have been effective in communicating to the "unreachable" poor, or the "invisible poor" as Michael Harrington called them, information about the aid programs now available and in getting them to make use of them. Partially as the result of this there have been sharp increases in welfare case loads throughout the country.

An ideological change is also involved here. Increasingly public welfare is being viewed not as a temporary expedient to meet some crisis, but as a basic right. Since it is a right, it is asserted, the government should place few or no restrictions or prerequisites. The fact of need is all that matters. Guaranteed annual income and negative income tax plans are consonant with this philosophy.

While billions of tax dollars are spent in an attempt to cope with the results of the problem of over-population, relatively little is appropriated to attack the cause. The 1969 budget calls for $3 billion for welfare grants to the states, in addition to the billions raised in taxes by the states themselves. However, only a little over 1% of this figure (about $35 million) is set aside for domestic population control.

Personal Results

Earlier we noted that the population explosion had two collective implications, which we have just considered, and two personal implications. The latter involve the problem of the burdened mother on the one hand and that of unwanted children on the other.

There is no way of measuring the amount of suffering experienced by mothers burdened by excessive progeny, where children are a curse instead of a joy, and childbearing is a tribulation instead of a blessing. The records of family planning clinics are replete with individual cases of physical, mental and emotional suffering. The rejected child, the abandoned child, and the battered child not infrequently are tragic testimonials to the burden of the too-often-pregnant mother.

It is only recently that we have become aware of the battered child syndrome and it was only in 1961 that the American Academy of Pediatricians first scheduled a symposium on this topic. While we have only scratched the surface in our etiological studies of the battered child, we do know that in many of the more severe cases which come to court attention a mother burdened with excessive pregnancies is involved. In one medium-sized midwest community three cases came to court attention in a six-month period.

>1) Mother A, having just borne her sixth child in six years, choked the baby, lit a charcoal fire and broiled it, and finally abandoned it in an open field. This middle-class mother with a stable marriage was not prosecuted because the prosecutor stated that it could not be determined which of the three acts resulted in the death of the child.
>
>2) Mother B, a meticulous housekeeper, found the fifth child in five years too much to cope with, but took out her hostility on the middle child. When the boy smeared his feces on the newly-cleaned bathroom wall, the mother swung him by the ankles, bashing his head against a door sill. Convicted of manslaughter, the mother was imprisoned.
>
>3) Mother C systematically starved her unwanted child over an extended period of time almost to the point of death. Eighteen months of hospital care was necessary before the child had adequately recovered to be placed in a foster home. Prosecution in this case failed because intent could not be proven. It is interesting to note that in none of these cases was insanity used as a defense.

Finally, there is the problem of the child who is unwanted and is told that in ways both subtle and blatant. Last Christmas season a newspaper did a feature series on families in poverty. The father of one of the families, shown in an adjoining picture with his wife and 14 children, was quoted for all to read in the paper: "I haven't wanted a one of them since the fifth, and after the ninth child I put my foot down and said that's enough." (He obviously learned that that is one of the least effective methods of birth control known to man.)

Not all unwanted children get to know they are unwanted in such a blatant way. However, our courts, clinics and institutions are filled with children who, somehow or another, get to feel quite correctly that no one wants them. Any fundamental attack on the problem of rapidly accelerating juvenile delinquency and crime rates will have to focus on the high production rate of unwanted children. We noted earlier that 32% of the white and 43% of the non-white couples in high delinquency areas bear unwanted children in a given year. Our lethargic efforts to help lower-class families get the same family planning information that the middle-class families have is another indication that our communities have just about as much crime and delinquency as they deserve. "Every child a wanted child" is more than a slogan. It is a realizable goal with beneficial consequences for communities, families and individuals.

CONCLUSION

Programs for family planning through birth control have been surrounded by controversy down through time. The opposition of church groups is today of no real consequence. Practically all major Protestant groups, who once had issued negative denominational statements, today align themselves with the family planning movement both theoretically and in active support. Whereas just a few years ago there was an unwillingness among Catholic church leaders to speak of "population explosion" and "family planning", and much insistence that the problem was one of food production and distribution, today there is much ferment over the issue.

Changes in the traditional position of the Catholic church

are being studied at the highest levels. Research in this country and elsewhere has found that Catholic couples use contraceptive devices to about the same extent found in the general population. Family planning clinics under church auspices are being organized both here and abroad, although limited to use of rhythm techniques. Catholic leaders, both lay and clergy, have been helpful in many cases in setting up new public birth control programs in health and welfare departments.

Fears about deleterious medical side affects of the pill have by now generally been placed in proper perspective. The most significant study of this problem to date was the British study reported in the British Medical Journal, April 27, 1968, in which it was shown that a woman on the birth control pill is more prone (although the likelihood is still extremely slight) to develop clots in blood vessels. The study found that the incidence of fatal outcome from use of the birth control pills is 1.2 per 100,000 users per year in the age group 20–34, and rises to 3.4 per 100,000 users in the 35–44 age group.

However, as Dr. Alan F. Guttmacher points out in Bulletin No. 32 of Planned Parenthood-World Population (May 20, 1968), one must take into account the risk of death from pregnancy and delivery in exactly the same groups of women. The risk for the 20–34 age group is 22.8 per 100,000 and for the 35–44 age group it is 57.6. This means that having a baby carries 18 times the risk of the pill in the younger age group and 17 times the risk in the older.

The newest area of controversy regarding family planning involves the opposition of the black power movement. Although previously held myths that lower-class Negroes were not interested in limiting births and that they lacked the discipline and foresight to maintain the regimen of a contraceptive program have been disproven by actual experience in programs both in this country and abroad, the opposition of black militants is increasingly being felt as that movement gains strength. The National Black Power Conference in Baltimore in June, 1967, officially opposed birth control programs. Reasons given for this opposition generally concern the imposition of white middle-class standards on the black community, the white desire to limit the number of "us beautiful blacks", and the desire of whites to use birth control as an easy way to solve the basic problems of society. Just how intensive and effective this opposition gets to be remains to be seen at this time. Right now other black power goals have higher priority than the one opposing family planning.

Mounting concern for the twin problems of over-population and the unwanted child is apparent at all levels, local, national and world-wide. Public policy and private attitudes concerning the problems have changed so drastically in so few years so that it is more of a revolution than just a trend. Interacting with this, as both cause and effect, are the technological and medical advances in the birth control area. In mid-1968 a major pharmaceutical company announced that it was ready to market a long-term birth control injection, effective for three months. On-going research suggests other significant developments in the near future.

Never before in history has the medical profession occupied such a critical role in determining the future course of events. While the older birth control techniques did not involve a doctor, all of the newer ones do. In the past our medical proficiency has been ever more effectively used to bring down the death rate. From both a social and personal perspective, the birth rate calls for similar attention today.

Chapter 18

GENETICS, SOCIETY
AND THE FAMILY

SUMMARY

V. Elving Anderson, Professor of Human Genetics at the University of Minnesota, outlines the present state of knowledge of human genetics as related to reproduction. The author describes the functioning of the DNA in the development of the fetus. The development of the blood and the nervous system are cited as examples where development of genetic disorders could have a major disabling effect.

Specific disorders are noted in which it is possible to predict with considerable accuracy whether a child born to a given set of parents will be effected. The possibility of genetic control is given extensive consideration, both in its positive and negative aspects. The Christian ethical and moral problems arising out of this possibility are discussed. Dr. Anderson sets forth principles on which individual and social decisions may be based.

V. ELVING ANDERSON, B.A., Ph.D. *Professor Anderson is Assistant Director and Professor of Human Genetics at the Dight Institute of Human Genetics, the University of Minnesota. He is a frequent contributor to scholarly journals. From 1946 to 1960, Dr. Anderson taught at Bethel College, St. Paul, Minnesota.*

GENETICS, SOCIETY AND THE FAMILY

by V. Elving Anderson

INTRODUCTION

The topic of "genetic control" has attracted a good deal of public attention as well as apprehension.[1] Some of the more speculative treatments of the topic have minimized the current gaps in our knowledge and may have contributed to a spirit of arrogant trust in the capabilities of science. They have also awakened the fear that some person or group might use technological advances in an authoritarian manner.

Although the possibility of misuse must be acknowledged, an awareness of future threats should not be permitted to obscure the need for a realistic and fair appraisal of problems right at hand. Genetic control does not have to be authoritarian. As Davis has pointed out, "When authors in

---

[1] Anderson, V. Elving. 1966. The control of man's genetic future. *J. Amer. Sci. Affil.* 18:97–101.

liberal societies wish to satirize genetic control, they depict the eugenic utopia as composed of hereditary castes; when they are serious about it, they depict the utopia as democratic." [2]

The primary concern of the physician must be for the individual who seeks his help, but the issues raised in this symposium can be viewed from other perspectives as well. For this reason some of the relevant genetic ideas are here considered under the three major functions of science: To explain, to predict, and to control.

GENETIC EXPLANATION

The development of any organism requires raw materials, energy, and information. The genetic material (DNA) forms the information which guides the division of cells and their subsequent differentiation into tissues and organs. It does this primarily through specifying the sequence of amino acids as they are fitted together to form one type of protein or another. Some proteins serve as structural components of cells, while others act as enzymes to regulate further chemical reactions. Thus, twenty different amino acids can be put together in different combinations to form hundreds of different proteins.

Genetic variability is responsible for many of the differences among individuals. In the blood, for example, both red cells and white cells have distinguishable blood types. Genes control the presence of enzymes in the red cells, the globulins essential for disease resistance, the factors necessary for clotting, and the proteins in the plasma that carry copper and iron. The role of genes in the development of the nervous system is shown by the existence of more than seventy-five different genetic disorders that can lead to severe mental re-

[2] Davis, Kingsley. 1966. Sociological aspects of genetic control. pp. 173–204 in *Genetics and the Future of Man*, ed. by J. D. Roslansky. New York: Appleton-Century-Crofts.

tardation. Some idea of the extent of genetic variability is seen in a recent listing of over 1500 human traits that follow a simple mode of inheritance.[3]

There is growing evidence that many aspects of human behavior may be conditioned by genes. A number of studies have demonstrated a strong familial tendency for schizophrenia. The possibility that this tendency is at least partially genetic is strengthened by the fact that biochemical alterations can induce psychosis-like states. More recently we have learned that an extra "Y" chromosome in males is associated with mild mental retardation combined with aggressiveness and other personality changes.

Nevertheless, there is no evidence for genes in man which rigidly specify behavior patterns. It is more reasonable to expect genetic differences in the way individuals respond to the various environmental forces during their growth and development. Identical twins show many similarities in mannerisms and other behavioral traits, but their DNA does not fully specify the uniqueness of each co-twin as a consciously responding individual.

Perhaps more relevant to our topic is the use of the "DNA dogma" to resolve questions about abortion. Hardin has argued that a set of blueprints is not a house; similarly the DNA of a zygote is not a human being. A key-point in his argument is that "a non-unique copy of information that specifies a valuable structure is itself almost valueless." [4] The DNA in a zygote is only a promise of things to come if the cell is nurtured and development is allowed to proceed. He recognizes that each zygote is unique, but concludes that the loss of a given zygote need not be a source of great concern, since liveborn children represent only an extremely small proportion of all possible zygotes.

[3] McKusick, Victor A. 1968. *Mendelian Inheritance in Man*, second ed. Baltimore: The Johns Hopkins Press.

[4] Hardin, Garrett. 1967. Blueprints, DNA, and abortion: A scientific and ethical analysis. *Med. Opinion & Review* 3:74–85.

Human ova are extremely complex cells, and they are already partly formed within the body of a newborn girl. The cytoplasm has a complex architecture with many types of structures, but the various enzyme systems are kept inactive. Years later when an ovum is released and fertilization occurs, the enzyme systems are released and a number of metabolic changes are rapidly initiated. Selected portions of DNA are "turned on" and begin to control the sequence of events. The developing embryo attaches itself to the lining of the uterus; although it is not yet understood why the strange tissue is not rejected as transplants would be. Early in development the fetus passively exchanges materials with the uterine lining, but progressively the fetus and its supporting membranes become more different. Within the placenta there develop enzymatic transfer mechanisms which pump materials needed by the fetus even though the concentration may be lower in the maternal blood supply.

A number of fetuses (perhaps as many as half) are lost through spontaneous abortion. Of those recovered in the earlier stages about ⅓ are found to have some gross chromosomal defect. Thus, spontaneous abortion can be a natural means of eliminating a defective organism. (It is possible that some types of therapy may prolong the life of a defective fetus and thus lead to a small increase in the frequency of defective liveborn children.) Toward the latter part of gestation, certain genes are turned off while others are switched on, as seen in the gradual change from fetal hemoglobin to adult hemoglobin.

I would conclude that it is more accurate to say that the zygote is potentially human than that it is fully human. Initially it is completely dependent upon the mother. As development proceeds, the fetus becomes increasingly more different from (and independent of) the mother. Our knowledge of DNA has greatly improved our understanding of the *mechanisms* involved, but it does not resolve finally the question as to the *value* of the zygote or the fetus.

GENETIC PREDICTION

The presence of a child with a serious malformation or genetic disease poses a specific problem to a family. If a couple is to make free and responsible decisions concerning future pregnancies, they should have: 1) The best information currently available about the genetic risks involved, 2) An interpretation of this information so that they can understand and accept it, and 3) Techniques for restricting conception if they so decide.[5]

The estimate of risk for the next pregnancy requires an accurate diagnosis and adequate information about the family medical history. If the condition clearly fits a genetic disease with known pattern of inheritance, the risk follows a theoretical probability based on the recombination of genes, usually 25 per cent or 50 per cent. If the pattern of inheritance is less clear, it is necessary to use "empirical risk" figures determined by studying a number of families with similar problems.

Some specific illustrations may help. Recently a 25-year-old man learned that his mother and two of her sisters had developed Huntington's chorea. A long letter from a neurologist made the diagnosis sufficiently clear. Genetic theory indicates that there is a 50 per cent chance that he has received the deleterious gene from his mother and will develop the condition. The man and his wife already have a 26-month-old child, who now has a 25 per cent risk of becoming affected. They have concluded that they wish to have no more children under these circumstances.

In another family with eight children, three were affected

---

[5] Reed, Sheldon C. 1964. *Parenthood and Heredity*. New York: John Wiley & Sons.

with cystic fibrosis, and one of these has died. All cases of cystic fibrosis appear to follow an autosomal recessive mode of inheritance, and the risk for the next (and each subsequent) pregnancy would be 25 per cent. Both the mother and father carry a "hidden" gene, and each affected child by chance received a "double dose."

The predictions for Down's syndrome (mongolism) are somewhat more complicated, since they are based upon empirical risks rather than genetic theory. In 95 per cent of the cases, the condition results from an extra chromosome, and the risk for another pregnancy is 2 to 3 per cent. In the remaining 5 per cent of the cases one chromosome has become attached to another in the form of a "translocation." In the translocation type the risk in a subsequent pregnancy is about 20 per cent for another affected child, 40 per cent for a child who is normal but carries the translocation, and a 40 per cent chance of a completely normal child.

The physician who makes the diagnosis of a genetic disease has the primary responsibility for seeing that the parents are informed of the genetic implications. The services of a geneticist as consultant may be helpful, particularly if the laboratory data are equivocal, or if the family history appears to contradict the provisional diagnosis. The parents may wish to consider other religious, emotional, or financial factors, but the final decision must be theirs.

GENETIC CONTROL

Three types of conscious genetic control are possible: 1) We can change the effect of genes through medical treatment. 2) We can change the frequency of genes. 3) At some time in the future it may become possible to add or modify genetic material.

1) The ability to control the effect of genes is part of the growing practice of medicine. For a few conditions there are special diets with reduced levels of the specific dietary com-

ponent that the body is unable to handle. In cystic fibrosis the
regular administration of pancreatic enzyme alleviates a significant part of the problem. For Huntington's chorea tran-
quilizers reduce some of the neurological signs, but do not
appear to slow the progressive deterioration. These advances
in "environmental engineering" are extremely beneficial to
families with affected children, but they do not replace efforts to prevent the occurrence of the problems. The treatments are seldom fully effective, and they require careful
monitoring to prevent over-control and possible damage.

2) A second avenue is to reduce the frequency of genes and
of deleterious genetic combinations. When parents learn
that there is a sizable risk of producing another child with
a serious defect, the responsible approach on their part is to
consider setting aside the privilege of further reproduction
in order to protect the "rights" of children to be born with
reasonably good health. This voluntary decision to forego
further reproduction will also make a modest contribution to
reducing the frequency of genetic carriers in the population.

The significance of such a choice was emphasized by the
late Pope Pius XII: "Better warned of the problems posed
by genetics and of the gravity of certain hereditary diseases,
men of today have, more than in the past, the duty to take
account of this increased knowledge so that they might forestall countless physical and moral difficulties for themselves
and others. They should be attentive to whatever could cause
lasting harm to their descendants and involve them in an
interminable succession of miseries." [6] The action of couples
in taking a chance when there is one chance in four of having
a seriously defective child is described by Paul Ramsey as
"genetic imprudence" and "gravely immoral." [7]

[6] Pope Pius XII: Discourse to the International Congress on
Blood Transfusion, September 5, 1958. *Dight Inst. Bull.* 11:9–21.

[7] Ramsey, Paul. 1966. Moral and religious implications of genetic
control. pp. 109–169 in *Genetics and the Future of Man*, ed. by J. D.
Roslansky, New York: Appleton-Century Crofts.

The means whereby a couple may restrict their own reproduction for genetic reasons include conception control,
sterilization, and abortion. The desirability of conception
control under such circumstances does not appear to need
further justification. Even Pope Pius XII stated that if both
husband and wife are found to carry "Mediterranean hema-
tologic disease" they may be dissuaded from having children
but not forbidden.[8] (He insisted, however, that such control
involve only use of the rhythm method.)

When there is a 25 per cent or higher risk of a severe
genetic defect the couple may prefer voluntary sterilization
rather than run any risk at all. In the case of Huntington's
chorea mentioned above, this would most appropriately involve the husband with the family history of the condition.
In cystic fibrosis, either husband or wife could be sterilized,
since both are assumed to be carriers. Sterilization is also
used by couples approaching the age of 40, a period when the
risks of defects in a child begin to increase.

Involuntary sterilization is a more complex problem. Yet
there are circumstances when a child is irreversibly retarded
and for whom reproduction may be possible but who will be
unable to care for any offspring. Under adequate legal safeguards, the parents or guardians should be able to exercise
their responsibility for the child by arranging for sterilization.

If conception control is attempted but fails, a sizable risk
for a severe genetic defect would appear to constitute a
reasonable fetal indication for abortion. Recently this option
has been further refined by the development of techniques
for prenatal diagnosis. This raises the possibility of selective
abortion, which can save the life of normal fetuses. The
diagnosis of Down's syndrome, for example, can be made by
a chromosome study of fetal cells obtained from the amniotic
fluid. A couple faced with the prospect of a second child with

---

[8] Pope Pius XII, *op. cit.*

translocation Down's syndrome might request a therapeutic abortion. Now they can be encouraged to wait until a firm diagnosis can be made, with an abortion only if the fetus has a mongoloid chromosome pattern. The techniques of prenatal diagnosis are being extended to genetic *biochemical* defects as well.

3) A third possible means of genetic control is the modification or addition of genetic material (genetic engineering). It would be extremely difficult to locate a specific gene and change it in a desired direction (a directed mutation). It would appear simpler to add extra DNA of the desired type by adaptation of the techniques used for DNA transfer in micro-organisms. One possibility for the future may be to prepare a virus able to infest human cells and use it as a carrier for the new DNA. Lederberg has described this as "genetic modification by viral therapy" and has compared the procedure to vaccination.[9] A more immediate prospect is to treat genetic defects in liver enzymes by a liver transplant, leaving the child's own liver intact.

FREEDOM AND RESPONSIBILITY

It may be helpful to stress the sequential nature of decisions concerning reproduction. A couple may start marriage with some initial assumptions as to the number of children they wish to have. But after each pregnancy, the new decisions will be altered by the reproductive experience and other factors up to that time. The basic problem is how to respect the freedom of the individual couple while protecting the reasonable interests of the broader society.[10]

Every culture places some restrictions upon the freedom to marry and reproduce, in the form of social pressures as well as legal control. A rapidly expanding population appears

---

[9] Lederberg, C. 1968. An unpublished paper read before the 1968 meeting of the American Society of Human Genetics.
[10] Ingle, Dwight J. 1967. Ethics of genetic intervention. *Med. Opinion & Review* 3:54–61.

to make necessary a more restrictive approach. The more freedom of choice is allowed, the less effective any progress toward a defined goal will be.

On the other hand, a number of countries have developed programs for population control which make the means for birth control available, but do not infringe markedly upon individual rights and freedoms. Similarly, genetic control does not have to be authoritarian. It is imperative to find a way to develop a pattern of genetic control which would be appropriate for a democratic society and for individuals with Christian presuppositions.

I would agree with Scanzoni [10] that there are two essential elements: 1) Responsible decisions concerning the use of conception control, sterilization, and abortion require the freedom implied in Christian liberty. 2) Individual couples, nevertheless, need some guidance as to the factors that should be considered in arriving at such a decision. These two points suggest the need for continuing public education about genetics, improved tests to detect the carriers of harmful genes, adequate facilities for genetic counseling, and modified laws permitting more freedom for couples to choose the appropriate means for restricting reproduction.

The Bible does not say much about conception control, but it does say much about the family. Physicians and other professionals can deal with reproductive problems in such a way as to strengthen the role of the family. For example, it is preferable for a physician or geneticist to discuss the genetic implications with husband and wife together, since both share in the need for understanding.

It is also clear that a Christian view of life is not wholly individualistic but includes the concepts of community and interdependence. A Christian will deny some of his personal rights out of a spirit of love and concern for others. In an

---

[10] See chapter 16, this volume.

area with severe population pressures, insisting upon a large family may appear to be an arrogant demand for the supporting services of society.

In this volume Hughes has argued for an "ethics of genetic duty" which takes the form of "an ethics of self-control, not imposed arbitrarily on society, but self-imposed by the individual on himself (or herself) both inside and outside of marriage." [12] But passive agreement upon this concept may not be sufficient. One of the best ways to reduce the threat of the misuse of genetic information may be to share in efforts to convince Christians and others of the importance of such an "ethics of genetic duty."

Just as we are stewards of God's other good gifts, we are also "stewards of the human gene pool." We wish to preserve our natural resources for our children. It is just as urgent to do what we can to reduce the frequency of genetic disease.

GOALS AND LIMITS

It is far easier to reach a concensus about traits that are harmful and should be reduced in frequency than it is to agree upon goals for positive selection. One of the more thoughtful proposals for positive selection is that by Muller, but treatment of that question goes somewhat beyond the scope of this symposium.[13] However, most biologists would agree that there is no one genetic combination that is best for all circumstances. Variety is biologically desirable, since a variable population is better able to withstand drastic changes in environmental conditions.

It is humbling to realize that we may have to settle for short-term goals. Our children may develop somewhat different ideas, and the developments in science and technology will create new possibilities and problems.

---

[12] Chapter 5
[13] Muller, H. J. 1968. What genetic course will man steer? *Bull. Atomic Scientists* (March) pp. 6–12.

Furthermore, the concepts of population genetics indicate that the total elimination of disease is not biologically possible and therefore is not a live option. When efforts are made to reduce a specific genetic cause of death, the population dynamics are such that over the course of many generations the deaths from this cause will tend to return to their original level. This does not deny the real immediate gain, but points out the arrogance of any claim or assumption that we can wipe out genetic disease in a single generation.

Finally, it is not reasonable to expect that genetic control will guarantee the "fruits of the Spirit" or a utopia without sin. Such an assumption would be quite inappropriate for one who is convinced that God is creator and sustainer of life and that responsibility toward God is the main distinctive of the human state.

SECTION 5

THE LEGAL
FRAMEWORK

Chapter 19

THE LAW AS IT GOVERNS
DECISIONS TODAY

SUMMARY

This article is an overview of the law as it currently governs decisions relating to contraception, sterilization and induced abortion. Historical legal developments and current trends are examined. Significant court cases are given as examples of controversy and precedent. The tensions between the right of privacy and compelling interests of the state are introduced. The author expresses as his opinion that difficult questions about the control of human reproduction are best solved in the legislatures rather than the courts. Doctors have already been subjected long enough to the hazards of too much ambiguity in this field. They are entitled to clarification. The impossibility of predicting what the Supreme Court might do if brought face to face with these issues is underscored in support of the need of legislation in this area.

TOM C. CLARK, A.B., LL.B. *Mr. Justice Clark is at present Director of the Federal Judicial Center, created recently by Congress as a continuing educational institute for federal judges. Justice Clark was nominated Associate Justice of the United States Attorney General, appointed in 1945. He was capacity through June of 1967. Prior to that he had been United States Attorney General appointed in 1945. He was born in Dallas in 1899, graduated from the University of Texas, practiced privately for several years, except for a term as Civil District Attorney for the County of Dallas. In 1937, Mr. Justice Clark joined the Department of Justice as an attorney where he remained until his appointment as Attorney General.*

THE LAW AS IT GOVERNS DECISIONS TODAY

by Justice Tom C. Clark

A study of the statutes of the various states indicates that 46 now specifically permit an abortion to save the life of a pregnant woman. Only four states, Louisiana, Massachusetts, New Jersey and Pennsylvania, have no statutory permission and the courts of two of these, Massachusetts and New Jersey, engrafted exceptions on their statutes. Massachusetts held abortion permissible where the woman's life or health was in great peril; New Jersey found that a physician may act to save a pregnant woman's life. This leaves but two states that bar abortion completely. Commencing in the early part of 1967 a mood for reform brought additional enlargement for medical action in five states. Colorado, North Carolina, California, Maryland and Georgia adopted laws based on the suggestions of the American Law Institute in its

Model Penal Code (1962). It specifically permits an abortion:
1) Where the continuance of the pregnancy might gravely
impair the physical or mental health of the mother; 2) Where
the child will be born with a grave physical or mental defect;
or 3) Where the pregnancy resulted from rape, incest or
other felonious intercourse.

The recent English rule is more liberal than the American
prevailing view. It permits therapeutic abortion in a variety
of circumstances, i.e., consideration of the "actual or reasonably foreseeable environment" of the pregnant woman in
determining whether the pregnancy must be interrupted.

The constitutionality of statutes prohibiting or restricting
an abortion have never been passed upon by the United States
Supreme Court. Any conclusion, even by one whose experience includes 18 years of service on the Court, is purely
speculative. There is no doubt, however, that serious attacks
can be made on such statutes, although they have the support
of history.

The early Hebrews sentenced one to death that destroyed
the foetus. Sparta followed suit. The Oath of Hippocrates is
said to have provided:

> I will use treatment to keep the sick according to
> my ability and judgment but never with a view to
> injury and wrongdoing . . . I will not give to a
> woman a pessary to cause abortion. But I will keep
> pure and holy both my life and my art.

Aristotle hypothesized that at conception the foetus is
vegetable; later it becomes animal and finally it achieves
human status. Thomas Aquinas modified this early view laying the foundation for the original common-law concept that
human life begins with quickening, i.e. when movement by
the foetus is actually felt by the pregnant woman. The quickening is said to occur between the period of fourteen and
twenty weeks of pregnancy.

In Roman Law, however, the foetus was treated as part of

the mother, having no separate human significance. It was said that the child ripens as does the fruit of the tree—only when it falls down.

In English Law abortion was held to be a crime as early as Bracton. In 1766 Blackstone tagged it a "heinous misdemeanour" if performed after the foetus quickened. Few American cases arose during the next 75 years. However, at least four states disapproved abortion after the foetus quickened. The problem caused little controversy until after the Civil War. The groundwork for the present statutes was laid during this period. It was supported by the moral precept that sexual activity was by nature designed to be procreative rather than gratifying.

To interrupt pregnancy was thought to be immoral. The intention of some of the permissive statutes was, therefore, solely to protect the life of the woman. *State* v. *Murphy*, 27 N.J.L 112 (1858). The general rule was to outlaw all abortions performed after conception. This conferred, by inference, a legal status upon the foetus at conception. See *Gleitman* v. *Cosgrove*, 49 N.J. 22 (1967). These statutes made no provision for the performance of an abortion in case of rape, incest or complications that might endanger the woman's life. Nevertheless, a permissiveness was recognized in practice when the pregnant woman suffered from a variety of physical disorders, such as heart disease, tuberculosis, diabetes, etc. However, recent medical developments have reduced the danger of pregnancy to the woman in such cases. This—together with a stronger enforcement policy—has reduced the number of hospital abortions.

As a result of this development, it is claimed that criminal abortions result in the loss of the lives of 10,000 American women each year. From 80 to 90 percent of these are married. On the other hand, only eight to nine thousand legal abortions are performed annually while an estimated two million illegal ones occur. Some claim that one out of every five pregnancies in the United States terminates in illegal abortion. This has possibly brought on the present rash of public controversy. Legislative action has been the chosen instrument of abortion reform. The American Law Institute proposed its Model Penal Code in 1962 and it has the support of the American Medical Association. The Civil Liberties Union proposes that abortions be made legal if performed by a duly-licensed physician. The Roman Catholic Church has taken a strong position against such legalization. Indeed, officially, it is opposed to all means of contraception, save the rhythm method. This has caused some schism in Catholic ranks, the extent of which might prove embarrassing to the hierarchy.

Of late, resort to the courts is advocated and we may well expect cases to arise testing state restrictions under the federal Constitution. However, there is a paucity of cases presently, because of the non-prosecutive policy of local authorities as well as the difficulty of proof. Prosecution of quacks results in pleas of guilty and hence no case law results. Another reason for a failure of cases is the rule as to "standing" which formerly required a party to have a specific interest. However, at the last term of the Supreme Court this rule was largely abrogated. In all likelihood the Court would take jurisdiction of a case raising the question in an appropriate action.[1]

In the area of the First Amendment the Court has gone far in permitting individual action such as in public modes of expression, association and personal political beliefs. The basic guideline as announced in *Bates* v. *Little Rock*, 361 US 516 (1960) is:

---

[1] At this point I emphasize that my discussion of the legal issues reflect my personal views and are not to be construed as reflecting any attitude of the Court or any of its members. Nor should any one assume that my views were formulated from my experience on the Court. The question never arose during my service and I have never discussed it with any of my brethren.

> Where there is a significant encroachment upon personal liberty, the State may prevail only upon showing a subordinate interest which is compelling. At 524.

Earlier, in *Pierce* v. *Society of Sisters,* 268 US 510 (1925), the Court found that Oregon's statute prohibiting parents from sending children to private schools "unreasonably interferes with the liberty of parents and guardians to direct the upbringing and education of children under their control." (At 534–535.) And in 1944, in *Prince* v. *Massachusetts,* 321 US 158, the Court spoke of "the private realm of family life which the state cannot enter." Finally, in *Griswold* v. *Connecticut,* 381 US 479 (1965) the Court declared Connecticut's statute on the use of contraceptives violative of the right to privacy. Specific guarantees in the Bill of Rights, the Court said, have penumbras that give life and substance to their guarantees. The Fourth and Fifth Amendments serve as a protection against all governmental invasions of the sanctity of a man's home and the privacies of life. In its opinion, the Court referred to *Mapp* v. *Ohio,* 367 US 643 (1961) where we held that the Fourth Amendment created a right to privacy, no less important than any other right carefully and particularly reserved to the people. Finding that Connecticut's statute concerned a relationship lying within the zone of privacy created by several fundamental constitutional guarantees the Court struck it down. The Court reasoned that rather than seeking to achieve its goals by regulation of manufacture or sale, the statute prohibited use, thus having a maximum destructive impact. It, therefore, violated the principle that a regulation must not have a sweep which is unnecessarily broad. See *NAACP* v. *Alabama,* 377 US 288, 307 (1958).

Many commentators cite *Griswold* as authority for striking down restrictive abortion statutes. And *Griswold* does speak of the sacred precincts of marital bedrooms and the repulsiveness of Connecticut's restrictions on notions of privacy surrounding the marriage relationship. But as my brother White points out in his concurrence, state interference is permissible only *if reasonably* necessary to the effectuation of a legitimate and substantial state interest and is *not* arbitrary nor capricious in application. And, as my brother Goldberg said in his opinion, judges are not left at large to decide cases in the light of their personal and private notions. Rather, they must look to the traditions and collective consciences of our people in determining which rights are fundamental and therefore protected under the Due Process Clause of the 14th Amendment. The inquiry boils down to whether the right involved is of such a character that it cannot be denied without violating those fundamental principles of liberty and justice which lie at the base of our civil and political institutions. Connecticut's act dealt with a sensitive area of privacy—the marital relation and the marital home. Likewise the Court in *Meyer* v. *Nebraska,* 262 US 390, recognized that the right "to marry, establish a home and bring up children" was an essential part of the liberty guaranteed by the 14th Amendment. Moreover, my brother Goldberg in his *Griswold* opinion asked a significant question: "Would a decree requiring that all husbands and wives be sterilized after the birth of ten children be valid?" And he concludes that it would not because it unjustifiably intrudes upon rights of marital privacy.

My brother Harlan struck down Connecticut's statute because it violated "basic values" which under the Due Process Clause were protected from invasion by the State. There were two dissents in the case, my brothers Black and Stewart.

The question, therefore, narrows to whether the decision to bear or not is a fundamental individual right which is not subject to legislative abridgement. *Griswold's* action was to prevent the formation of the foetus, while abortion is to destroy it. Both deal with procreation in which the state has a vital interest. However, the difference lies in the fact that after the foetus is formed, life is present, and barring unusual circumstances, it will grow and in due course become a human being. At what stage does the state interest become substantial and its restriction reasonably necessary to its legitimate purpose to protect life and the propagation of the human race? If, as I am told, some medical men say life is present at conception, would it be reasonable to protect it from that time forward? If not, at what time would the foetus be subject to state protection—at quickening? It seems that the crux of the problem of control is where does the foetus assume the status of a living human being?

This question is largely controlled by the medical evidence, despite the fact that some states permit recovery of damages for injury to the foetus even when born dead. It is submitted, however, that such a rule would not control the question raised here. Still, it is argued, even the mass of cells must have some life—otherwise there would be no necessity for the abortion. Perhaps it is biologically alive? If so, is it expendable?

These are difficult questions and in my view a court is not the place to get an answer. Control could be the better solved in the legislative arena. There the give and take of accommodation is available. A more flexible rule would be obtainable. The courts are not able to reach out and deal with such reform. The problem reaches the court only in the form of a justiciable issue—a case or controversy. Its decision is directed to the narrow question involved. Its rule is, therefore, narrow and exacting. The legislature, on the other hand, can investigate, hold hearings without evidentiary restriction and enact broad formulae of national application. In addition, in these litigious days the medical profession needs more adequate protection than a case by case method permits. Doctors have already been subjected too long to the hazards of too much ambiguity in abortion law. They are entitled to clarification to which a case by case method would not lend itself.

As a first step the Model Penal Code of the American Law Institute might be the vehicle. It does not sweep so broadly as does the English rule which takes into account the "actual or reasonably foreseeable environment" of the pregnant woman. Nor does it extend to the patient's total environment, actual or reasonably foreseeable, as recommended by the American College of Obstetricians and Gynecologists. Still it is more liberal than any present state law, unless it be North Carolina. Even there the residency requirement is quite restrictive. The present climate seems fair for legislative action. Indeed, five states have enacted liberalizing rules in the last two years. It is to be expected that many more will follow suit. I rather doubt that the courts will interfere in the process.

We now turn to the problem of sterilization. No state has a specific statute banning sterilization. However, Kansas, Utah and Connecticut have general statutes that make it an offense to destroy the power to procreate the human species. These acts, it is submitted, are aimed more at contraception than sterilization. However, the courts of the states have not decided if their broad sweep includes sterilization. I, therefore, raise a *caveat* as to them.

Virginia and North Carolina have specific statutes that permit sterilization. Indeed, in *Buck* v. *Bell*, 274 U.S. 200 (1927) the Supreme Court of the United States permitted Virginia to sterilize the insane under, of course, proper safeguards. The case arose under a factual situation where both the mother and grandmother of the subject had been found mentally defective. Mr. Justice Holmes, in writing for the Court, said that it was better for all the world that instead of waiting to execute degenerate offspring for crime or to let them starve for their imbecility, society can prevent those manifestly unfit from continuing their kind. The principle, he said, that sustained compulsory vaccination is broad enough to cover the fallopian tube. Three generations of imbeciles are enough, he concluded.

On the contrary, however, in *Skinner* v. *Oklahoma*, 316 US 535 (1942), the Supreme Court of the United States struck down a statute authorizing sterilization of habitual criminals defined as any person who has been convicted three times of felonies involving moral turpitude. Certain offenses were specifically excepted from the Act. The case came on against one who had been convicted once of stealing chickens and twice of robbery. It was held in an opinion by my brother Douglas that the statute was violative of the Equal Protection Clause.

Aside from these cases, it appears to me that where one requests sterilization and a vasectomy is performed, no state or federal criminal problem arises with perhaps the exception of the three states above listed. However, if the subject is married, it is suggested that the specific consent of the wife be secured along with her husband's.

Some questions are also posed as to the use of artificial insemination in inducing pregnancy. Some say that it is an act of adultery. I submit that this is hardly true under standard adultery statutes. Certainly the injection of the semen by the husband with the consent of the wife would raise no problems, in the absence of specific prohibitory statute, of which I could find none. The better practice would be to secure the consent of both the husband and wife where an injection is made. Horribles, of course, can be hypothetically posed, such as diseased semen, etc. However, if the usual tests are made of the donor and the semen and they are negative, the doctor would run little risk. This assumes that he would use the ordinary skill and technique followed by current approved practices.

Normal vital-statistic-reporting practices include a statement as to the parents of the child. Would a doctor in a case of artificial insemination perjure himself in signing such a certificate? I doubt it. First, the prosecutor has a large discretion in the adminstration of criminal justice and he would hardly take such a step. Second, the proof would be quite difficult unless abstention from intercourse by the parties was followed during the period. Nor do I believe it necessary that the child be formally adopted by the husband. Having been born in wedlock it is presumed that the child is legitimate. And as to the donor, I submit that he would hardly be accountable for child support under the average circumstances. This is not to say that there might not be unusual cases—horribles we call them—that might support parent-child responsibility.

In closing, it is well to point out that abortion, sterilization and artificial insemination are all in a field that has not yet been explored by legal process. These have been cases on the periphery but they are not controlling. The right to privacy in such intimate personal relations is exceedingly great. The necessity of the state would have to be most compelling to permit an invasion of it. However, if science teaches that beyond doubt the foetus lives from the moment of conception —and that it has human qualities—the decision against a state restriction of its interruption is made quite difficult. If, on the other hand, this not be factually true, the constitutional protection would be nigh absolute—in my view—until the foetus reached that stage when human life was interrupted and destroyed.

As to what the Supreme Court might do, your prediction would possibly be as valid as would mine. I do not engage in this pastime. Having had considerable difficulty in reaching a decision on many questions while sitting there, I know of the many imponderables that go into Supreme Court adjudication. Each Justice does his best, with the tools he has, to build a temple, case by case, that will afford equal justice for all men. It might be well to remember, though, that of the majority in *Griswold* only four now remain on the Court. Hope even among lawyers and litigants springs eternal. In this connection some say that it will continue only to spring until someone brings the Court face to face with it once again.

Chapter 20

THE LEGAL RIGHTS
OF THE FETUS

SUMMARY

Characteristics of the legal process and the legal mind are described, especially as bearing on problems of the control of life. The introduction underlines the fact that in difficult dilemmas the right questions, in themselves, can be illuminating. The first section of the paper is devoted to considerations related to prenatal injury with a critique of traditional doctrines which in the past have blocked just decisions in the courts. Despite the difficulties traced back to unrealistic precedents a recent tide in the direction of allowing recovery for prenatal harm is examined and is supported as a trend with illustrative cases. A discussion of cases bearing on damages to a child when its birth is the result of unwanted pregnancy ensues. The second major part of this paper introduces laws related to abortion. It begins with a description of the extent

370   BIRTH CONTROL AND THE CHRISTIAN

of the problem and continues with a distillation of proposals
made by the American Law Institute in its Model Penal Code.
Subsequent positions adopted by the American Medical Association and the American College of Obstetrics and Gynecology are summarized and their significance is discussed. The
new liberalized statutes of four U.S. states are sketched
and the impact of the Constitution on decisions in this arena
of controversy is shown. The paper concludes with a defense
of the hypothesis that *"good medicine cannot be bad law."*

THOMAS F. LAMBERT, JR., A.B., B.C.L. (OXON.). *At
present Mr. Lambert is Editor-in-Chief of the American
Trial Lawyers Association. He was selected in 1955 by Dean
Roscoe Pound to occupy this prestigious office. Mr. Lambert
graduated with honors in Political Science from U.C.L.A. He
was then awarded a Rhodes Scholarship to Oxford University, England, where he studied jurisprudence and was granted
a B.A. in 1938 and the B.C.L. in 1939. At age 25 he became
the youngest Dean of Law School in the history of American
legal education having been appointed to that position in the
John B. Stetson College of Law. His achievements in the legal
field have been innumerable and cannot be listed here completely. Of special significance, however, are three distinctions: Mr. Lambert was Trial Counsel in the Nuremberg
trials where he prepared the U.S. Trial Brief against the
Nazi Party and against its Chief of Staff under Hitler, Defendant Martin Bormann. Both Party and Bormann were
convicted. He participated in the planning and operational
phases of military government from London to Rhineland
at the end of World War II. He was professor of Law, Boston
University School of Law from 1946–1955.*

THE LEGAL RIGHTS OF THE FETUS

by Thomas F. Lambert, Jr.

INTRODUCTION

Professor Paul A. Freund reminds us that an ancient Chinese curse carried a terrible doom. "May you live," it ran, "in a time of transition." He goes on to assure us that painful as the experience may be, it is apt to be fruitful for the principles of social action.[1] The current religious revolution and the ferment, if not crisis, in law offer a stimulus to enlarge the awareness of moral claims, and sharpen the sensibility to social injustice. Questions are raised specifically as to both the rights of the unborn child and its vulnerability to the pressures for sympathetic recognition of therapeutic abortion.

This paper will focus on two topics—the *law relating to prenatal injury* and the *law of abortion*.

In view of the ferment of our times, the resurgence of "situational ethics," the decline of dogma, ecumenical breakthroughs, future-oriented theology and doctrinal pluralism, the law cannot be expected at this time to yield precise answers to the ethical questions and congeries of cautions

---

[1] Freund, *Civil Rights and the Limits of Law*, 14 Buffalo L. Rev. 199 (Winter 1964).

raised by prenatal injury and abortion. Conferences such as
the New Hampshire Symposium will advance the time and
prospect for such detailed guidance by providing a closer interchange among medicine, theology, and law. Each discipline
helps to clarify the issues in the light of its own experience
and its own ways of thinking, thereby encouraging a mounting consensus, if not a detailed legal code, by contributing
the advantages of cross-lights and cross-fertilization without
the risks of cross-sterilization.

In any such dialogue it is well to understand certain characteristics of the legal process and the legal mind. In the
first instance the law is conservative. Some say that one of
the troubles with lawyers and judges is that "they sit like
the figure on the silver coin, ever looking backward." As part
of its conservatism, the law tends to generalize on the basis
of a balance of risks, as in the collision between fair trial
and free press; or between the individual's right of privacy
and the public's right to know. There is also the dilemma of
a free press in an open society and the interest of public
officials in protecting their reputations against defamatory
statements, resolved by allowing recovery only when the
public official can show "malice" on the part of the defendant.
Other conflicts arise between individual rights and law enforcement; and between civil disobedience and the duty of
law observance.

Not only is the law conservative, but it is deeply solicitous
of human integrity and life. The slightest offensive touching
of another, if not consented to, is an actionable battery re-
dressible in an action for trespass to the person. And since
the ancient case of the tavern keeper's wife [2] who successfully dodged the hatchet cast at her by an irate customer,
juries have been allowed wide latitude in fixing damages in

---

[2] I de S et ux. v. W de S (1348) Y.B. Lib. Assis. f. 99, pl. 60;
(1366) Y.B. 40 Edw. III 40, pl. 19; Prosser, Torts (3d ed. 1964)
37–41.

such "near miss" or "assault" cases. They may give the untouched plaintiff reparation for the indignity and outraged feelings and as a deterrent to such breaches of peace. In short, law is protective of our basic liberties, all those that are central to our civilization, such as bodily integrity, freedom from emotional disturbance, liberty of locomotion, right of privacy, freedom of speech, reputation, family rights, and the right to enjoy property and to do business.[3]

However, there are counterconsiderations that bear closely on our topics. For, if the law is conservative, it is also creative, innovative and responsive. As Dean Roscoe Pound wisely summed it up, "The law must be stable, and yet it cannot stand still." The great mission of the law is to monitor and accommodate the interplay between continuity and change and thereby hold heritage and heresy in fruitful tension. When the time is right, the legal soil is well prepared to bring forth out of the old fields the new wheat.[4] The common law is not a closed system of rules immutable unless changed by legislation. Both courts and legislatures have a responsibility for law reform, a nondelegable duty which extends to the unfinished tasks of rationalizing, updating, and, where necessary, correcting the law relating to both prenatal injury and induced abortion. To state this proposition is merely to attest faith in the common-law tradition which teaches that the life of the law is response to human needs.

---

[3] Seavey, Cogitations on Torts (1954) 304.

[4] Keeton, *Creative Continuity in the Law of Torts*, 75 Harvard L. Rev. 463–509 (Jan. 1962); Keeton, *Judicial Law Reform—A Perspective on the Performance of Appellate Courts*, 44 Texas L. Rev. 1254–68 (July 1966); Peck, *The Role of the Courts and Legislatures in the Reform of Tort Law*, 48 Minnesota L. Rev. 265 (1963); Clark & Trubeck, *The Creative Role of the Judge: Restraint and Freedom in the Common Law Tradition*, 71 Yale L.J. 255 (1961); Pound, Interpretations of Legal History (1923) 1; 3 Pound, Jurisprudence 560–66 (1959); Cardozo, The Growth of the Law (1924); James, *Tort Law in Midstream: Its Challenge to the Judicial Process*, 8 Buffalo L. Rev. 315, 340–44 (Spring 1959); Lambert, *The Jurisprudence of Hope*, 31 ATLA L.J. 29–41 (1965); Lambert, *The Common Law Is Never Finished*, 32 ATLA L.J. 741–800 (1968).

This means that through knowledge and understanding and immersion in the realities of life, law can be made, in Lord Mansfield's phrase, to work itself pure.

What is incontestably clear about the issues of prenatal injury (contemplate the Thalidomide horror and the prospects for the Thalidomide Generation [5]) and abortion ("The Terrible Choice" [6]) is that all the disciplines concerned— medicine, theology, law, ethics, social science—confront anguished issues of extreme delicacy and difficulty. As Karl Barth acutely observed, "A drowning man cannot pull himself out by his own hair." Any and all human beings, whether as subjects, advisers or practitioners, who are caught up in the decisional web of these racking questions need all the help they can get from the professions, and are legitimately claimant on the compassion of all the rest of us. Somebody said, "We are placed on this earth not to see through one another but to see one another through." While there are probably no single-minded, single-sentence solutions to such life-and-death questions as prenatal injury and abortion, by pooling information and insights, and by avoiding the cardinal sin of narrowing specialization—"one-dimensional thinking, all warp and no woof, making for glibness of mind that knows the answers without really knowing the questions" [7] —we can emphasize the spirit of tolerance, the distrust of slogans, a bent toward accommodation of conflicting views and a civilized abidance of the irreducible dissents which cannot be composed.

There is one thing law can do in the joint quest for a principled solution to the problems at hand. It can facilitate the yielding of absolutes where worthy conscientous risks press for acceptance. It can show that the first step to wis-

---

[5] See *Life*, July 26, 1968, 46–64.

[6] *See* The Terrible Choice: The Abortion Dilemma (Bantam Book, April 1968).

[7] Freund, On Law and Justice, (1968) 115.

dom is to recognize that the matching of wooden maxims or granitic dogmas will not produce the principled decision. Then it can search for inner checks and safeguards to be observed by the concerned professions that will mitigate and justify the socially useful risks. For example, the great traditional safeguard of medicine is the disciplined fidelity of the physician to his patient, guided by his dominant therapeutic aim and responsibility, considering the patient as an end and not as a means. Other safeguards come readily to mind in the physician's duty to make a full disclosure to an adult patient of sound mind and stable personality of serious risks arising from contemplated surgery or other treatment, and/ or approval by a higher echelon of medical advice.

Society does not condemn the taking of risks or the subjection of others to risk. Life without risk is like food without salt. We still build our cities on the slopes of Vesuvius. What is condemned and discouraged by law is the creation of unjustifiable, excessive, inordinate, indecent risks—as to which the social judgment is, "the game is not worth the candle."

We know that the automobile is the great meatgrinder of American life. Cars have killed more Americans since 1900 than the death toll of all U.S. wars since 1775. Roughly 24 million cars crashed in 1966 alone, injuring 4 million people, disabling 1,900,000 and killing 53,000. The economic loss caused by this carnage is well over $12 billion a year. Although we can calculate quite accurately the risk of mortality from permitting automobiles to be designed for high speeds and to congest our highways, we take and accept the risk. Just as when we contemplate the risk of loss of lives from explosives used in tunneling or highway construction, or of workmen from falling in the course of building skyscrapers, our social decision is deliberately to elect to take the known risk of loss of life.

Does therapeutic abortion performed under proper medical

safeguards represent a justifiable social risk, e.g., in cases where there is substantial danger that the continuance of the pregnancy would gravely impair the physical or mental health of the mother; when there is substantial risk that the child would be born with grave physical or mental defects; and when the pregnancy resulted from rape, incest, or other felonious intercourse, including statutory rape of girls under 16?

I believe the above represents a proper and pivotal question with respect to the abortion debate.

While a question may be 180 degrees away from presenting its answer, we cherish the insightful reminder of Mr. Justice Frankfurter that the most meaningful answer may well be the question.[8] And it is ancient or at least authenticated learning that education resembles ignition more than injection. As Gertrude Stein lay on her death-bed she spoke feebly to a cluster of friends. "What is the answer?" There was an embarrassed silence. "Well, then," she said, "what is the question?" [9]

If an interdisciplinary dialogue succeeds merely in putting and pondering the most searching questions in the anguished areas of prenatal injury and abortion, it will take a long stride toward putting us on the high road leading to viable and principled social solutions.

PRENATAL INJURY

The Background

Anglo-American courts unfortunately began by denying recovery for prenatal injury or death in the absence of statute. The first case in which the issue arose, in England or

---

[8] *See* the expression of his critically probing philosophy in Larson *v.* Domestic and Foreign Commerce Corp., 337 U.S. 682, 705–6 (1949) (dissent).

[9] Freund, On Law and Justice (1968) 161.

America, was Dietrich *v.* Northampton, 138 Mass. 14 (1884), in which Justice Holmes (later to be elevated to the U.S. Supreme Court) wrote the opinion denying recovery for the child's death. The action for the death of the child was against a city for negligent maintenance of a street, causing the expectant mother to fall and her previable child to be prematurely born and die a few minutes after birth.[10]

Justice Holmes, unable to find any precedent for the action, believed that the common law provided no remedy. It would have been more accurate to say that there was no Anglo-American authority either way,[11] and that the lawsuit merely raised the recurrent, commonplace situation of the "open-and-unprovided" case. If it was enough to deny a remedy or refuse recognition to a legal interest for which no enabling act was on the books and no existing precedent authorized the remedy, then the common law would have remained frozen in its Plantagenet moulds.

When Massachusetts went over the cliff in 1884, it took droves of nay-saying courts from other states with it, *e.g.,* Allaire *v.* St. Lukes Hospital, 184 Ill. 359, 56 N.E.638 (1900) (superb dissent by Justice Boggs which over the years has been a rallying point for the more liberal view); Walker *v.* Great No. Ry., 28 L.R. Ir. 69 (1890) (defendant common carrier owed no contractual duty to the "nonexistent" child in the womb, but only to the mother—conceptualistic jurisprudence with a vengeance). Thus a restrictive rule grew up denying *civil liability* for wrongfully inflicted prenatal injury or death. This immunity or no-duty rule hurled the unborn child into outer darkness, beyond the pale of the law's protection. In a melancholy succession of calamitous cases it ruled in effect that the unborn child, if lucky enough to

---

[10] Viability is that stage of development in the womb when the fetus, if born, is capable of extra-uterine existence, i.e., capable of independent life if prematurely born.

[11] Salmond, Torts 346 (10th ed. Stallybrass, 1945).

escape death in the womb, would have to make his way through life uncompensated, with the seal of the defendant's negligence upon his body.[12]

Criticism of the "No-Liability" Rule

Two main reasons were advanced to support the old restrictive rule refusing to protect from negligent invasion the interest of the unborn child in freedom from bodily harm or death or the interests of the after-born child from the risk of prenatal harm: (1) the aridly formalistic notion that the unborn child is owed no duty of care since, *for purposes of protection from prenatal injury*, it lacks legal personality, and (2) the practical difficulty of proving causation and the resulting fear of spurious suits or faked claims.[13]

As to the first, the lack of a "person" to whom a duty of care may be owed surely should not trouble courts in cases where the child is born alive and suffers after birth the results of the prenatal injury.[14] The term "legal personality" should be defined in relation to the purpose at hand, in terms of consequences as much as essences. The fetus or child in the womb should be treated as a person *for purposes of tort law* whenever that is necessary to prevent injustice. In Thellus-

---

[12] For an excellent history of liability for prenatal harm, beginning with the original denial of recovery and the subsequent spectacular reversal of the negative rule and adoption of the protective rule of liability, see Gordon, *The Unborn Plaintiff*, 63 Michigan L. Rev. 579–627 (Feb. 1965) ; Winfield, *The Unborn Child*, 4 U. Toronto L.J. 278 (1942), also published in 8 Camb. L.J. 76 (1942) ; Prosser, Torts (3d ed. 1964) 354–57; Del Tufo, *Recovery for Prenatal Torts*, 15 Rutgers L. Rev. 61 (1960) ; 2 Harper & James, Torts (1956) 1028–31; 27 ALR2d 1256 (1953) ; 15 ALR3d 992 ("live-birth" doctrine rejected, most courts allowing recovery where prenatal injury results in death of child before birth) ; 35 Cornell L. Q. 648 (1950) ; 63 Harvard L. Rev. 173 (1949) ; 19 NACCA L.J. 230–39 (1957) ; Lintgen, *Impact of Medical Knowledge on the Law Relating to Prenatal Injuries*, 110 U. Pa. L. Rev. 554 (1962) ; 31 ATLA L.J. 178–85.

[13] Harper & James, Torts (1956) 1029.

[14] Prosser, Torts (3d ed. 1964) 355; Herzog, Medical Jurisprudence (1931) §§ 860–975; Malloy, Legal Anatomy and Surgery (1930) 669–687; 1 Gray, Attorney's Handbook of Legal Medicine (3d ed. 1949) 611; and see especially Gordon, *The Unborn Plaintiff*, 63 Michigan L. Rev. 579, 586–97 (Feb. 1965).

son *v.* Woodford, 4 Ves. Jr. 227, 332, 31 Eng. Rep. 117 (1798, 1799), answering a disdainful contention that a child *en ventre sa mère* was a nonentity, Justice Buller said, "Let us see what this nonentity can do. He may be vouched in a recovery, though it is for the purpose of making him answer over in value. He may be an executor. He may take under the Statute of Distributions. He may take by devise. He may be entitled under a charge for raising portions. He may have an injunction; and he may have a guardian." In appropriate cases, the criminal law protects the unborn child and regards it as a separate entity. See, *e.g.,* Clarke *v.* State, 117 Ala. 1, 23 So. 671 (1898) (child born alive died as result of criminal beating of mother; *held,* murder of child). The law of wills and property, as indicated above, considers the fetus in being for purposes which are for its benefit and where justice so requires. As Dean Prosser sums up in his discriminating discussion of the point, "All writers who have discussed the problem have joined in condemning the old rule, in maintaining that the unborn child in the path of the automobile is as much a person as the mother, and in urging that recovery should be allowed upon proper proof." [15]

While in most legal systems, legal personality may begin or be assigned at live birth, this is not a necessary or inevitable state of affairs but reflects that expediency and justice were found to require that imputation. It is emphasized that *for purposes of tort law* protection of the child *in utero* may well commence from the moment of conception,[16] and this without involving the law in the embarrassment of holding that the negligent dropping of a test tube of spermatozoa will expose the careless person to tort liability.

A Texas court has incredibly stated that the reasonable

---

[15] *Cf.* Nekam, The Personality Conception of the Legal Entity (1938) 24; Graveson, Status in the Common Law 111 (1953); C. K. Allen, Legal Duties 28–70 (1931); Dias & Hughes, Jurisprudence 283 (1957) (all cited by Gordon, *The Unborn Plaintiff,* 63 Michigan L. Rev. 579, at 587 (Feb. 1965).

[16] Gordon, *op. cit. supra,* note 15, 579, 586–97 (Feb. 1965).

man "reckons life from the time of birth. His conscious care and solicitude are for the expectant mother and not for the unborn child apart from her." Magnolia Coca Cola B. Co. *v.* Jordan, 124 Tex. 347, 78 S.W.2d 944, 949 (1935). With respect, this bizarre statement strikes one as "nonsense on stilts." As Professor James said of this wayward dictum, "If this amazing statement means that present traumatic injury to a woman cannot reasonably be seen to endanger the foetus or the after-born child, it flies in the face of medical knowledge which is widely shared (in its rough outlines) by laymen. If it is meant in any narrower sense, it misses the point. If I negligently run into a bakery truck, my 'conscious care and solicitude' may be only for the solitary driver, the truck, and the pies. Yet if the back of the truck is filled with children, I am liable to them too if they are hurt. And the improper canning of baby food today is negligence to a child born next week or next year, who consumes it to his injury. The limitation of the *Palsgraf* case [leading case confining scope of duty in negligence cases to those persons or things which are within range of apprehension and thus foreseeably endangered by defendant's conduct] contains no requirement that the interests within the range of peril be known or identified in the actor's mind, or even be in existence at the time of the negligence." [17] It is submitted that the first objection to liability for prenatal injury, based upon doubts as to the legal existence of the child in the womb, is more than met *for purposes of tort law and the right to compensation* by the foregoing arguments, as well as by modern medical-legal principles which recognize the unborn child as a separate entity from the time of conception or viability. Thus legal separability tends to correspond to and accord with biological separability of the child *in utero*.

Difficulty of Proof

The second objection to recovery for prenatal harm, based

---

[17] 2 Harper & James, Torts (1956) §18.3, p. 1030.

upon the asserted difficulty of proof and the concomitant opportunity to fabricate groundless claims, does not justify wholesale denial of all remedy for prenatal harm. The paralyzing fear that to allow recovery for prenatal injury will make of our courts a dumping ground for false claims, because of difficulty of proof, shows a cynical lack of faith in the ability of our courts and juries to sift the false from the true. In the leading case of Woods *v*. Lancet, 303 N.Y. at 356, 102 N.E.2d at 695 (1951), the New York Court of Appeals stated: "The question of causation, reasonable certainty, etc., which will arise in these cases are no different in kind, from the ones which have arisen in thousands of other negligence cases decided in this State, in the past. It is an inadmissible and insupportable concept that uncertainty of proof can ever destroy legal rights." [18]

Incidentally, bearing in mind the gauche and amazing generalization of the Texas Supreme Court in Magnolia Coca Cola B. Co. *v*. Jordan, *supra*, declaring with awe-inspiring error that the reasonable man "reckons life from time of birth," thereby setting up the Q.E.D. of denying all remedy for prenatal harm, it is a pleasure to report that the Texas

---

[18] *See, e.g.*, Dillon *v*. Legg, 69 Cal. Rptr. 72, —P.2d— (Cal. 1968) (California Supreme Court, reversing prior inconsistent cases, upholds right of mother outside area of injurious impact, to recover for psychic injury and shock of witnessing sudden death of her young daughter by negligence of defendant-motorist: "[T]he possibility that fraudulent assertions may prompt recovery in isolated cases does not justify a wholesale rejection of the entire class of claims in which that potentiality arises"); Scott *v*. McPheeters, 92 P.2d 678, 682 (Cal. App. 1939) (similar); Steggall *v*. Morris, 258 S.W.2d 577, 580 (Mo. 1953) (similar); and compare the forthright rejection of the bromidic argument, that all claims should be barred because some may prove groundless, in Justice Crockett's excellent opinion in Samms *v*. Eccles, 358 P.2d 344 (Utah 1961), 26–27 NACCA L.J. 184–87, upholding a complaint for emotional distress caused by defendant's illicit solicitation of sexual intercourse: "To forbid all such actions because groundless charges may be made is not a good reason for denying recovery. That some claims may be spurious should not compel those who administer justice to shut their eyes to serious wrongs and let them go without being brought to account. It is the function of courts and juries to determine whether claims are valid or false, a responsibility which should not be shunned merely because the task may be difficult to perform"); see 28 NACCA L.J. 33, 39–42 (1961–62).

Court has recently re-examined and revised that erroneous conclusion. In Leal *v.* C.C. Pitts Sand & Gravel, Inc., 419 S.W.2d 820 (Tex. 1967), *reversing* dismissal of plaintiff's claim for injury to a viable fetus who lived two days after birth, the court, overruling prior contrary authority and adopting the "contemporary trend" of authority, *held* that a death action was maintainable.[19]

Turning of the Tide—New Majority Rule Allowing Recovery for Prenatal Injuries

The foregoing rather devastating criticisms of the "no-recovery" rule have had their effect, and arguments favoring recovery for prenatal harm have at last borne fruit. Since 1946 the "no-liability" rule has been breached in a series of more than 35 cases, many of them expressly overruling prior negative holdings, thus bringing about the "most spectacular abrupt reversal of a well settled rule in the whole history of the law of torts." [20] Writing in 1964, Dean Prosser could declare with satisfaction, "So rapid has been the overturn that at the time of publication nothing remains of the older law except decisions, not yet overruled, in Alabama, Rhode Island, and Texas." [21] Since 1964, both Rhode Island and Texas have bridged the abyss of the "no-recovery" rule and now protect the unborn child.[22] A scant 22 years ago, immunity for negligently caused prenatal injury was virtually

---

[19] See Personal Injury—Actions, Defenses, Damages ["PIADD,"] "Children," §1.06 (Matthew Bender & Co., 235 E. 45th St., New York, N.Y. 10017).

[20] Prosser, Torts (3d ed, 1964) 355–56.

[21] *Ibid.*, 356.

[22] Sylvia *v.* Gobeille, 220 A.2d 222 (R.I. 1966) (in reversing dismissal of child's action, Rhode Island Supreme Court overruled a 65-year-old inconsistent case and also repudiated the arbitrary "viability" rule, thus extending tort law's protection to even the pre-viable unborn); Leal *v.* C.C. Pitts Sand & Gravel, Inc., 419 S.W. 2d 820 (Tex. 1967) (Texas Supreme Court, reversing prior mistaken rule, holds that where pregnant wife was injured in auto-truck collision and her viable fetus is born alive and then dies from such prenatal injury, defendant is liable).

universal. But since 1946 and the pioneering decision in Bonbrest *v.* Kotz, 65 F.Supp. 138 (D.D.C. 1946), a virtually
unbroken line of cases, a groundswell of reforming jurisprudence, has since held that an infant born alive may sue for
prenatal harm, and that an action for wrongful death will lie
where it dies as a result of such injuries after birth.[23]

In the ground-breaking *Bonbrest* case, *supra,* a trial court
held that an infant born alive had a cause of action for prenatal harm suffered while in a viable state—in that case,
brain damage caused by an obstetrician. The court persuasively reasoned that the unborn child was a separate biological, and hence legal, entity from the mother. The child in
the womb has its own system of circulation, without communication between the circulatory systems of child and
mother; the heartbeat of the child is not in tune with that
of the mother but is more rapid; there is no dependence of
the child on the mother except for sustenance, which would
be true of a 2-year-old child. And the dramatic point was
made that even upon the death of the mother, the child may
be removed from her alive by Caesarian section. In short,
medical science has long recognized the separate existence of
the child from the instant of conception, and its legal existence has been recognized by the criminal and civil law for
all purposes which were to its benefit (such as taking by will
or descent). Therefore, a floodtide of modern cases have concluded there is no convincing reason why tort law should not
take the unborn child within its protective province, for the
purpose at least of redressing unprivileged tortious harms
inflicted upon it by the acts of wrongdoers.

---

[23] Cases are collected in 32 ATLA L.J. 774–75 (1968); 31 *id.* 32–
33; 29 NACCA L.J. 107–12; 26–27 *id.* 143–46; 25 *id.* 156–60; 23 *id.*
117–20; 19 *id.* 230–39; 18 *id.* 376; 16 *id.* 386–91; 13 *id.* 19, 22–23; 9
id. 216–17; 8 *id.* 163–65; 6 *id.* 195; 5 *id.* 277; 10 ALR2d 634 (1949);
27 ALR2d 1256 (1953); Del Tufo, *Recovery for Prenatal Torts,* 15
Rutgers L. Rev. 61 (1960); Gordon, *The Unborn Plaintiff,* 63
Michigan L. Rev. 579 (1965); Lintgen, *The Impact of Medical Knowledge on the Law Relating to Prenatal Injuries,* 110 U. Pa. L. Rev.
554 (1962).

Note that the "no-recovery" rule has even been discredited and excised in Massachusetts, the state of its birth.[24] This indicates that tort law, even in the most conservative states, is not hobbled by a disability at self-correction and can free itself from the fetters of demonstrable error.

Eclipse of Viability Rule

In spite of the repudiation of the "no-liability" rule, two nagging problems have remained to agitate the general subject of recovery for prenatal injuries—the viability problem and the "live-birth" doctrine of recovery for stillbirth as the result of the tortious injury.

The viability rule would limit protection of the unborn child to cases where the fetus is viable, i.e., far enough advanced in fetal life to be capable of independent, extra-uterine life in an incubator if prematurely born.[25] While many, if not most, of the cases allowing recovery have involved a viable fetus, this would appear to be fortuitous happenstance. When actually faced with the issue for decision, most states (a clear majority of those passing on the issue), have allowed recovery even though the injury occurred during the early weeks of the pregnancy, when the child was neither viable nor quick.[26]

---

[24] See Keyes v. Construction Service, Inc., 165 N.E.2d 912 (Mass. 1960), 25 NACCA L.J. 159–60 (Massachusetts Supreme Judicial Court, reversing prior inconsistent cases, holds that an infant born alive could maintain an action for prenatal harm suffered by the child when *viable* in its mother's womb); Torigan v. Watertown News Co., 225 N.E.2d 926 (Mass. 1967) (properly rejects "viability" rule and holds that death action was maintainable where pre-viable (3½-month-old fetus at time of rear-ender auto accident which injured its mother) was fatally injured, born alive, and died 2½ hours after birth).

[25] Dorland, American Illustrated Medical Dictionary (21st ed. 1948) 1616; 1 Gray, Attorney's Handbook of Medicine §58.01 (3d ed. Supp. 1964); Schmidt, Attorney's Dictionary of Medicine 870 (1962).

[26] For collections of cases rejecting the viability rule, see Prosser, Torts (3d ed. 1964) 356–57; 19 NACCA L.J. 230; 23 *id.* 118; 25 *id.* 156–160; 26–27 *id.* 143–46; Note, *Prenatal Injuries and Wrongful Death*, 18 Vanderbilt L. Rev. 847, 852–54 (1965); Note, *Torts: Prenatal Injuries—Viability and Live Birth*, 21 Oklahoma L. Rev. 114

Out of the praiseworthy pack of cases rejecting the viability rule as an unyielding prerequisite of recovery for prenatal harm, perhaps it will be instructive to quote from two. In Smith *v.* Brennan, 157 A.2d 497, 504 (N.J. 1960), the child *in utero* was born with deformity of legs and feet as a result of injuries suffered by his mother and himself in an automobile accident 2 months and 13 days prior to his birth. In *reversing* dismissal of the child's complaint, the New Jersey Supreme Court overruled a prior 1942 inconsistent precedent and added, with respect to the viability rule, that it could see no reason for denying recovery for a prenatal injury because it occurred before the infant was capable of separate existence: "Whether viable or not at the time of injury, the child sustains the same harm after birth, and therefore should be given the same opportunity for redress" (at 504). In the celebrated case of Sinkler *v.* Kneale, 164 A.2d 93 (Pa. 1960), 26–27 NACCA L.J. 143–46, a child was allegedly born a Mongoloid as a result of injuries received when she was a previable one-month-old fetus when her mother was the victim of a rear-ender automobile collision caused by the negligence of defendant-motorist. In *reversing* dismissal of the child's complaint, Justice Bok stated, "The real catalyst of the problem is the current state of medical knowledge on the point of the separate existence of a foetus" (at 95). After pertinently observing that medical authorities have long recognized that a child was in existence from the moment of conception, and not merely a part of its mother's body, he astutely added, "As for the notion that the child must have been viable when the injuries were received, which has claimed the attention of several of the

---

(1968) ("the majority of jurisdictions allow recovery for injury or death occurring during viability" (at 116), citing: 27 ALR2d 1256 (1953) ; 3 ALR2d Later Case Service (1965)) ; Del Tufo, *Recovery for Prenatal Torts: Actions for Wrongful Death,* 1961 Personal Injury Annual 175, 186–92, reprinted from 15 Rutgers L. Rev. 61 (1960) ; Gordon, *The Unborn Plaintiff,* 63 Michigan L. Rev. 579, 586–602 (Feb. 1965).

states, we regard it as having little to do with the basic right to recover, when the foetus is regarded as having existence as a separate creature from the moment of conception. . . . The question is primarily one of medical causation, and since medical proof of that is necessary, we now remove the bars *in limine*" (at 96).[27]

If I plant a bomb in a house which explodes a month after a baby's conception, or if I negligently can baby food which poisons a baby a week or a year thereafter, by fundamental principles of tort law it is no defense to me that the baby was not within the range of peril of my tortious acts at the time of commission, was unknown and not identified to me at the time of my misconduct or was not even in existence at that time. So viability is a false prerequisite to recovery for prenatal harm and need not be fulfilled.[28] A successful plaintiff may well be unknown, unknowable or not even in existence at the time of the defendant's negligent act. It is therefore submitted that the modern prevailing rule rejecting the viability doctrine is right both in its rationale and result.

Live-Birth Doctrine Rejected

In addition to rejection of the viability doctrine, as described above, a second dramatic development in the field of prenatal injuries since World War II is the repudiation of the restrictive "live-birth" doctrine. Where the child is *stillborn*, recovery for its death depends upon the construction of the wrongful death act of the applicable state and whether the fetus is to be considered a "person" within the intent of

---

[27] See Prosser, Torts (3d ed. 1964) 357; Puhl *v.* Milwaukee Auto Ins. Co., 99 N.W.2d 163 (Wis. 1960) (similar to *Sinkler* case, *supra.* in text, but holding that plaintiff's proof on medical causation was not sustained); Note, [1962] Wisconsin L. Rev. 554; Note, Lintgen, *Impact of Medical Knowledge on the Law Relating to Prenatal Injuries*, 110 U. Pa. L. Rev. 554 (1962); Culner, *Trauma to the Unborn Child*, 5 Trauma (No. 1, June 1963) 5–126.

[28] 2 Harper & James, Torts (1956) 1030; Kine *v.* Zuckerman, 4 D. & C. 227, 230 (Phil. Pa. C. P. 1924); 63 Harvard L. Rev. 173 (1949); Seavey, Book Review, 45 Harvard L. Rev. 209, 210 (1931).

the statute. On principle, since as we have seen by the majority rule the infant could have sued had he been born and survived, it would clearly seem that his representative or estate should be able to sue for his stillbirth.[29] The regressive live-birth doctrine says that the child must first be born alive, be it only for an instant, in order to permit recovery under a wrongful death act. This apparently rests upon a conclusion that the stillborn fetus was never in being, was never a "person" within the meaning of the death act. Yet if the child *en ventre sa mère* is considered to have a separate existence at the time of injury, for the purpose of commencing an action if born alive for injuries inflicted while still in the womb, that personality is not defeated, defeasible, eclipsed nor extinguished *ab initio* by the stillbirth. Should the tortious destroyer of a child *in utero* be able to escape scotfree by killing instead of by maiming? Should the law adopt as its central theorem in the stillbirth cases the proposition, "It pays to kill"? As was acutely observed by the Wisconsin Supreme Court in recently allowing recovery for the wrongful death of a child stillborn as a result of prenatal injury, "Such a legal rule [live-birth requirement] would produce the absurd result that an unborn child who was badly injured by the tortious acts of another, but who was born alive, could recover while an unborn child, who was more severely injured and died as a result of the tortious acts of another, could recover nothing." [30] The absurdity would be augmented even more bizarrely where one twin fetus was born alive and the other dead, where both injury and death were the result of the same negligent act.[31] The absurdity of

---

[29] Del Tufo, *Recovery for Prenatal Torts: Actions for Wrongful Death*, 15 Rutgers L. Rev. 61 (1960), reprinted in 1961 Personal Injury Annual 175, 193–203 (Matthew Bender & Co.).

[30] Kwaterski *v.* State Farm Mut. Auto. Ins., 34 Wis. 2d 14, 148 N.W.2d 107, 110 (1967).

[31] Note, *Torts: Prenatal Injuries and Wrongful Death*, 21 Oklahoma L. Rev. 114, 116 (1968).

drawing the line of liability at survival is also shown by the recent action of a Pennsylvania court in granting letters of administration to the estates of two of a set of triplets while denying them to a third. In this case all three were allegedly killed by prenatal injuries sustained in an automobile accident, but while two survived birth for a few minutes, the third was stillborn.[32] This is a real feast of unreason, drawing an arbitrary distinction without a difference. It is both bad embryology and grievously bad law. The opposite rule, abrogating the live-birth requirement and allowing recovery in the stillbirth situation, would in fringe cases raise substantial and difficult questions as to showing causal relation between the alleged negligence and the eventuating stillbirth. This raises problems of proof, with the burden and risk of nonpersuasion resting on the plaintiff, and not to recognition or existence of the right. Vexed questions will also remain in establishing a basis for the evaluation of damages for the wrongful death of an unborn infant.[33] But these problems go to the application rather than to the existence of a right.

---

[32] *Philadelphia Evening Bulletin*, Feb. 15, 1962, p. 28, col. 5; Note, Lintgen, *The Impact of Medical Knowledge on the Law Relating to Prenatal Injuries*, 110 U. Pa. L. Rev. 554, 556 n. 18 (1962).

[33] How much more difficult or intractable or unmanageable or speculative is it to calculate or measure damages for the death of an eight-month-old fetus than for one wrongfully killed 3 days after full-term birth? In National Homepathic Hospital *v.* Hord, 204 F.2d 397 (D.C. Cir. 1953), $17,000 was awarded and *affirmed* for the wrongful death of a new born baby, 2 or 3 days' old); *cf.* Gullborg *v.* Rizzo, 331 F.2d 557 (3d Cir. 1964), 31 ATLA L.J. 178–85 ($5,000 award for stillbirth of 6-months-old fetus); Greenberg *v.* Stanley, 153 A.2d 833 (N.J. 1959) ($5,000 for death of 5-month-old baby). For a cloudburst of cases granting or affirming substantial awards for the wrongful death of minor children, see 32 ATLA L.J. 628–36; 26–27 NACCA L.J. 207–214; 51 Cornell L.Q. 425 (1961); Speiser, Recovery for Wrongful Death 325 (1966); 3A Personal Injury— Actions, Defenses, Damages ["PIADD,"] "Wrongful Death," 173– 193 (1967 Supp. 26–29); Prosser, Torts 931–32 (3d ed. 1964); Magner, *Plaintiff's Proof in Infant Death Cases*, The Practical Lawyer (No. 8) 27–36 (Dec. 1957); 4 Am. Jur. Proof of Facts 170– 84 (1960); 18 NACCA L.J. 373–80; 23 *id.* 121–28; 28 *id.* 78; 30 *id.* 188–98; *cf.* 31 ATLA L.J. 294–98.

They should be met under the general canons of proof, not by capitulation to unjust immunity rules.[34]

Moreover, claims to recover for prenatal harm and for the stillbirth of unborn children are buttressed (as to their alleged "speculative" nature) by the maxim that the defendant will not be allowed to profit by his own wrong where such wrong has complicated an innocent victim's problem of proof. With praiseworthy liberality, courts have held that where defendant's tort liability has not only caused harm but also contributed to the difficulty of showing its extent, defendant cannot complain if plaintiff comes forward with all the evidence practically available to him under the circumstances, even though it is less than would otherwise be required.[35] The proposition sticks like a fishbone in the throat that the law should allow recovery for a child who is born alive and who dies a minute after birth from being negligently dropped on his head, but fails to provide for an identical child who is slaughtered in the womb one minute before delivery. Maybe borderlines are inevitable but they need not be contrived, fostered or cultivated. As Del Tufo persuasively concludes, "There is no reason to draw a borderline. In fact, as the cases which have raised such a barrier demonstrate, it is intolerable to hinge the right to sue upon the circumstance of birth. (Footnote omitted). In terms of a right of action, no justifiable distinction exists, for example, between the stillbirth of a foetus in an advanced stage of development and the birth alive of a comparable foetus with death shortly ensuing. Protection from tortious injury should be afforded

---

[34] Del Tufo, *Recovery for Prenatal Torts: Actions for Wrongful Death*, 15 Rutgers L. Rev. 61 (1960), reprinted in 1961 Personal Injury Annual 175, 193–203. *Contra*, Gordon, *The Unborn Plaintiff*, 63 Michigan L. Rev. 579, 591–95 (Feb. 1965).

[35] McCormick, Damages 102 (1935); 4 Restatement of Torts §912, Comment *a*; Story Parchment Co. *v.* Paterson Parchment Paper Co.. 282 U.S. 555, 563 (1931).

an interest in being born alive and in living a complete life after birth." [36]

Accordingly, to underpin tort law's solicitude for the unborn child, the modern prevailing view thus allows recovery for stillbirth resulting from prenatal injury. However, it rejects as skewed distortion of fundamental principle the discredited live-birth restriction on recovery.[37] More specifi-

---

[36] Del Tufo, *Recovery for Prenatal Torts: Actions for Wrongful Death*, 15 Rutgers L. Rev. 61 (1960), reprinted in 1961 Personal Injury Annual 175, 199.

[37] Eleven state courts and three federal courts construing state law have now allowed recovery for the death of stillborn infants with ten state courts and one federal court denying recovery. For the *majority view*, see Todd v. Sandidge Construction Co., 341 F.2d 75 (4th Cir. 1964), 8 ATL News L. 105 (May 1965); Gullborg v. Rizzo, 331 F.2d 557 (3d Cir. 1964), 31 ATLA L.J. 178–85; [note that contrary to affirmative forecast in *Gullborg, supra*, that when squarely faced with the problem the Pennsylvania Supreme Court would allow recovery where the child was born dead, that court subsequently confounded many students by denying recovery for stillbirth: Carroll v. Skloff, 202 A.2d 9 (Pa. 1964)]; Wendt v. Lillo, 182 F.Supp. 56 (N.D. Ia. 1960); Gorke v. LeClerc, 181 A.2d 448 (Conn. Sup. 1962); Prates v. Sears Roebuck & Co., 118 A.2d 633 (Conn. Sup. 1955); Worgan v. Greggo & Ferrara, Inc., 128 A.2d 557 (Del. 1956); Hale v. Manion, 368 P.2d 1 (Kan. 1962), 29 NACCA L.J. 107–12; Mitchell v. Crouch, 285 S.W.2d 901 (Ky. 1955); Valence v. Louisiana Power & Light Co., 50 So. 2d 847 (La. App. 1951); Cooper v. Blanck, 39 So.2d 352 (La. App. 1923); Maryland, Use of Odham v. Sherman, 198 A.2d 71 (Md. 1964), 31 ATLA L.J. 183–84; Verkennes v. Corniea, 38 N.W.2d 838 (Minn. 1949) (original case activating trend toward recovery in stillbirth cases); Poliquin v. MacDonald, 135 A.2d 249 (N.H. 1957); Stidam v. Ashmore, 167 N.E.2d 106 (Ohio App. 1959); Fowler v. Woodward, 138 S.E.2d 42 (S.C. 1964); Kwaterski v. State Farm Mut. Auto Ins. Co., 148 N.W.2d 107 (Wis. 1967), 10 ATL News L. 107, 118 (April 1967); Hatala v. Markiewicz, 224 A.2d 406 (Conn. Sup. 1966) (injury to viable fetus subsequently stillborn; action maintainable, difficulty of proving causal relation no reason for denying a cause of action: "The burden of proof would have been almost insurmountable in the days of Blackstone and Holmes and probably greatly influenced their conceptions of the law. The physicians of today, however, have less trouble with the problem, and the right to bring an action is clearly distinguishable from the ability to prove the facts"); cf. Personal Injury—Actions, Defenses, Damages ["PIADD"] "Children." §1.06 (Matthew Bender & Co.); Porter v. Lassiter, 87 S.E.2d 100 (Ga. App. 1955) (indicating recovery should be allowed where child is stillborn); Amann v. Faidy, 114 N.E.2d 412 (Ill. 1953) (similar); 27 ALR 2d 1256 (1953); 3 ALR 2d Later Case Service (1965); 3 ALR 2d 1002 (1965); 15 ALR 3d 992 ("live-birth" doctrine rejected; cases collected rejecting the doctrine).

cally, at this writing 14 states reject the live-birth requirement,[38] whereas only 11 states follow it.[39]

The dynamic element of tort law, working itself pure from rules drawn from the fountain of justice, has thus eroded and displaced the dead and empty legalism which too long denied reparation for prenatal injury and death. The no-liability rule is headed for oblivion and the boneyard of discredited error.

The Thalidomide Tragedy

The world has become aware that we have on our hands thousands of members of the thalidomide generation. These are the children born in the late 1950's and early 1960's with misshapen limbs, dim hearing and other irremediable effects of a tranquilizing drug their mothers used early in pregnancy. The drug thalidomide (alpha N–Phthalimide glutarimide) achieved wide popularity because it did not produce the usual side effects of sedatives. It was sold literally by the ton in Western Europe, England, Canada, Brazil, and Japan. There were more than 10,000 of these stricken children, and half of them, in a score of countries, survived infancy. When awareness finally seeped into the consciousness of parents and officials that an epidemic of monster births had afflicted West Germany, England, and, to a lesser extent, other countries, the officials of the producing firm of Chemie Grüenthal were brought to court on charges of criminal negligence.[40] Nine hundred thalidomide children were born in

---

[38] See cases cited *supra* note 37.

[39] See cases cited in Note, *Torts: Prenatal Injuries—Viability and Live Birth*, 21 Oklahoma L. Rev. 114, 115–16, 121 (1968).

[40] On the thalidomide tragedy, see *N.Y. Times*, August 13, 1968; Gordon, *The Unborn Plaintiff*, 63 Michigan L. Rev. 579, 619–21 (Feb. 1965); Mellin & Katzenstein, *The Saga of Thalidomide* (pts. 1–2), 267 A.M.A.J. 1184, 1187–90, 1238 (1962); Taussig, A Study of the German Outbreak of Phocomelia: The Thalidomide Syndrome, 267 A.M.A.J. 1106 (1962); Trueta, *Care of Thalidomide Babies*, 1962–3 The Lancet 1162.

England alone. Some 450 of them are alive today. A few—
the real wreckage of the thalidomide generation—are gradually being sealed off from the world by the "glaze of institutional care." But most live at home with their mothers,
fathers, sisters and brothers. The shock and guilt of the
parents of these children, who at first suspected their own
"heredity" and genes rather than a drug as the causative
agent, can only be imagined.

While the United States was largely spared the thalidomide curse, since the drug was not generally available here,
an undetermined number of American women did obtain it:
From physicians to whom the drug company had sent samples
for testing; from Canada, where it was legally on sale;
from Americans who had traveled in Europe. As a result,
perhaps a dozen native-born thalidomide children—including
a pair of twins—are growing up in America right now. When
considering the merits of allowing or withholding a remedy
for prenatal damage, one need only recall and contemplate
the excruciating emotional trauma and crushing economic
burden suffered by the survivors of the 10,000 children and
their afflicted families who comprise the thalidomide generation.

Expectant Father Protected—Husband
Has Cause of Action Against Abortionist

In 1962 the legal waters were rippled by report of a case
of "paternal annoyance." [41] A husband apparently recovered
damages against an abortionist who had performed an illegal
operation upon the wife with her consent. The California
court ruled that the husband had a cause of action, based on
injury to his "marital interest," against one who performs
an abortion on his wife without his consent. The case is

---

[41] See Foote & Sander, Cases on Family Law 5B–21a (temp. ed.
1962); Note, 110 U. Pa. L. Rev. 908 (1962); Note 14 Stanford L. Rev.
901 (1962); 5 NACCA News L. 182 (Aug. 1962).

Touriel *v.* Benveniste, Civil Docket No. 766790, Los Angeles Super. Ct., Oct. 20, 1961. In overruling defendant's demurrer, the trial court held that plaintiff-husband had a legally protected interest in the unborn child which was separate from his wife's interest in the child and thus unaffected by her consent. The court ruled that the action was not for the wrongful death of the unborn child, (hence, the California death statute was deemed inapplicable), but for the direct invasion of the father's legally protected "marital interest" in the unborn child. The legal implications of this decision are self-evident in those cases in which the husband-father has not consented to the illegal abortion arranged by the wife and the abortionist.

Pregnancy Following Failure of Sterilization Operation

Custodio *v.* Bauer, 59 Cal. Rptr. 463 (Cal. App. 1967), has important implications for several aspects of the over-all subject "Legal Controls of Human Reproduction." In that case pregnancy followed the failure of a sterilization operation. In an action filed by the husband and wife before delivery of the child against the attending physician, the court *held* that causes of action were well stated for negligence, misrepresentation, fraud and deceit, and breach of contract. The court also *held* that the parents could properly recover damages for the unwanted birth of even a healthy, normal child.

Allegations were held sufficient to state the following causes of action: (1) *Negligent performance of the sterilization operation* in that there was insufficient cutting of the Fallopian tubes and failure to relocate them so as to avoid regeneration; (2) *Post-operative failure to correctly apprise of the consequences of the operation*, i.e., of the operation's possible temporary nature, so that plaintiff failed to use protective devices that would have avoided conception of her tenth child; (3) *Failure to fully advise* of several surgical procedures that would accomplish complete sterilization, suggesting the operation was unwarranted and showing possible battery on plaintiff for lack of effective consent; (4) *Misrepresentation, fraud, and deceit* in that representations that plaintiff could engage in sexual intercourse with safety and that contraceptive devices were not necessary, were negligently made and known to be false; (5) *Allegations charging breach of contract* were sufficient to withstand general demurrer in that they permitted the interpretation that plaintiffs and defendants agreed in writing that the latter would sterilize plaintiff-wife by operative procedure and that she agreed to pay a reasonable fee for the service.

As to the absence of proximate cause, the court gave this defense short shrift: sexual relations between the parents were *not* a superseding cause. The general test as to whether an independent intervening cause has broken the chain of causation is *foreseeability*. "It is difficult to conceive how the very act the consequences of which the operation was designed to forestall, can be considered unforeseeable."

As to the invoked defense that the action for misperformance of a sterilization operation offended the state's public policy, the court held that a sterilization operation either for therapeutic purposes to protect physical or mental health, or for the purpose of family limitation motivated solely by personal or socio-economic considerations, was *not* against public policy. "Where not prohibited by statute, the matter would appear to be one of individual conscience."

With respect to *damages*, since the action was filed before delivery of the child, the extent of plaintiffs' damages could not be ascertained. But if successful on the issue of liability, plaintiffs established the right to more than nominal damages. Plaintiffs were at least entitled to be reimbursed for any outlay for the unsuccessful operation. Further, they were entitled to recover for all foreseeable consequences of the failure of the sterilization operation. The court stated with high plausibility, "The mental suffering attendant to the unexpected pregnancy because of the complications which may or may not result, the complications that do result, and the delivery of a child, are all foreseeable consequences of the failure of the operation. If the mother dies in childbirth from foreseeable complications of the prescribed pregnancy, the defendants may be chargeable therewith. . . . If she survives but is crippled from the same causes and no longer able to perform her maternal and conjugal duties, the physicians would have to compensate her for her injuries, and her husband for loss of services and medical expenses."

The court emphatically rejected the flawed contention that no recovery could be had for normal delivery or for the costs of rearing a child. "Where the mother survives without casualty there is still some loss. She must spread her society, comfort, care, protection and support over a larger group. If this change in the family status can be measured economically it should be as compensable as the former losses. . . . With fears being echoed that Malthus was indeed right, there is some trend of change in social ethics with respect to the family establishment. City, state, and federal agencies have instituted programs for the dispensing of contraceptive information with a view toward economic betterment of segments of the population. One cannot categorically say whether the tenth arrival in the Custodio family will be more emotionally upset if he arrives in an environment where each of the other members of the family must contribute to his support, or whether he will have a happier and more well-adjusted life if he brings with him the wherewithal to make it possible."

In holding that a cause of action was stated for *breach of contract*, the court was "not unmindful that the subject of this controversy has implications which may affect the manufacturer, . . . purveyers and prescribers of proprietary drugs" [birth control pills]. In this connection the court referred to an Iowa case (verdict directed for physician for lack of proof of damages in action based upon normal but unexpected pregnancy following prescription and use of birth control pills) and a Washington case (action against pharmacist for substituting dehydrating pills for birth control pills). The jury were permitted to consider medical expenses in connection with birth of the child (but not the usual pain and suffering of childbirth) and aggravation of the mother's pre-existing varicose vein condition; and an $8,000 verdict was returned.

The court also noted on the damages issued that "ramifications of this case also embrace the subject of 'wrongful life' . . . or the right of a child to recover from a tortfeasor whose conduct was a contributing cause of his conception," citing Williams v. State, 223 N.E.2d 343 (N.Y. Ct. App. 1966) (no remedy to bastardized child conceived and born because negligent supervision of its institutionalized mother permitted rape of mother, a mental patient in state mental hospital, by another patient), to be discussed hereafter.[42]

---

[42] For a recent case involving substantially similar facts as Custodio v. Bauer, 59 Cal. Rptr. 463 (Cal. App. 1967), see Bishop v. Byrne, 265 F. Supp. 460 (S.D.W. Va. 1967), holding cause of action was stated by wife and husband against physician on theory of negligence in performing operation but not on theory of breach of warranty in absence of express warranty by defendant of operation's success. See Louisell & Williams, Trial of Medical Malpractice Cases, §§4.02, 8.03–8.06, 8.09, 8.10 (1960) (Matthew Bender & Co.). Cf. Doerr v. Villate, 220 N.E.2d 767 (Ill. App. 1966) (held, reversing dismissal of wife's complaint, where she had given birth to retarded and deformed child after defendant had performed operation to sterilize husband, wife's action was not time-barred as it was governed by 5-year general limitations period, rather than by 2-year period for personal injuries; plaintiff was held to be seeking damages not for any personal injury to her resulting from the operation (which would have been caught and barred by the 2-year statute) but rather for "injury to her property" (which rendered the 5-year statute applicable and her action timely). See 99 ALR2d 1398 (1965) (liability of physicians and surgeons for injuries to children in pregnancy and childbirth cases).

"Wrongful Life?"

Two recent cases, *Zepeda* and *Williams*, raise the arresting question as to whether the law should allow compensation for what might be termed "wrongful life" or for the harmful effects of illegitimacy.[43] The problem not only has interesting implications for the prenatal injury issue and the entire abortion syndrome but also for its own sake.[44] In 1960, there were 224,330 illegitimate births in the United States.[45] A recent unpublished Department of Labor report indicates that from 1940 to 1963 the illegitimacy rate among Negroes rose from 16.8% to 23.6%; the comparable statistics for whites indicate a rise from 2% to 3.07%.[46] The illegitimate child has traditionally been regarded by society as an inferior being, if not an outcast or outlaw, to be endured but always resented. Even in our "enlightened" day, the illegitimate, born with the stigma of bastardy, will very likely suffer not only from legal disabilities but also from subjective feelings of inadequacy generated and perpetuated by oppressive so-

---

[43] See Ploscowe, *Wrongful Life*, 38 N.Y.U.L.Rev. 1078 (1963). For comments on Zepeda v. Zepeda, 41 Ill. App. 2d 240, 190 N.E.2d 849 (1963), *cert. denied*, 379 U.S. 945 (1964), see 49 Iowa L. Rev. 1005 (1964); 11 S.D.L.Rev. 180 (1966); 28 Albany L. Rev. 174 (1964); 14 Am. U.L. Rev. 84 (1964); 2 Duquesne U.L. Rev. 125 (1963); 77 Harvard L. Rev. 1349 (1964); 25 Ohio St. L.J. 145 (1964); 112 U.Pa. L.Rev. 780 (1964). For a discussion of Williams v. State, 18 N.Y.2d 481, 223 N.E.2d 343, 276 N.Y.S.2d 885 (1966), see *N.Y. Times*, June 26, 1965; p. 1, col. 2; at lower court level, see 15 Am. U.L. Rev. 407 (1966); 38 Colo. L. Rev. 285 (1966); 40 Conn. B.J. 88 (1966); 4 Dusquesne U.L.Rev. 315 (1965); 12 Harvard L.J. 179 (1966); 50 Minn. L.Rev. 593 (1966); 43 N.D.L.Rev. 99 (1966); 41 N.Y.U.L.Rev. 212 (1966); 40 St. John's L.Rev. 116 (1965); 40 Tul.L.Rev. 685 (1966); 68 W. Va. L. Rev. 345 (1966); 18 Syracuse L.Rev. 657 (1967).

[44] Note, 26 Brooklyn L.Rev. 45 (1959); 64 Columbia L.Rev. 376 (1964); Davis, *Illegitimacy and the Social Structure*, 45 Am.J. Sociology 215 (1939); Fodor, *Emotional Trauma Resulting from Illegitimate Birth*, 54 Archives of Neurology and Psychiatry 381 (1945); Note, *Compensation for the Harmful Effects of Illegitimacy*, 66 Columbia L.Rev. 127 (Jan. 1966).

[45] *Time*, Aug. 27, 1965, p. 17.

[46] *Ibid.*

cial attitudes. The two recent cases mentioned above raised the pivotal question as to whether the handicaps of bastardy could be remedied in part by a tort action on behalf of the bastard child.

This novel question was first raised in a 1963 Illinois case, Zepeda v. Zepeda, 41 Ill. App. 2d 240, 190 N.E.2d 849 (1963), *cert denied*, 379 U.S. 945 (1964).[47] A bastard child, conceived when his mother was induced to engage in sexual relations by the defendant-father's fraudulent promise of marriage, sued his father in tort. The child sought to recover for the deprivation of the "right to be a legitimate child, to have a normal home, to have a legal father, to inherit from his father, to inherit from his paternal ancestors and for being stigmatized as a bastard." At trial, defendant (who was already married) successfully moved to dismiss the complaint for failure to state a compensable claim. On plaintiff's appeal, the reviewing court, although agreeing that a legal wrong had been committed—it characterized defendant's misconduct as both wilful and tortious—and that plaintiff had suffered a genuine injury, nevertheless affirmed denial of any legal relief. It felt that such refusal was dictated by the possibility that any recognition of the child's interest would swing wide the "doors of litigation" to all persons "born into the world under conditions they might regard as adverse." Declaring that judicial creativity and "lawmaking, while inherent in the judicial process, should not be indulged in where the result could be as sweeping as here," the court reasoned that any more inclusive rescue or alleviation of the illegitimate's plight must come from the legislature.

Zepeda was followed by a recent New York trial court decision laying down unequivocally that reparation for the illegitimate's injuries could and should be given in a court of law. In Williams v. State,[48] action was brought on behalf of

---

[47] See Note 43 *supra*.
[48] See Note 43 *supra*.

a bastard child born to a mentally deficient mother as a result of rape by a fellow patient in a state mental institution. The basis of the action was the state's negligent care, supervision, and protection of the vulnerable mother. Damages sought were essentially the same as those listed by plaintiff in *Zepeda*—the stigma of illegitimacy, deprivation of property rights, and loss of a normal home life. The New York trial court (Court of Claims) denied the state's motion to dismiss, holding that claimant could recover if her proofs matched her allegations. The court agreed with the concession in *Zepeda* that the injuries suffered by an illegitimate were substantial, real, and merited reparation. Moreover, the requisite elements of this tort claim—negligence, foreseeability, and proximate cause—were held to have been properly pleaded. The state's bromidic contention that allowance of the action would open the courts to a spate of similar suits was rejected as "unrealistic, illogical, and unsupportable." As a result, instead of buckpassing the question to the legislature, the courts should carry out their nondelegable responsibility to accommodate change and continuity in the law, and to recognize a new interest clamoring for legal protection, instead of getting walleyed with novelty-phobia.

Upon the state's appeal in *Williams,* the intermediate appellate court *reversed,*[49] holding that no cause of action was stated by a bastard born because of alleged negligent supervision of mental-patient-mother raped in a state mental hospital. Upon plaintiff's further appeal, the Court of Appeals affirmed the no-cause-of-action ruling of the Appellate Division, reasoning that no wrong had been committed for which the infant had standing to complain. Judge Keating stressed that the measure of damages would not be the stigma or handicaps of being born illegitimate rather than legitimate, but would rather be the injury suffered in the

---

[49] See Williams *v.* State, 269 N.Y.S.2d 786 (App. Div., 3d Dept 1966).

event plaintiff could show that *nonexistence* is preferable to the stigmatized, disadvantaged life of this particular illegitimate. Absent the defendant's wrong, the argument contends, plaintiff would not have been born at all, and hence assessing his damages would require the weighing of handicapped existence and nonexistence. Is any something better than nothing? Must we say that the "Gift of Life" is always or almost always certain to exceed the stigma and disabilities which are the daily bread of the adulterine bastard?

One commentator [50] has responded that conceding the metaphysical and symmetrical appeal of the Gift-of-Life argument, it does "not seem sufficiently weighty to justify denial or relief. Certainly it is doubtful whether permitting the suit would necessarily imply a value judgment that an illegitimate's infamy is worse than non-existence. In any case, acceptance of the 'being versus nothingness' argument would require an almost impossible abstract computation placing a monetary value on the 'benefits' conferred instead of focussing the inquiry on the plaintiff's suffering from being born illegitimate."

LAWS RELATING TO ABORTION

Extent of the Problem

Statistical information concerning the number of abortions, legal and illegal, in the U.S. is notoriously sketchy, slippery, and unreliable.[51] This is due not only to the clan-

---

[50] Note, *Compensation for the Harmful Effects of Illegitimacy*, 66 Columbia 127, 139 (Jan. 1966).

[51] *The Desperate Dilemma of Abortion*, Time, Oct. 13, 1967, at 32. On the problem of the statistical background of abortion, see, *e.g.*, The Terrible Choice: The Abortion Dilemma (1968) 40–46; Fisher, Criminal Abortion in Therapeutic Abortion: Medical, Psychiatric, Legal, Anthropological and Religious Considerations 3, 6 (Rosen ed. 1964) : "Although it is impossible to verify the figure, it has been estimated that between 300,000 and a million or more criminal abortions are performed each year in the United States." *Cf.* Ridgeway, *One Million Abortions*, New Republic, Feb. 9, 1963, p. 14.

destine nature of illegal abortions but also to the obvious fact that for legal abortions there is no central federal, state, regional, or city registry keeping books on the number of legally induced abortions. Estimates as to the number of illegal abortions range from 200,000 to 1,500,000 annually with about 1,000 deaths.[52] The figure of about 1½ million is a recurrent one, as is indicated in a recent study: "Surveys indicate that between 1,000,000 and 1,500,000 abortions take place annually—or, one abortion for every four to five pregnancies." [53] "The so-called 'back-street abortionists,' whether amateur or professional, each year cause the death of 5,000 to 10,000 women who are forced to seek their services." [54]

In short, while we have no study even approaching the Gallup poll in scientific validity, there is good reason to believe that the number of abortions annually in the U.S. is of considerable magnitude. Whether the availability of the "pill" and the enlarged knowledge and efficacy of contraceptive methods has decreased the number of abortions, as would seem logical, is not definitely known. Moreover, Pope Paul's recent encyclical, condemning all means of birth control except rhythm, may, to the extent that it is obeyed by Catholics, generate new pressures for abortion by those who are confounded by rhythm control.

---

[52] Legislation, *Abortion Legislation: The Need for Reform*, 20 Vanderbilt L.Rev. 1313 (Nov. 1967); Leavy & Kummer, *Abortion and the Population Crisis; Therapeutic Abortion and the Law; Some New Approaches*, 27 Ohio St. L.J. 647 (1966). While a number of studies have reached the same approximate figure (1 million to 1½ million annually), note that Modern Penal Code §207.11, Comment (Tent. Draft No. 9, 1959) reported estimates from 333,000 to 2,000,-000 annually.

[53] Trout, *Therapeutic Abortion Laws Need Therapy*, 37 Temp. L.Q. 172, 178 (1964); Comment, *The Legal Status of Therapeutic Abortion*, 27 U.Pitt L.Rev. 669, 677 (1966).

[54] Modern Penal Code §230.3(2) (Proposed Official Draft, 1962); Grannella, *The Difficult Quest for a Truly Humane Abortion Law*, 13 Villanova L.Rev. 257, 258 (Winter 1968).

The ALI Proposal

A central force in the current drive to liberalize modern abortion laws is the proposal of the American Law Institute completed in 1962. In that year the ALI, a prestigious group of 1,500 lawyers, representing practicing attorneys, judges, and law teachers, finished work on its 10-year study of the substantive criminal law and published a Modern Penal Code. Among countless improvements proposed was a reformation of antiquated abortion laws. National attention has been focused on abortion developments by the enactment in Colorado, North Carolina, California, and Georgia of modernized abortion laws patterned on the Model Penal Code. The ALI proposal does not authorize abortion on demand. Indeed it makes "unjustified termination of pregnancy" a crime and defines the three types of cases in which abortions would be justified: (1) when there is "substantial risk that the continuance of the pregnancy would gravely impair the physical or mental health of the mother"; (2) when there is "substantial risk . . . that the child would be born with grave physical or mental defect"; and (3) when "the pregnancy resulted from rape, incest, or other felonious intercourse," including statutory rape of girls under sixteen.[55] The operation must be performed by a licensed physician in a licensed hospital. At least two licensed physicians must make a written certification of the justifying circumstances. Termination of pregnancy would be justifiable only *before viability.*[56]

To the pragmatic eye, this is a very conservative liberalization of the abortion laws. Professor Louis B. Schwartz of the University of Pennsylvania School of Law, Co-Reporter of the ALI's Model Penal Code, has made the short-fall impact of the ALI's proposal clear: "The first of the justifica-

---

[55] B. James George, Jr., *Current Abortion Laws: Proposals and Movements for Reform,* 17 Western Reserve L.Rev. 371 (1965), reprinted in Abortion and the Law 1, 26–30 (D. Smith ed. 1967).

[56] Schwartz, *Abortion and 19th Century Laws,* TRIAL (June/July 1967) 41.

tions listed above mainly codifies the practices of reputable physicians in 'therapeutic abortion.' Such a codification is extremely important in view of the ambiguity of existing laws. A typical present statute makes 'unlawful' abortion a felony, but does not tell the physician which abortions are lawful and which are unlawful. Such precedent as exists makes it clear that necessity to preserve the mother's life will justify termination of pregnancy, but the situation is hazier regarding protection of her health, particularly her mental health. Doctors should not be required to gamble with the prospect of prosecution, where one district attorney may take a narrower view than his predecessor.

"Permitting termination of pregnancy where the child is likely to be born defective broadens the legal justifications. But ethical physicians commonly perform such operations even in jurisdictions where the law seems to make them illegal. German measles in early pregnancy carries a substantial risk of gross defects in the child. The thalidomide tragedy of a few years ago is a reminder of the horrors that can lead to a compelling demand for termination of pregnancy, where children will be born without legs, or minds, as a result of the mother's taking a widely described drug.

"The rape justification likewise conforms to widely-held moral views. It seems to many people intolerable that a woman who has been made the victim of a brutal assault should be compelled to bear the child of her ravisher. In one widely-publicized case, the rape victim was a married woman who faced the ugly alternative of raising such a child as part of her own family or giving it away at birth to be raised in an institution.

"Opposition to liberalized abortion is based on a reverence for life which should be shared by all faiths. Among Catholics and some other groups this is expressed in the view that 'natural law' forbids any termination of pregnancy from the moment of conception.

"Insofar as natural law refers to religious or moral views, none can quarrel. However, there are leading Catholic theologians and philosophers who carefully distinguish between natural law and man-made laws.

"Man-made laws, unfortunately, often have consequences as bad as the evils they are supposed to cure. For example, total repression of abortion causes thousands of women to risk death in procuring illegal abortions, and millions of women to suffer imposition and degradation at the hands of criminal abortionists.

"The rich can avoid the law easily by going to foreign countries where abortion is not prohibited; existing laws, therefore, hit the poor the hardest. We all remember the hypocrisy and corruption that resulted from the nobly-motivated effort to deal with alcoholism by national 'prohibition.' " [57]

AMA Endorses ALI Approach

In June 1967 the American Medical Association executed an about-face when its House of Delegates approved the first revision in 96 years of organized medicine's stance on abortion. In effect, the AMA endorsed the ALI proposal by sanctioning abortion when pregnancy threatens the life or health of the mother, when the fetus is in grave danger of being deformed or mentally retarded, or in pregnancies resulting from legally established rape or incest.[58]

The Legislative Reform Movement

The ferment generated by the ALI proposal has doubtless had an impact in accelerating modernization of abortion laws on the legislative front. Prior to 1967, while 39 states permitted abortions where necessary to save the life of the

---

[57] The Terrible Choice: The Abortion Dilemma (1968) 53; *AMA Policy on Therapeutic Abortion*, 201 J.A.M.A. 134 (Aug. 14, 1967).

[58] B. J. George, Jr., *The Law Governing Abortion* 5 (University of Chicago Conference on Abortion, 1967).

mother, only 4 approved abortions to save the life or health of the mother. Since 1967, however, 4 states (California, Colorado, North Carolina, and Georgia) have expanded their laws to permit abortions if they are necessary to preserve the life or health (specifically including the mental health) of the mother; in cases of rape, including statutory rape and incest; and (excluding California) if there is a substantial risk of fetal deformity. Additionally, in late October of 1967, the English Parliament enacted the Abortion Act of 1967, with even broader authorization for abortion than its American counterparts, since it contains a so-called social clause permitting doctors to consider the pregnant woman's "actual or reasonably foreseeable environment" and such factors as overcrowding in a large family, inadequate housing, strain on the mother, and the like. Let us turn to a brief sketch of each statute.

The Colorado Statute

After violent opposition from religious groups that may have encouraged the Colorado Legislature to act,[59] House Bill No. 1426 was enacted into law.[60] The law signed in April, 1967, permits termination of a pregnancy in an "accredited hospital," defined to mean one licensed by the Colorado State Department of Health and accredited by the Joint Commission on Accreditation of Hospitals, following hospital-board determination that (1) continuance of the pregnancy would result in the death of or serious mental or physical damage to the mother (when an abortion is allowed because the mother's health is endangered, a psychiatrist must be one of the doctors to certify the need); (2) the child will be born with grave and permanent physical de-

---

[59] Colo. Rev. Stat. Ann. ch 40, art. 2, §50 (1967). See *Legislation —Colorado's New Abortion Law*, 40 U. Colo. L. Rev. 297 (Winter 1968).

[60] *Legislation—Colorado's New Abortion Law*, 40 U. Colo. L. Rev. 297, 309–10 (Winter 1968).

formity or mental retardation; or (3) that less than 16 weeks of gestation have passed, and the pregnancy resulted from forcible rape, statutory rape or incest. There is no residency requirement, but fears that Colorado would turn into an "abortion mill" or "abortion mecca" have apparently not materialized.[61]

The North Carolina Statute

The North Carolina statute [62] also requires that a lawful abortion be performed by a doctor licensed in North Carolina, and that it take place in a hospital licensed by the State Medical Care Commission. Grounds for justified medical termination of a pregnancy are: (1) substantial risk that continuance of the pregnancy would threaten life or gravely impair health of the mother; (2) substantial risk that the child would be born with a grave physical or mental defect, or (3) if the pregnancy resulted from rape or incest. In the latter event, the rape, though not incest, must have been reported to a law enforcement agency or court official within 7 days after the commission of the offense. A major difference between the Colorado and the North Carolina abortion laws is the latter has a 4-month residency requirement.

The California Statute

California's old anti-abortion law, on the books since 1861, was relaxed by the 1967 legislature after a great deal of controversy and 7 years of study, to allow termination of pregnancy for specific therapeutic indications. The Therapeutic Abortion Act [63] became effective on November 8, 1967,

---

[61] N.C. Gen. Stat. §14–45.1 (1967).

[62] Cal. Health & Safety Code §§25950–54 (West Supp. 1967). See Leavy & Charles, *California's New Therapeutic Abortion Act: An Analysis and Guide to Medical and Legal Procedure*, 15 U.C.L.A.L. Rev. 1 (1967).

[63] See Leavy & Charles, *op. cit. supra*, 1, 3–4, 22–23 (1967). The authors state: "Finally, there is the difficult question of induced abortion for probable fetal deformity, which is often caused by

and permits termination of pregnancy if a 3-man committee of the medical staff of an accredited hospital unanimously agrees that there is (1) substantial risk that its continuation would gravely impair the physical or mental health of the mother or (2) when the pregnancy resulted from rape or incest.

California's abortion law is less liberal than the Colorado, North Carolina, and Georgia enactments in that it does *not* permit legal abortions on eugenic grounds for fetal deformity. Just prior to the Therapeutic Abortion Act coming to a vote in the 1967 Regular Session, Governor Ronald Reagan publicly announced that he would oppose the bill if it allowed abortion for fetal deformity. The bill's author then caused that portion to be amended out, in order to obtain the Governor's signature.[64] In California, as in North Carolina, a psychiatrist's participation is not required for approval of an abortion on mental grounds. For the purpose of securing a therapeutic abortion on the ground of statutory rape, a girl must be under the age of 15. This is a deviation from California's ordinary 18-year age limit for statutory rape. Cal. Penal Code §261 (1) (West 1957).

The Georgia Statute

Georgia has recently joined Colorado, North Carolina, and California in modernizing its abortion statute. The enabling act passed the Georgia General Assembly and became law, although Governor Lester Maddox withheld his signature.

German measles contracted in early pregnancy. This indication for therapeutic abortion, which is embodied in the Model Penal Code provisions and in the Colorado and North Carolina laws, is recognized as sound and scientific by the overwhelming majority of the medical profession and is a common reason for abortion in hospitals throughout the United States [citing Niswander, *Medical Abortion Practices in the United States*, 17 W. Res. L. Rev. 403 (1965); Packer & Gampell, *Therapeutic Abortion*, 11 Stan. L. Rev. 417 (1959)]. Yet this exception to the prohibitory law was deleted at the last moment from the California legislation, albeit through political necessity." *Ibid.*, at 3.

[64] *Medical World News*, May 3, 1968, p. 15.

Georgia's new law provides that a therapeutic abortion may be performed if a majority of not less than 3 members of a special hospital committee agree that continued pregnancy would result in serious or irremediable damage to either the pregnant mother or the fetus. Moreover, rape victims will qualify for the legalized operation.[65]

Obstetricians Back Liberalized Abortion Laws

In an historic action, The American College of Obstetricians and Gynecologists, at its May 9th, 1968, meeting in Chicago, not only took an official position on therapeutic abortion but went further and endorsed abortion on medical grounds for indications that are far broader than even those in the recently liberalized laws of Colorado, North Carolina, California, and Georgia. The ACOG's executive board adopted, 11 to 2, an abortion policy described as the most liberal approved by any professional medical organization.[66]

Prime mover in activating the new policy was outgoing college president, Dr. Duncan Reid, Chief of Ob.-Gyn. at Harvard. He headed the college's *ad hoc* panel on abortion reform which drafted the policy statement. In releasing the statement, Dr. Reid told reporters that it goes far beyond all statements made thus far by medical groups, in giving the physician more latitude in deciding what abortions were medically justifiable.

The key sentence in the statement reads, "In determining whether or not there is serious threat to [a woman's] health, account may be taken of the patient's total environment, actual or reasonably foreseeable." This merits favorable comparison with England's new and liberal abortion law, whose so-called social clause permits physicians to consider such stress on the mother, or the neglect or privation of

[65] *N.Y. Times*, May 11, 1968: *Medical World News*, May 24, 1968, p. 23.
[66] *Medical World News*, May 24, 1968, p. 23.

other children, as are generated by overcrowding in inadequate housing and the psychic stress and emotional trauma engendered by too large a family.

The new ACOG abortion policy provides as follows: [67]

> Therapeutic abortion may be performed for the following established medical indications:
> (1) When continuation of the pregnancy may threaten the life of the woman or seriously impair her health. *In determining whether or not there is such a risk to health, account may be taken of the patient's total environment, actual or reasonably foreseeable.*
> (2) When pregnancy has resulted from rape or incest: In this case the same medical criteria should be employed in the evaluation of the patient.
> (3) When continuation of the pregnancy would result in the birth of a child with grave physical deformities or mental retardation.

The policy statement made little reference to existing inconsistent laws or to the risk that an obstetrician who operated on the basis of the new policy statement might find himself confronted with criminal charges or disciplinary proceedings. However, Dr. Reid and the college are quoted as denying emphatically that they are counseling disobedience to law, and state that they believe college members, affirming the efficacy of effort, will seek implementation of the new policy by lobbying and laboring for legislative change.

While the ACOG policy is hopefully designed to achieve and infuse a modicum of reason into the resolution of one of the most anguished problems of the human hive, it clearly is not aimed at the accommodation of abortion on demand, the cultivation of abortion mills, or even to support abortion as a woman's inalienable right. "The college will not condone or support the concept that an abortion be considered or performed for *any* unwanted pregnancy or as a means of population control." The college is committed, however, to

---

[67] *Rewriting the Law of Abortion, Medical World News,* September 29, 1967, p. 52.

getting medically justifiable abortions off the back street, out of the offices, and into accredited hospitals.

Questionnaires mailed to 8,540 fellows of the college 10 days before the meeting asked them to vote on the "specific indications" proposition and also on the "addendum"—the key sentence on "total environment." As of May 6, 1968, the day the annual meeting opened in Chicago, 65% of the college had responded. Eighty-eight per cent favored the specific indications and 77%—representing more than half of all ACOG fellows—approved the "total environment" proposition. The ACOG policy statement may help provide a climate of accommodation to aid in legalizing and evoking official toleration of what have been termed "gray area" abortions, i.e., to legalize what many conscientious physicians have been doing all along.

In most states it is virtually an open secret that such "gray area" abortions are constantly being performed on one legal pretext or another or for reasons which patently strain, if they do not overload, the limited allowable legal reasons. During the rubella epidemic of 1964, for example, 329 pregnancies were terminated in New York City hospitals alone, although New York law sanctions abortion only to save the mother's life.[68] The ACOG policy may also help in meeting such candid criticism of existing abortion laws as that voiced by Dr. Eleanor B. Easley, Chief of Services in obstetrics-gynecology at Watts Hospital in Durham, N.C. "The law," she bluntly declares, "does not touch the core of the abortion problem—women who suffer genuine socioeconomic distress, who are unmarried, or who are too old to raise children." [69]

Impact of the Constitution

While the foregoing liberalized abortion statutes and poli-

---

[68] *Ibid.*, p. 52.

[69] Leavy & Kummer, *Abortion and the Population Crisis: Therapeutic Abortion and the Law: Some New Approaches*, 27 Ohio St. L. J. 647, 674 (1966).

cies provide available models and patterns for other legislatures contemplating revision, there is the possibility that the law-making bodies may move too slowly or remain inert. If they do, is there any likelihood of judicial intervention which may take the form of invalidating and shooting down, on constitutional grounds, the old abortion statutes used as the basis of a criminal prosecution against a physician who performs a "medically justifiable" abortion for therapeutic or eugenic reasons? Those who contend that the old abortion statutes are flawed by a fatal constitutional vice pin their argument in large part on Griswold v. Connecticut, 381 U.S. 479 (1965), the Connecticut anti-birth-control case which recognized privacy as a constitutional right, and voided a statute prohibiting dissemination of contraceptives, at least to married couples. Mr. Zad Leavy, an attorney, and Dr. Jerome M. Kummer compare the traditional abortion laws and the Connecticut contraceptives statute and conclude: (1) "[B]oth statutes are at war with currently accepted standards of medical practice; (2) both statutes invade the sacred realm of marital privacy by denying married couples the right to plan the future of their family; (3) both statutes force the birth of deformed children, or leave abstinence the alternative; (4) both statutes are largely unenforced; nevertheless the prosecution hangs like a cloud over the medical profession; (5) both statutes result in discrimination against people in lower economic brackets; (6) both statutes are in conflict with one of the world's most critical problems today, the population explosion; (7) both statutes involve the imposition of a religious principle on the entire community by government action." [70]

When Is a Human Being?

It is pertinent to note Professor Louis B. Schwartz's em-

---

[70] Schwartz, *Abortion and 19th Century Laws*, TRIAL (June/July 1967) 41.

phatic view, as Co-Reporter of the ALI's Model Penal Code, that early termination of pregnancy is *not* equivalent to homicide. He adds, "From the legal point of view, no state requires a certificate of death in such cases. From a religious point of view, few carry the notion of humanity so far as to call for baptism at this point of development. Among those who have, for debating purposes, called early termination of pregnancy 'murder,' I have never heard it proposed that therapeutic abortion be made a capital offence. 'Life' in a general sense is certainly there, but not yet human life, any more than the life in the sperm or unfertilized egg can be called a human being." [71]

CONCLUSION

It is believed that there is a mounting consensus in the United States that the traditional abortion law is unnecessarily strict, even Draconian, and should be liberalized. The path of reform may follow a ragged or wandering line (the "calfpath" often known to the law) between the ALI proposal and that of the American College of Obstetricians and Gynecologists, i.e., an oscillation between medical grounds, including fetal deformity, and those plus socio-economic grounds. Indeed, progress may pursue the line of advance of moving first to the ALI position and thereafter, as awareness of social and moral claims is enlarged, to the ACOG position. When the art of military advance was described by Marshal Foch in terms of the movement of a parrot in his cage, he was describing the art of legal and social advance as well: grasp and pause, grasp and pause.

It has been acutely observed that the freedom of competent physicians to treat their patients as *total persons* (a woman carries a child not only *in utero* but suffused and implanted in her psyche as well) is probably the strongest interest that can be advanced in favor of therapeutic abortion. It is a

---

[71] *Ibid.*, p. 45.

parade of imaginary horribles to suppose that the enactment of the ALI's proposal or even the ACOG proposal on justified termination of pregnancy will evoke "abortion mills and meccas" in any state. Not only are the legitimizing circumstances narrowly defined in the ALI proposal (though somewhat broader or more elastic in the ACOG proposal), but the necessity that the operation be performed in a hospital brings the whole procedure squarely under the scrutiny and control of organized medicine.

In general, accredited hospitals have committees of doctors review each proposed interruption of pregnancy. "The country will be in a bad state indeed if we cannot trust committees of doctors, acting openly, not to affront the law and morality of the community." Would not society be better off to rely on the judgments of its legitimate medical practitioners, than to remit millions of wretched women to the unskilled and unscrupulous, operating in secrecy and in the shadows?

There are those who will surely insist that the ALI proposal is not permissive enough in failing to include the socio-economic factor. Most abortions are sought by married women who may have a number of children and want no more, or by unmarried women over the "age of consent," or by married women who find themselves pregnant after the husband has deserted them or been killed. Here the prospective mother faces the necessity of raising a fatherless child while working for a living. It may be that sometime in the future, a generation or so hence, society will be sympathetic to the broader justifications for abortion embodied in the socio-economic and "reasonably-foreseeable-environment" clauses of the English Act and the ACOG proposal.

Surely good medicine cannot be bad law. Behavior can affect attitudes no less than attitudes can affect behavior. Social science has a term, "cognitive dissonance," to describe the strain between behavior and attitude, a tendency to ameliorate this tension by bringing the two into conformity. This often may be done under present archaic abortion laws by the doctor rationalizing an enforced prohibition against abortion by hostility to it, when his medicine urgently insists upon the interruption of indicated pregnancies. Hypocrisy, a great civilizing trait, is a bridge thrown up between attitude and behavior. Will not much of the tension of the medical profession be resolved when archaic abortion laws are altered and liberalized to bring them into conformity with good medicine?

It may be that there is no law of human jettison. The question for our generation, however, is whether we do not throw overboard the mother and those dependent upon her if we refuse to sacrifice the fetus. These are not easy questions, especially to professionals who do not wish to play God with human lives, whether in being or inchoate with life.

In any event, in an unfinished universe, one generation cannot commit to the next its views of public policy or human destiny. What we can do both for our generation and the next is to inform our judgment concerning problems of awesome complexity by the widest interchange, airing and consensus. Humility is a large part of every professional's code. "We are all ignorant. We are just ignorant about different things." Consciousness of our limitations enables us to find freedom in the fetters of our professionalism—"fetters that somehow make it possible to surmount the agony and absurdity of human decisions," including those flowing from the desperate dilemma.

SECTION 6

A HISTORICAL REVIEW

Chapter 21

VIEWS AND POSITION
OF THE CHRISTIAN CHURCH—
AN HISTORICAL REVIEW

SUMMARY

This chapter is an overview of official and unofficial statements set forth in the history of the church. Teachings on
sexual intercourse, marriage, contraception, abortion, sterilization and artificial insemination are considered. Special attention is paid to Roman Catholic moral theology, which has
the fullest development in matters of marriage and reproduction. Recent developments in medical science, changing social
conditions and growth in world population are reflected in
current statements of Protestants and Catholics. The trend
of change within the churches on the subject is indicated,
with special reference to the tensions within Catholicism.

LLOYD A KALLAND, Th.M., Th.D. *Dr. Kalland is Professor of the Philosophy of Religion at Gordon Divinity School, Wenham, Massachusetts. In addition to his teaching responsibilities, he has served the school in several administrative posts, including that of Acting Dean. He has earned degrees from the following schools: Gordon College, The Theological Seminary of the Reformed Episcopal Church, Westminster Theological Seminary, Northern Baptist Theological Seminary and the University of Pennsylvania. Professor Kalland is a frequent lecturer and participant in scholarly discussions in the Northeast United States. His articles and book reviews appear in a number of religious periodicals.*

VIEWS AND POSITION
OF THE CHRISTIAN CHURCH—
AN HISTORICAL REVIEW

by Lloyd A. Kalland

INTRODUCTION

This chapter surveys the control of human reproduction as discussed, declared, and exercised during the history of the Christian Church. In that Roman Catholicism characterizes most of the history of the Church and in that the papacy was the chief authority in the interpretation of faith and conduct, it follows that the greater part of the struggle with which we are dealing will take place within the confines of the Roman Catholic communion.

The subject matter deals with contraception, abortion, sterilization, and artificial insemination. Our account will show, however, that while abortion, sterilization, and artificial insemination were seriously considered by the Church on occasion, it was contraception that constituted the basic problem throughout the greater part of the history of the

Church. In the light of this, plus the fact that the other topics are dealt with in depth elsewhere in this volume, we shall concern ourselves mainly with the problem of contraception.

Our task, then, is to reveal as clearly as possible the primary influences, the kinds of arguments used, the feelings and aspirations of all concerned which make up the struggle to determine what man's responsibility is in the control of human reproduction.

As we proceed it will become clear that we are not dealing with the cool calculations of sophisticated, philosophical minds, nor the products of dedicated biblical exegetes, but rather our concern is with both the learned and the unlearned, the healthy-minded and the anxious, the laity and the clergy, perhaps even the pure and the lustful. It is a record of life as it was and is.

Although the line of discussion becomes rather unclear at points, and the progression of thought somewhat lost in the maze of redundancy, at the end there will emerge a prevailing theological-moral mentality, suggesting what man feels to be his responsibility in the crucial business of controlling human reproduction.

Furthermore, it will be noted that the contributions on this subject by the early Church Fathers are somewhat disjointed. It remained for St. Augustine to produce the first full-orbed position.

THE OLD TESTAMENT AND SOME JEWISH INTERPRETATIONS

The records of the Old Testament and ancient Jewish religious beliefs do not always agree. However, with the foundational structure of society as designed and produced by the Creator, there is basic agreement. At the roots of all creation there is a divine order, and marriage comes first in the formation of human relationships. Marriage is both wholesome and significant.

Speaking to this point in his exposition of Deuteronomy, Dr. Kline says:

> Man was indeed set as king over the earth with the whole order of nature under his dominion, but man's rule is a vicegerency in the Creator's name. Human authority must therefore be exercised according to the pattern God appoints . . . the distinction between man and woman should not be blurred by the one appropriating the characteristic articles of the other. . . .[1]

It is from this thesis that the author of Deuteronomy reveals God's declarations on the value of human life, the sanctity of marriage and the family, the concern for the young virgins, and the censure of adultery and divorce.

The Jews held that husband and wife were propagating a holy people under the command of the covenant God. The family was not only the foundational unit of society but it was the duty of every male to marry and produce children.[2] A woman who bore no children was a reproach to her father.[3]

While the woman was viewed as subordinate and inferior to the man, she nonetheless occupied a place of respect and esteem in the home with her family. Despite the lesser station of the wife, the Jewish concept of marriage by Christian standards was never surpassed in antiquity by that of any other culture.

The Babylonian Talmud substantiates this concept of marriage and procreation where it specifies that the judgment of death is deserved by a male who "emits semen in vain." [4] This legacy of a high esteem for human life in general and marriage in particular, since the time of the prophets, is always noticeable in the stream of human history.

---

[1] Kline, M. G., *Treaty of the Great King*, p. 110, see also Genesis 2:23 and Deut. 22:1–30.

[2] *Babylonian Talmud*, Kiddushin 29b.

[3] *Babylonian Talmud*, Yebamoth 64a, etc.

[4] Niddah 13a and Yebamoth 34b. Cf. Genesis 38:8–10.

THE GREEKS

There is a sharp dichotomy in the attitudes expressed by the Greeks concerning the use of genital powers. On the one hand there were the Hetairai and those who practiced male homosexuality and pederasty and others who were ascetics, rejecting extramarital intercourse. The Stoics believed that marital intercourse was morally right but was exclusively for the purpose of procreation. Pleasure was wrong.[5] The Neo-Pythagoreans also maintained that marriage was for procreation exclusively.[6] The basic contribution of the Stoics which appears throughout the history of the formulation of the doctrine and practice of birth control is that they believed there is no direct connection between intercourse and love.

THE ROMANS

The purpose of marriage according to Roman law was the procreation of children. Government officials praised procreation as a civic duty; however, the upper class Romans did not always agree with the Hebrews that large families were a mark of a happy union.[7] In fact, the birth rate among the aristocracy in the first century was a concern of the government.[8]

Although the Roman empire was noted for its many laws, it found it to be virtually impossible to interfere with family life. One reason for this condition was that it faced some extremely sobering problems with plagues and wars.

---

[5] *Stoic Fragments*, ed., G. Haase, Leipsig, 1897, no. 84.

[6] *Sentences of Sextus*, Greek and Latin Texts, ed., Henry Chadwick, Cambridge, 1959, no. 231. See Carl F. H. Henry's *Christian Personal Ethics* for a concise coverage of philosophical schools of thought.

[7] Williams, Gordon, "Some Aspects of Roman Marriage Ceremonies and Ideals, *Journal of Roman Studies*, 48 (1958), 16, 28.

[8] Boak, Arthur E. R., *Manpower Shortage and the Fall of the Roman Empire in the West*, Ann Arbor: 1955, pp. 15, 113. See also *Daily Life in Ancient Rome*, translated by E. O. Lorimer, New Haven: 1940, p. 90.

Although laws existed on the books concerning the sale and use of abortifacients and contraceptives (mainly potions), expeditions of the law were infrequent.[9] The absence of any significant reference to the matter of contraceptive practices in Roman classical literature suggests to John T. Noonan that there may have been a rather general calm acceptance.[10]

THE NEW TESTAMENT

While there is a clear expression of love in the Old Testament,[11] the concept is emphasized in the New Testament and plays a major role in the Christian concept of marriage. There is also emphasis on virginity in the New Testament. In the Gospel of Matthew it is related to the Kingdom. There is a stronger emphasis in the Lukan account [12] where Christians are told to hate their parents, their wives, etc. and there is a reward for leaving a wife.[13] Virginity is mentioned in Revelation 14:1–5 where it speaks of the 144,000 not being defiled by the woman and that virginity is possible (I Cor. 7:7). All of this, however, appears to be related to the shortness of the time available to the Christian pertaining to his earthly pilgrimage.[14] And yet, through the New Testament, marriage is upheld as being good. Particularly so in Ephesians 5:25–33, where husbands are required to love their wives, and intercourse is viewed as being holy and is not necessarily linked to procreation. Also it is to be noted that where Mark 10 and Matthew 19 establish monogamy as the correct relationship, the words of Genesis

---

[9] Hadrian, *Digest*, 48.8.4.2, 28.8.5.

[10] Noonan, John T., *Contraception: A History of its Treatment by the Catholic Theologians and Canonists*, Cambridge: 1966, p. 28. This significant volume was used freely for several of the sections of this chapter.

[11] Deut. 6:5; Lev. 19:8; etc.

[12] 14:26.

[13] 18:29; 20:34–36.

[14] I Cor. 7:32–34.

to increase and multiply are not repeated. Although the Apostle Paul in his Corinthian letter advises widows not to remarry, in I Tim. 5:14 he suggests that young widows should marry and bear children.[15] Another stress of the New Testament is that intercourse is due to the husband and the wife. It is a debt that must be paid.[16]

It is to be noted that whereas the New Testament exhorts Christians to love other humans, in no place in the New Testament do we find a suggestion as to when a being becomes human. The New Testament usage of the word "begotten" contains the idea that one is born from the father. A possible interpretation would be that beings are determined as human at the time of insemination. However, there appears to be no definitive expression on this point in the New Testament.

From the brief sketch above it should be noted that some statements are clear as to their basic meaning, whereas many other statements appear to complicate matters and must be viewed with a very critical eye. The whole social structure of the people of the New Testament, the engagements of the believers with false philosophies and religions, and the particular doctrinal and practical problems which faced them, due to the inroads of these ideas, all must be carefully analyzed in order to attempt a formulation of a "biblical" position on the control of human reproduction.

THE GNOSTICS

The gnostics claimed to have special revelatory knowledge. Although there were various schools of thought and many teachers with varying emphases, gnosticism was basically dualistic, claiming that the evil Demiurge created both material things and the moral law. Consequently both were to be despised.

---

[15] Gen. 1:22; I Cor. 7:8.
[16] Rom. 13:7 and Matt. 18:32.

The following chart presents a general picture of the positions held by the gnostics as compared to other elements of their contemporary society: [17]

Left: 1. Intercourse in all possible ways is mandatory for salvation. Believers in all possible experience.

2. Intercourse in any way is permissible for anyone. Strict antinomians

3. Intercourse is permissible for anyone as long as procreation is avoided. Dualists

Center: 4. Intercourse for women is decent only in marriage; intercourse for men is permissible with wives, concubines, prostitutes. Conventional Roman Society

5. Intercourse in marriage alone is permissible; within marriage there are no limits or specific purposes. Much of Old Testament

6. Intercourse in marriage alone is permissible provided it is not against nature. A few Church Fathers

Right: 7. Intercourse in marriage alone is permissible and then only for procreation. Stoics

8. Virginity is preferred, but intercourse in marriage, for procreation only, is permissible. Most Church Fathers

9. Intercourse is never permissible. Strict ascetics

---

[17] Noonan, *op. cit.*, p. 57. See S. Benko's excellent article, "The Libertine Gnostic Sect of the Phibionites" in *Vigiliae Christianae*, Vol. 21, No. 2, May, 1967.

It is Noonan's contention that the first three positions are those advocated by the gnostics and that Christian reaction was mainly against those positions.

To cite a few examples, Tatian, as reported by Clement of Alexandria, condemned sexual intercourse by saying that Paul's words, "Lest Satan tempt you because you lack self-control" means that to lack self-control is to desire intercourse. Marcion and his followers based their position on metaphysics. Marcion, who had been excommunicated by the Roman Catholic Church in 144 because of his rejection of the Old Testament, viewed the world as being basically evil. In the light of this he held that all marriages were evil.

On the other side were the Antinomians. Carpocrates and his son, Epiphanes, claimed that all women were free property.[18] Clement claimed that some of the gnostics practiced intercourse because it brought them into the mystery of the Kingdom of God. They used Matthew 5:42, "give to him who seeks," to justify their actions.[19] The Valentinians also gave special significance to intercourse. To them the emission of seed by the spiritual men hastened the coming of the pleroma, that is, the consummation of the divine hierarchy of aeons.[20]

THE EARLY FATHERS

The school which proved to be a potent threat to the gnostics was the Manichaean.[21] In a sense, however, the Manichaeans were a continuation of some of the emphases found within gnosticism.

---

[18] Clement maintained that after these Antinomians had eaten the Eucharistic feast they had intercourse wherever and with whom they wanted (see *Stromata*, 3.4.25, 3.28. See footnote 17).

[19] Clement, however, refuted them with an exegesis of Eph. 4: 20–24 and 5:1–11 (see *Stromata*, 3.4.27–29).

[20] *The Pretended Gnosis*, 1.6, PG, 7:511.

[21] Quasten, J., *Patrology*, p. 365 (for recent findings on Manichaeism).

Tertullian, in his zeal to refute gnosticism, all but condemned intercourse in any marriage. In the Eastern Church, Gregory of Nyssa reacted to the gnostic antinomian thinking to the place where he declared that a virgin is "deified." [22]

In the West, Ambrose declared that a virgin in fact marries God.[23] When Helvidius denied that Mary remained a virgin after the birth of Christ and referred to several texts speaking of "brothers of the Lord," Jerome claimed him to be a blasphemer. According to Jerome, Joseph was a guardian of Mary rather than a husband.[24]

One of the crucial areas around which much of the discussion took place, beginning with the early centuries of the Christian Church and continuing to the present, is that of the natural order formulated by God in His creation. Clement stimulated this type of thinking by constructing a natural law of marriage. Although there is an occasional reference to biblical data, there is little doubt that most of his material came from the writings of the Stoics. Although natural law is not always identified with precisely the same definition, there was a general agreement on the overall definition. Clement, Origen, and Ambrose all agreed that natural law constitutes that process in nature which has received no contamination by human sin or error. Building upon this, they maintained that animals do what is natural because they are without sin. Furthermore, it is self-evident then that human organs also function apart from sin.

Exemplifying the above, Clement of Alexandria stated clearly that Christian husbands were to use their wives

---

[22] *Virginity*, PG, 46:319. Chrysostom rather picturesquely said that marriage is a nest for birds that cannot fly. In a more direct fashion he posed the question: Who can make the journey to heaven encumbered by a wife and family? (*Virginity*, PG, 48:540, 545, 567).

[23] *Virgins*, 1.23, 28, 52.

[24] *Against Helvidius: The Perpetual Virginity of Blessed Mary*, 16, PL 23:210, 213.

moderately and only for the raising of children.[25] Origen
from the Eastern Church expressed precisely the same idea
when he said, "intercourse with his wife only for the sake
of a posterity." [26] In a collection of canons from the Syrian
Church (about 220–250) entitled *Didascalia* we read
that husbands are forbidden to have intercourse with their
pregnant wives (6:28) because such an act would not produce children and thus would constitute an act merely for
pleasure.

So general was the acceptance of this interpretation that
only two exceptions can be found—Lactantius and Chrysostom. Lactantius, writing in the last part of the third century, states that God made animals to reject their mates
when they were pregnant but made the woman to yield to
her husband so he would not be driven to lust after other
women. However, even here it is to be noted that although
the wife will not sin in so doing, neither does she uphold
"the virtue of her modesty." [27] Chrysostom's allowance has
to do with the practice of intercourse by older people after
the opportunity for procreation has passed.[28] With this allowance, however, there is no yielding to the idea that contraceptives are allowed. He considered contraception as
worse than homicide, a mutilation of nature. Pope Sixtus II
(martyred in 258) said an adulterer is also anyone who is
shameless with his own wife. And Jerome said an adulterer
is he who is too ardent a lover of his wife.

Eusebius, the celebrated historian of the early fourth
century, entertains the question as to why Christians ne-
glected marriage and the procreation of children if they

[25] *Stromata*, 3.11.71.4, *Die Griechischen Christlighen Schriftsteller Der Ersten Jahrhunderte*, 15:228.

[26] *Third Homily on Genesis Six*, GCS, 29:47. See *First Apology of Justin, XXIX, the Anti-Nicean Fathers*, Vol. 1, p. 172 for a similar statement.

[27] *Divine Institute*, 6.23,1326 *Corpus Scriptorum Ecclesiasticorum Latinorum*, 19:566–568.

[28] *Homily* 5 on the *Epistle to Titus*, PG, 62:689.

had the same roots as the Jewish people who enjoyed large families. His answer is threefold: (1) the Jews were concerned about the beginning, and the Christians about the end. (2) The Jewish "holy men" procreated in order to have others to whom to give their revelation, while the Christians found people everywhere with whom to share their gospel. (3) The Christian's everyday life is far more complex and filled with church work and business so that raising a family becomes an additional chore.

The practice of infanticide, abandonment, and abortions apparently were accepted practices among many peoples. Philo states that there was a terrible plight of parents who practiced infanticide, stranglings and drownings, exposing in desert areas to wild beasts, etc. Justin claimed that these persons were killers of men.[29] Moreover, in the *Apology* we read that Christians were forbidden to destroy even the fetus (9.8). In the *Didache* or the *Teaching of the Twelve Apostles* this practice was looked upon as identical with the killers of children (5.2). In the *Letter of Barnabas* (early second century) we read, "Thou shalt not kill the fetus by an abortion or commit infanticide" (19.5). The same interpretation was made by Tertullian, Cyprian and others.[30]

In the Eastern Church, in the basic legislation which was the *Canons of Saint Basil*, there was a condemnation without qualification of all women who committed abortion, whatever the state or development of the fetus.[31] In the West, Jerome also condemned this practice.[32] This means that for all intents and purposes, the life-giving process was viewed as identical to life itself and it was equally wrong to kill a fetus as it was to take the life of a child.

---

[29] *Apology for Christians*, 1.27, 29. Tertullian claimed that these were the works of pagans in *To the Nations*, 1.15.

[30] *Apology*, 9.8 and *Epistles*, 52.2.

[31] *Letters*, 188, PG 32:672.

[32] *Letter 22 to Eustochium*, CSEL, 54:160. See John Calvin's critical remarks on Jerome's "false views" in Calvin's *Commentary on the Epistle of Paul the Apostle to the Corinthians*, I. Cor. 7:7.

A factor which had a great deal to do with these doctrinal and practical interpretations are the biological theories prevalent in that day. Aristotle,[33] Jerome, Augustine, Lactantius and Clement of Alexandria all believed that the male seed was primary in procreation. The Stoics held that the body was from the male seed whereas the soul was the contribution of both the male and the female. Soranos, in his famous *Gynecology*[34] stated that the male seed is primary and the female only supplies the food for growth.

The subject of ensoulment, or when the soul enters the body, was understood by Aristotle as taking place in the fetus of the male 40 days after conception. In the female it takes place 90 days after conception.[35] According to Tertullian, the embryo has a soul when it attains final form.[36] He followed Aristotle's formula plus an interesting interpretation of Leviticus 12:1–5, believing the final form to be when the soul unites with the body, in the male 40 days following conception and in the female 80 days. Understandably, this type of thinking was a prime factor in determining the "correct" evaluation of abortion and the use of contraceptives.

In order that procreation and human life, even in the form of a fetus, be protected there was throughout the Middle Ages a general condemnation of contraception.

During the Nicean Council (325) it was declared that the clerics who had voluntarily castrated themselves could not be ordained, and if they had been ordained they were not allowed to continue their ministries.[37] Chrysostom, in his

---

[33] Aristotle, *Generation of Animals*, 1.20, 729a; 2.3, 737a.
Jerome, *On Ephesians* 5:30.
Augustine, *On Genesis According to the Letter*, 10.18.32.
Lactantius, *The Worker of God*, 12.6.
Clement of Alexandria, *Paedagogus*, 1.6.39, GCS, 12:113.
[34] 1.12.43.
[35] *History of Animals*, 7.3.
[36] *The Soul*, 25.21; 37.2.
[37] *Mansi*, 2:668.

Homily on Matthew 19, states that the clerics that had castrated themselves were murderers.[38] In his Matthew 5 *Homily*, Chrysostom views those who attempt to avoid children as a burden:

> (they) mutilate nature, not only killing the newborn, but even acting to prevent their beginning to live.[39]

Jerome in his *Letter* (22), *to Eustochium* (13), urges a young teenage girl to remain a virgin, stating that others will drink sterility and murder a man not yet born, and yet others will use poisons to commit abortions—these were parricides.

The Manichaeans, although differing from the gnostics, had some characteristics in common. There were those who believed that the light which had come from God was released by man in his eating and in his sexual actions, making these actions good. However, others believed that virginity and continence were to be upheld and they denounced all intercourse as being fornication. Both the East and the West Churches repudiated Manichaeism.[40]

ST. AUGUSTINE

A contribution which was to claim full treatment throughout the history of the Church was that made by St. Augustine. The greatest human influence in Augustine's life was that of his mother, Monica. She was a fine Christian woman and gave her son a respectable Christian education during his childhood. However, Augustine chose rather to live a life of lust which left him "half drowned in a whirlpool of abominable sins." Augustine first joined the

---

[38] 62, PG, 58:599.

[39] *Homily*, 28, PG, 57:357.

[40] So vicious was the attack on the Manichaeans that the imperial government decreed that all of their property was to be confiscated and those who believed and practiced according to the Manichaean doctrines would be exiled from the empire. Theodosian, 16.5.18.

Manichaeans who taught that the Fall consisted of Adam's yielding to urgings of his genital appetites. This, however, did not deter Augustine from following his own genital appetites. For fifteen years he lived with a mistress who bore him a son. He became dissatisfied with the Manichaean teachings and after considering several religious and philosophical schools of thought, he finally became convicted of his sin and became a Christian. He soon married, but as he says in his *Confessions*, "not being so much a lover of marriage, as a slave to lust, procured another, though no wife. . . ." [41] All of this is important to the understanding of Augustine, because, despite the depth of his theological insights and his submission to the tenets of Scripture, he found it virtually impossible to detach his guilt feelings from his exposition of the texts relating to marriage and procreation.[42]

Due to the lustfulness of man's heart as a consequence of the Fall, Augustine believed that intercourse could not be experienced apart from concupiscence which is evil. Even to have intercourse with a desire and intention for procreation was judged a venial sin. Coupled with Augustine's reaction to his early life of lust was his revulsion of the teachings of the Manichaeans. For example, Augustine knew that the Manichees practiced *coitus interruptus* in a religious rite. This in turn intensified his detestation of contraception. A group called the Catharists similarly came under the wrath of Augustine.[43]

Augustine's clearest statement on the problem of con-

---

[41] Book VI, Chapter 15.

[42] So repugnant was the act of intercourse to Augustine that he wrote, "Continence from all intercourse is certainly better than marital intercourse itself which takes place for the sake of begetting children, *The Good of Marriage*, Chapt. 6, Vol. 27, *The Fathers of the Church.*

[43] In his *Heresies* he brings to the attention of his readers that some Catharists after intercourse take the semen, mix it with grain and eat it as an eucharist (46, PL, 42:36).

traception is found in his work entitled *Marriage and Concupiscence*. Here he says:

> Sometimes this lustful cruelty, or cruel lust, comes to this, that they even procure poisons of sterility (*Sterilitatis venena*), and if these do not work, extinguish and destroy the fetus in some way in the womb, preferring that their offspring die before it lives or if it is already alive in the womb to kill it before it is born. Assuredly if both husband and wife are like this, they are not married, and if they were like this from the beginning they come together not joined in matrimony but in seduction. If both are not like this I dare to say that either the wife is in a fashion the harlot of her husband or he is an adulterer with his own wife.[44]

This passage constitutes Augustine's key consideration of artificial contraceptives and it is the source from which the later canon laws quoted the phrase, "poisons of sterility."

Additional opinions along the same line are offered by Augustine in his reply to Pollentius. He refers to Onan as one who was shameful and lawless when he refused to father a child in behalf of his deceased brother by spilling his seed upon the ground. Augustine claimed that God took Onan's life because Onan was guilty of *coitus interruptus*. Although often interpreted in this way, Genesis 38:1–10 does not state specifically that God killed Onan for that purpose. However, this interpretation of the Onan story was used by leading theologians for many centuries in their attack on the use of contraceptives.

For approximately a thousand years after the death of Augustine, the monks, who were outspoken in their traditional interpretation, echoed and re-echoed the basic expressions of Augustine and other Fathers who spoke similarly on these matters. The first bishop to press these ideas on a province was Caesarius, a bishop of Arles from

---

[44] 1.15.17, CSEL, 42:229–230.

503 to 543. His claim was that too many people were living with concubines, which was the cause to make some rather rigid regulations on marital morality. He agreed with Augustine that the sole purpose of marriage-intercourse was for procreation.

One of the first pieces of Church legislation against contraception is viewed today as an interpolation. Nonetheless, it was useful to many groups in their advancement of the cause of "purity." The canon reads:

> If any woman has fornicated and has killed the infant thence born or has desired to commit an abortion and kill what she has conceived, or take steps so that she may not conceive, either in adultery or in legitimate marriage, the earlier canons decreed that such women might receive communion at death; we, however, in mercy judge that such women, or other women who are accomplices of their crimes, should do penance for 10 years.[45]

Pope Gregory also advanced this type of traditional thinking. While enjoying a high personal prestige, he declared an absolute condemnation of the contraceptive practice. This did much to assure the continuation of these ideas throughout the Middle Ages, yet his declaration was not an *ex cathedra* proclamation.

During the twelfth century there was the distribution of the penitential documents which proved to be something of a rebirth of Augustinianism. There was also a reaction to a group called the Cathars. The Cathars were a group of troubadours who functioned around the middle of the twelfth century in southern France who believed in pure love. That is, what they called carnal love, love of man for woman, extramarital love which terminated in sexual acts but did not consummate in insemination. They attempted to disassociate sexual intercourse from procreation. In other

---

[45] Chapters from the Synods of the Eastern Fathers 77 in Martin, Opera p. 142.

words, they attacked procreation but not intercourse as such. Naturally this free interpretation received a storm of reaction. Gratian, an important figure during the twelfth century deferred to Origen in stating that the Holy Spirit Himself would not be in evidence at the time when congenital acts were being accomplished. This was another way of saying that peace of heart or pleasure had no part in intercourse. Gratian continues by saying that even to have pleasure in intercourse when this pleasure was not sought was to commit a venial sin.[46] All of this, obviously, spoke against contraceptives. To what extent the practice of the people agreed with the theory of the Church will become increasingly clear as we pursue our study.

Contraception in general, during the medieval days in Europe, was linked closely to the medical knowledge derived basically from the Arabs' [47] *Canon of Medicine*. This work which covers many subjects in the general area of physical health includes several specific ideas on contraception.[48] There were several other lesser works including a Persian treatise, *The Book for Almansor,* which offered remedies for both abortion and contraception. Albert the Great (1206–1280), a Dominican bishop who was the teacher of Thomas Aquinas, wrote two treatises—*Vegetables and Plants* and *Animals.* In these he considers many types of contraceptives and abortive potions. Three other medical writers who contribute substantially to the subject were

---

[46] Noonan, *op. cit.,* pp. 198–99.

[47] *Canon of Medicine* written or compiled by ibn-sina was known in the Latin world as Avicenna. This work was translated into the Latin about 1150 and for approximately 500 years it dominated western medical thought.

[48] It states that cedar placed on the penis before coitus prohibits impregnation and it kills the fetus (2.2.163, Chitran). It also speaks of drinking various plants, acids, etc. Various movements of the human body particularly that of the woman after receiving the semen are advocated as ways of rejecting the male seed (see Noonan, p. 202). Some of the above methods were supposed to curb the desire for coitus rather than destroy the semen or the fetus.

Arnold Zenanova (1238–1311), John of Gaddesden (1280–1336), and Magnino of Milan (about 1300). It is a point of special interest that these Catholic writers in the thirteenth and fourteenth centuries speak of contraception without mentioning the moral condemnation that was given to it by the theologians. Later the medical writers actually recommend the use of contraceptives. In the *Canon of Medicine*[50] Avicenna states that prevention of pregnancy is necessary when the birth endangers the mother. It must be remembered, however, that these men were giving medical information rather than promoting a cause for the use of contraceptives. Nor, most certainly, were they speaking for the Church.

In his *Summa of Theologia* Antonius lists some habitual sins, mentioning the selling on the feast days of certain articles wherein wrong weights were being used. However, there is no mention of the selling of contraceptives. On the other hand, Noonan[51] claims that in the confessional there is mention of selling of ointments for abortion and the selling of poisons, etc., which could refer to any type of contraceptive.

One of the fourteenth century Canonists, a layman, Joannes Andreae (1270–1348), points out that a motive for the use of contraceptives was that it may not appear to be fitting for some women to appear in public while pregnant. Noonan regards this as being a motive of preventing shame, or yielding to social or legal pressure. There is also the motive of economics. Peter de Palude, a Dominican, stated that a motive in *coitus interruptus* was that a man may feel

---

[49] Similar examples are listed with some rather cruel events, both fiction and real in Dante's *Divine Comedy* (cantos 15.16 in the *Inferno*) and in the *Cantebury Tales*. In England and on the Continent, it would appear from the few laws then in existence, there was little interest in judging contraception as being a special menace.

[50] 3.21.1.2.

[51] Noonan, *op. cit.*, pp. 215 ff.

he has more children than he can feed.[52] Apparently at this point in medieval history there were several motives given as legitimate reasons for justifying the use of contraceptives. Among these were jealousy, or avarice, economic necessity, shame and medical, and social pressures.[53]

Another important factor in the overall problem is that of growing population. Generally speaking, populations in Western Europe rose continuously from the eleventh through the thirteenth centuries. For example, France in the ninth century totaled 10 million population and in the early part of the fourteenth century there were 17 million in that country. England went from 1,100,000 in 1100 to 3,700,000 in 1350. When we come to the mid-fourteenth century, however, we run into a sharp decline because of the black death plague. From 1348 to 1377, England declined 40 per cent in her population.[54]

There was a stabilization of population during the last part of the fourteenth century and throughout the fifteenth. It has been suggested that this population control was at least in part due to the use of contraceptives. This, however, is conjectural. Population explosions were not taken seriously in the late Middle Ages. This may be due in part to the frequent occurrences of wars, plagues and famines.

---

[52] *On the Sentences*, 4.31.3.

[53] Noonan, *op. cit.*, p. 222.

[54] Russell, Josiah Cox, "Late Medieval Population Patterns," *Speculum*, 20. The matter of population reappeared about 1800. In 1798 Thomas Malthus published an essay on the *Principles of Population*, which claimed that the populations if allowed to go unchecked would double themselves in 25 years. For example, England would become a nation of 170 million by 1900 and that the anticipated food supply would feed no more than 55 million persons (2nd ed. London: 1803, pp. 5, 8). See Himes, *Medical History of Contraception*, Baltimore: 1936, pp. 224–27. Also specifically on population see the *Catholic Encyclopedia* (suppl, 1922) where it is stated that the food problem will be met with new methods in food production, and evils like volcanoes, famines and earthquakes will keep the population under control, and the *62nd Annual Congress on Medical Education*—selected papers, Chicago: 1966, "An Expanding Populace in a Contracting World."

THOMAS AQUINAS

The most important voice in the history of the Catholic Church after Augustine was Thomas Aquinas. He made no outright radical changes from Augustine. However, his theological mentality, based upon Aristotelian thought, was argued from the premise of man's rational apparatus which in turn opened the door for a serious challenge to Augustine's conclusions. Aquinas held that natural coitus was instituted by God. Just as right reason proceeds from man, so the order of nature proceeds from God himself. Therefore, when sins are committed which are contrary to nature, which challenge the very order of nature, injury is done to God, the ordainer of nature. As for the unnatural use of coitus, Aquinas in his early commentary appears to include intercourse during pregnancy, intercourse with a sterile wife or even intercourse by an aged man.[55] However, in a later work, *Summa Against the Gentiles*, he clarifies what he means by natural over against unnatural. A natural act is when semen is deposited in the vagina and an unnatural act is when insemination is made impossible. Therefore, intercourse of the pregnant, or of the sterile, or of the aged would be classified as natural, consequently not sinful.

Furthermore, Aquinas argued that a diseased organ may be sacrificed, and in some circumstances, even society may be maimed as a punishment. However, this challenge to the natural order must be done only for good rational reasons. This brings out something of the balance not seen in Augustinian thought. Yet, it should be clearly understood that the use of contraceptives was judged as being unnatural and, therefore, was condemned equally by Aquinas and Augustine.

Although there were those who were critical of Thomistic

---

[55] *On the Sentences*, 4.33.1.3, and *Summa Theologica*, 2–2.154.12, obj. 1.

thought, it was generally agreed that when a man of the calibre of Aquinas followed basically a man of Augustine's stature, it was pretty much a foregone conclusion that the resistance to his thinking would be meager.[56] Noonan points this out when he says:

> In this European society, in this theology dominated by Augustine, reason itself appeared to condemn contraception. The contraceptive act destroyed potential life. It frustrated the inseminating function by *coitus interruptus*. It violated the principal purpose of marriage and the principal, if not the only, purpose of marital intercourse. Authority had condemned contraception. The Cathar enemy had been the prototype of a people denying the procreative purpose. Reason now showed that authority was right, that the Cathars were wrong, and that contraception was behavior contrary to the good of man.[57]

Although the sanctions of the various doctrines were not enforced legally, Noonan concludes that a Catholic practicing contraception could not consider himself in the state of grace, that is, he was not spiritually alive or open to God. He was also cut off from receiving the sacraments until he had repented of his act.[58]

Another stress of Aquinas was his constant reiteration of the glories of virginity, celibacy, and continence in marriage rather than the values involved in the procreation of new life. He preferred the perfection of existing life over against the realization of large families.[59]

Another significant element in this discussion is the viewing of marriage as a sacrament. Albert in his *Sentences* claimed that not only was marriage a sacrament, but there was an independent sacramental value for intercourse.[60]

---

[56] Alexander of Hales in *Summa Theologia* 2–2.3.5.2.1.3. and Peter de Palude in *On the Sentences*, 4.31.2 and 3.

[57] Noonan, *op. cit.*, p. 257.

[58] *Ibid.*, p. 258.

[59] *On the Sentences*, 4.32.1.4.

[60] 4.31.27 and 4.26.11.

Aquinas did not follow this particular interpretation but he did maintain that the essence of marriage was sacramental.[61] Although Aquinas saw marriage in this significant way, due primarily to his rationalistic stance, he allowed certain exceptions to exist. For example, he thought it right that intercourse be practiced by those who had abnormal menstruants.[62] As stated previously, he also allowed intercourse of the aged who naturally could not produce offspring. And in his *Summa Against the Gentiles* he claimed that intercourse by sterile women would not be considered a sin.[63] Between the years 1450 and 1750, when man's free spirit was venting itself, there is a rather graphic departure from some of the Augustinian theories and a general yielding to the less rigid style of thinking introduced by Aquinas.

Due to the openness of investigation during the Renaissance and the Protestant Reformation, sexual ethics received a fresh examination. Also, by the end of the fifteenth century there was the growth of the educated lay class which caused the ecclesiastical writers to place additional confidence in the moral evaluations of the laity. Aquinas' rationalism, which allowed for serious contemporary reflection, was being heard while Augustinian thought was challenged at its very roots. Noonan points up the distinctives of this trend when he says:

> The firm distinction between grace and nature, the insistence on the value of nature, the application of reason to the data of revelation, the Christian adaptation to Aristotle, these Thomistic accomplishments underlay the latter innovations.[64]

One of the innovations of this period was produced by Denis the Carthusian (1402–1471) in his work entitled

---

[61] *On the Sentences*, 4.31.1.2.2.
[62] *On the Sentences*, 4.32.1.2.2.
[63] 3.122.
[64] Noonan, *op. cit.*, p. 303.

The Praiseworthy Life of the Married. This was in effect a type of catechism of moral life for married people. Here Denis stresses the idea that love between husband and wife should be spiritual, natural, social and even carnal. Pleasure comes from engaging in a certain type of act. And in that the act of marital intercourse is good, pleasure derived from this act is also good. This, to Denis, brings together the spiritual and the carnal, both being good. Commenting on this point recently, Coenraad A. H. van Ouwerkerk says:

> The conflict lies precisely in that contraceptive intercourse is no longer experienced as a contradiction of love and of the function of marriage.[65]

Another important work of the fifteenth century was *Moral Questions,* authored by Martin Le Maistrae (1432–1481). His work was published posthumously about 1490. Le Maistrae claimed that the marital act itself was lawful. He believed there was a happy mean which was conjugal chastity. This mean lay between immodesty and insensibility, and was related specifically to the individual's intention. Therefore, he concludes, not every copulation of the spouses in which there was no intention of generate offspring was an act opposed to conjugal chastity.[66] Not only was an allowance made but the theological justification for this emphasis was gained primarily from the thinking of

---

[65] Bockle, Franz, ed. *Moral Problems and Christian Personalism, Vol. 5 on Concilium: Theology in the Age of Renewal,* New York: 1965, p. 20.

[66] This thesis was accepted and elaborated upon by John Major, a Scot Theologian (1470–1550)—a professor who taught in the Sorbonne, and the Universities of Glasgow and St. Andrews. It was also advanced by three Dominicans—Sylvester da Prierio (1460–1523), Thomas de Vio, known as Cardinal Cajetan (1469–1534) and Dominie Soto (1494–1560). Also manifesting the same interpretation generally was the Roman Catechism of 1566 which was drawn up at the direction of the Counsel at Trent and prepared under Pope Pius V. All of these were strong evidences of the fact that the inherent goodness of marriage did not depend upon the insistence that marriage was only for procreative purposes.

Aquinas. According to Aquinas, original justice was lost at the time of Adam's sin, but this did not impair any essential constituent part of human nature. Concupiscence was an effect of original sin, but in fact did not make man's natural sexual tendencies evil. Even though original sin was transmitted by generation, this did not mean specifically that sexual lust or sexual concupiscence were involved.

Another instance of this thesis was that of Peter de Ledesma, a student of Soto, who claimed that the good of offspring was not preferred to the duty of intercourse. Furthermore, income and education were included in the principle of the "good of offspring." Thomas Sanchez (1550–1610), a man who spoke on marriage with considerable authority, manifested basic agreement with the above thinking in his *The Holy Sacrament of Matrimony*.[67]

It is to be noted, therefore, that the introduction of financial and educational reasons in the definition of the moral validity of marriage moved much of the basic thinking of the Church from the thesis of Augustine, namely, that intercourse was to be experienced exclusively for procreation. Nevertheless, it ought not be forgotten that this shift did not relieve the general condemnation of the use of contraceptives. In fact, not until the nineteenth century was there an important group within or outside the Church which was urging the adoption of birth control.[68]

It is obvious to the readers of this subject in history that there was a sizable gap between the practice of the people and the theological-moral interpretations of the matter. If reasons are to be sought for this dichotomy, undoubtedly they ought to include the particulars that the Church writers were celibates and, therefore, not personally interested; the married laity for the most part were educationally un-

---

[67] 9.25 n.
[68] Noonan, *op. cit.*, p. 341.

able to enter into serious debate with the clergymen; and that effective contraceptives had not been developed.

The allowances gained through Thomistic rationalism were obvious to all interested persons. It remains a fact, however, that progress was slow and indefinite. Noonan sums things up well when he says:

> The lack of institutional involvement, the lack of interest by professional groups, the absence of invention, little change in population pressures, Protestant rigidity, the close connection of the arguments against contraception and against other sexual sins—all the reasons why the doctrine on contraception resisted the impact of the new evaluations of procreative purposes, pleasure, and education, and the feeble pressure of the laity for revision . . . the doctrine had been largely shaped in reaction to gnostic, Manichaean, and Cathar repudiations of the perpetuation of life . . . the old doctrine was in peaceful possession of the field.[69]

LUTHER AND CALVIN

Two of the most able theologians participating in the Protestant Reformation were Martin Luther and John Calvin. Luther's initial treatment of marriage was in keeping with the thinking of Augustine. Marriage was supported by three basic theological tenets: 1) It was a means of grace (*sacramentum*); 2) It was of mutual consent and fidelity (*fides*); 3) It was for the procreation and education of children. Marriage then was a sacrament that consisted of a life-long covenant of fidelity, the main purpose of which was the procreating and rearing of children.

Within one year, however, Luther changed radically in his interpretation of marriage. In 1520 he concluded in his work *The Babylonian Captivity of the Church*, that marriage was not a sacrament in that it is not grounded in redemption but in creation. He writes,

---

[69] *Ibid.*, p. 358.

> We have said that in every sacrament there is a word
> of divine promise, to be believed by whoever receives
> the sign, and that the sign alone cannot be a sacrament.
> Nowhere do we read that the man who marries a wife
> receives any grace of God. There is not even a divinely
> instituted sign in marriage, nor do we read anywhere
> that marriage was instituted by God to be a sign of
> anything.[70]

Furthermore, Luther contended that jurisdiction over
marital matters should not reside in the Church but under
the civil authorities. God's laws still prevail over marriage,
but in that the transaction came under the creation ordinance the civil court's authority prevailed.

Added to this is Luther's strong emphasis on the necessity
of love in the relationship between husband and wife. Love
is of the very essence of marriage. This emphasis is em-
blematic of Luther's dramatic switch from scholasticism to
the freedom afforded by the gospel of grace.

Nowhere does Calvin treat in a definitive way the control
of human reproduction. In his *Institutes of the Christian
Religion*,[71] he states that marriage is not a sacrament, but
he does not move to the consideration of the purpose of
marriage. In his commentary on *First Corinthians*,[72] Calvin
points out with candid clarity that celibacy is a preferred
state; however, it is reserved for those who have received
the gift of perpetual continency. Due to the insistence that
all priests remain unmarried, despite the absence of the
evidence of this gift, the Roman Catholic Church, says
Calvin, has become blemished by "horrible acts of filth-
iness." Luther enunciated the same principle when he wrote,

> Therefore we should and must acknowledge that God
> has left them free to marry, and they cannot be bound

---

[70] Luther, *Works*, Vol. 36, 92. See also Vol. 44, 5 ff. and Vol 45,
13 ff.

[71] Trans. by John Allen, IV, XIX, 766 ff.

[72] See footnote 32.

by any vow contrary to God's Word, nor obligated to the teachings of the devil.[73]

Marriage itself is understood by Calvin as a holy estate which demands of both husband and wife a concern and love for each other. The point of importance with Luther and Calvin is that both emphasized the love relationship in marriage and their attitudes against a scholastic mentality were so decisive that both refused to be bound where the Scriptures were not explicit and thereby kept the channels open for further study on subjects such as the control of human reproduction. This constitutes a radical departure from both Augustinian and Thomistic thought.

SOME ADDITIONAL INFLUENCES

On October 29, 1588, the second Roman act, the bull *Effraenatam,* was issued by Sixtus V. The decree itself was basically Augustinian in emphasis, and was reactionary in essence. Sixtus V, a Franciscan pope, was all but vicious in his search for criminals of even twenty years prior to his reign and carried the same spirit into his pursuit of virtue. Particularly, it seemed, was he interested in connecting mortal sin with sexual intercourse. As a consequence of his labors,

> all abortion and all contraception by potion or poison were to be treated as murder. The ultimate ecclesiastical penalty of excommunication was invoked, and, to make the penalty even more stringent, only the Holy See could release the excommunication unless the sinner were in *articulo mortis.*[74]

The contribution of Sixtus V, however, was short-lived because Gregory XIV repealed all the penalties established by

---

[73] *Works*, Vol. 36, 260. See also W. H. Lazareth's *Luther on the Christian Home,* pp. 166 ff.

[74] Noonan, *op. cit.,* p. 362. See also Ludwig Pastor, *History of the Popes,* St. Louis: 1899–1953, XXI, 90; and *Codex Luris Cononici,* 2350.1, 985 n.4 in *The New Catholic Encyclopedia,* Vol. 1, p. 29.

Sixtus except those which applied to abortion of the ensouled 40-day fetus. Actually the *Effraenatam* bull lasted for only two and a half years.

Another interpretation which restrained progress in the control of human reproduction was the linking of contraception and abortion with homicide by those who emphasized the gravity of sexual sins. However, Noonan clarifies the matter as to the degree of following enjoyed by these proponents when he says:

> In the period 1450–1750, the analysis of contraception as homicide was far from universal. It was ignored by Denis, Major, Cherubino, Sylvester, Soto, Navarrius, Lessius, DeSales, Ledesma, Diana, Liguori. It was invoked by Le Maistre, Angelus, Cajetan, the Roman Catechism, Sixtus V, Laymann, Lapide, Marchant, Pichler. It was rarely applied to *coitus interruptus*. Its survival in any form was owed principally to the Canon law and the Roman Catechism. To the extent that the Canonical and the Catechistical classification was followed, the designation as homicide remained an objection to contraception by potion and poison.[75]

A development of gigantic proportions which contributed to the evolution in the areas of theological description and moral practice was that of the invention of the printing press. Although the masses could not yet read, the intellectuals became familiar with many types of literature, including treatises on morals. This widening of communications among the people also stimulated some clergymen to preach more particularly on the subject. Preaching on morals was not extensive, but it was developing.

Added to this picture was the situation of the confessional booth. There was a substantial amount of discussion throughout the Middle Ages pertaining to the manner in which a clergyman was to discuss the married life with the

---

[75] Noonan, *op. cit.*, p. 365.

penitents. Liguori,[76] among others, discussed this problem fully. Common among the clergy was the conclusion that the confessor could do as much harm as good were he to attempt to instruct the penitents during the time of confession. Although contraception as such was not the issue, intercourse was. The obvious point here is that even in this more intimate relationship of Church and Church members, there was not a strong insistence on prescribed moral responsibility. Although contraception was repeatedly designated as not only a sin but a crime, a vice against nature, a form of homicide, a king of infidelity, a violation of marriage, the actual condemnation of it occurred infrequently, especially among the peasants or common people.

In this struggle the control of contraceptive information was very important (yet increasingly difficult) to the Church's cause. Although much of the control was ineffective, the Counsel of Trent with its authorized index of prohibited books aided its cause somewhat. In the bull of Pius IV (Rule 7) he condemned all books of necromancy or those works which contained information on sorceries or poisons. Medical books, however, were exceptions to the rule, and were a significant force in the dissemination of information.

Also, the annulment of marriage remained on the books.[77] That is, a marriage could be annuled if a prenuptial condition against the goods of marriage existed. These goods referred to here are mainly the goods of offspring. Another violation was that committed by either the husband or the wife in the matter of meeting the conjugal debt. These items in the Canon Law as well as the Roman Catechism

---

[76] *Moral Theology*, "Conscience."

[77] For an incisive review of the "Index of Forbidden Books," see *The New Catholic Encyclopedia*, Vol. 7, p. 434; for the "Canon Law of Marriage" see vol. 9, pp. 271 ff.

remained on the books in spite of their being challenged seriously, especially by the middle of the eighteenth century.

From about 1750 to the present time, as has been stated, there has been a general spread of birth control practice. Perhaps the basic reasons for this are simply that more individuals and groups have spoken with considerable dedication and have followed up with practical application in the distribution of birth control propaganda. Also, the accessibility of a growing number of types of contraceptives contributes to this trend.

Corresponding to these factors is the philosophical-theological shift, namely, that man was viewing himself more and more as a manageable individual, which led to an increasing number of people rejecting openly the ecclesiastical establishment. It will be seen that when psychology emerges as a distinct discipline, man as a decision-making being will rival both God's law of nature and the laws of reason as the significant area of concern in reaching solutions to problems in the control of human reproduction.

There was a major upset in the prestige, and consequently the effectiveness, of the Catholic Church when the Jesuits in 1762–1778 were ruled illegal. Some 6,000 Jesuits responsible for over 200 colleges were expelled from France by Louis XV. Clement XIV completely suppressed the order in 1778. This all but broke the theological structure which was supported by the teachers within the Roman Catholic Church. Humanistic nationalism became the dominant force. The Bible was no longer the book of authority, scholasticism was discredited; clergymen were viewed as of no consequence and even as parasites on the community.

After several years of ineffective operation of Roman Catholism, Rome gradually again became a force as the authority of the Church. Although the *Diet of Manuals*, which enunciated moral conclusion in the form of a code, was being advanced by the Church, some individual writers in moral theology geared more to the public mind were being heard.[78] All of this meant that the laity was asking questions of the Church on birth control and their questions deserved answers.

It will be recalled that up until now various possibilities of having intercourse without ejaculation of the semen were allowed; however, there was no allowance for the use of the condom (1843) in particular nor contraceptives in general. According to Noonan more and more wives were submitting to their husbands on the basis of practical reasons, including their inability to educate their children, working under a limited financial program, keeping their husbands from committing adultery and in order to preserve their own health. According to the terms in use, they were practicing in "good faith." Going along with this whole idea was Liguori when he advised in his *The Practice of the Confessor:*

> as to sins in marriage, ask the wife only whether she paid the marital debt; about other things be silent, unless asked.[79]

Gousset echoes substantially the same idea when he says:

> better that the married sin materially than be exposed to the danger of sinning formally . . . should not confessors hear lest they offend penitents by interrogating them importunely? [80]

It was against this general trend that the Inquisition under Pius IX (1851) attempted to stymie the progress by calling the trend scandalous and erroneous. It is interesting to note, however, that the term heretical was not used.

---

[78] Among these were John Gury's (1801–1866) *Compendium of Moral Theology* (following basically Liguori's Moral Theology), Thomas Gousset's (1792–1860) *Justification de la Theologie, Morale de St. Alphonse de Liguori* and John Baptist Bouvier's *Dissertation on the Sixth Commandment of the Decalogue and Supplement to the Treatise on Marriage* (1785–1854).

[79] Section 4.

[80] *Moral Theology for the Use of Cure's and Confessors.*

Although the Inquisition spoke out against the general trend of expanding birth control, nothing of importance was accomplished. When the official directives from Rome were made, which restored the Church in France and the reign of Pius IX was ended, there was nothing of significance accomplished concerning the combating of birth control. However, by 1851 a tightening of the lines can be observed. But even with the specific rejection of condoms, birth control continued to sweep France. By and large it was left up to the local episcopates, and these established groups appeared to move with little authority or effective rational argumentation. The arguments against contraception, as was evident throughout the history of the struggle, were based on general ideas regarding the purpose of marriage, but they were not well worked out and the masses among the members remained unconvinced. With this ineffective operation going on within the Church, it is to be expected that regarding a social issue which involves so many people in such a crucial area of everyday living, the forces outside the Church would make significant advances. This is precisely what the reformers, the men of medicine, the scientists and other knowledgeable individuals did. Yet with all of this effective opposition to the claims of Catholicism and the obvious progression of birth control, Catholicism again found enough strength to produce a rather vigorous crusade against this force. This was accomplished mainly through the leadership of Leo XIII. Concurrently with this effort was the revival of Thomism. Even these efforts, however, which were substantial, did not successfully curtail the steady advances of the control of human reproduction.

AMERICAN PROTESTANTS

In Colonial America among the Protestants there was no serious debate on birth control. Children were needed to help with the household chores and to assist on the farms.

Large families were the rule. Families of seventeen and eighteen children were not uncommon.

During the eighteenth and the early part of the nineteenth centuries factories and mills hired child-labor for economic reasons. Children were taken from the streets in England and Ireland and shipped to America to help alleviate the labor shortage.[81] "Men and women married early and remarried promptly and repeatedly." [82] Some girls were grandmothers at twenty-seven years of age.[83] Spinsters and eligible bachelors were observed with suspicion.

However, when the industrial revolution advanced to the stage where the demands for child-labor were lessened and large numbers of immigrants from Europe came to the new world the size of families became a household concern.

One of the first, if not the very first book on the subject of birth control written in America, was Robert Dale Owen's *Moral Physiology* published in 1831.[84] By the 1840's birth control information was widely circulated. A book written by Frederick Hallick [85] was advertised by use of a host of celebrated endorsees.[86] There were several reasons why interest ran high among Protestants on the subject of birth control.

First, the basic theological structure of Protestant thought (as stated in the section on Luther and Calvin)

---

[81] Calhoun, *A Social History of the American Family*, Vol. III, New York: Barnes and Noble, 1946, pp. 285 ff.

[82] Calhoun, *op. cit.*, Vol. I, p. 163.

[83] Calhoun, *op. cit.*, Vol. II, p. 13.

[84] Yates, Herschel Wilson, Jr., *American Protestantism and Birth Control: An Examination of Shifts within a Major Religious Value Orientation*. An unpublished Harvard thesis, 1968, p. 35.

[85] Hallick, Frederick, *The Marriage Guide*, New York: T. W. Strong and Boston: G. W. Cottrell, 1850.

[86] Among these were: Noah Porter, President, Yale College; Mark Hopkins, President, Williams College; Rev. C. P. Sheldon, President, New York Baptist Convention; Bishop T. A. Morris, Methodist Episcopal Church; Prof. Austin Phelps, Andover Theological Seminary; Rev. Horace Bushwell and a number of physicians, as well as presidents of several universities.

allowed for the inclusion of companionship and pleasure as values in the marriage relationship. Secondly, Protestant individualism advocated the worth and dignity of man, which, in turn, promoted the rights of the individual. The progression from rights to the control of human reproduction was swift. It is important to note here, however, that control did not lead automatically to the acceptance of contraceptive devices. The use of contraceptives was rejected on moral and medical grounds. It was assumed that the use of preventives would result in excesses. Even the advancement of prostitution was attributed to the use of contraceptives.[87]

Woman's suffrage also led to the regulation of the number of children a mother should bear. The prerogatives of a mother, stressing the right of physical and psychological health plus the right to gain employment outside of the home were advocated with passion by a Protestant laywoman, Emma Angell Drake in her popular book, *What a Young Wife Ought To Know*.[88]

One of the earliest and most effective forces in the birth control movement outside of the Church was the establishment of the Malthusian Leagues. The first league was established in England in 1878.[89] Due to the publicity gained through an unsuccessful prosecution of the Court of England of Annie Besant and Charles Knowlton for distributing Knowlton's book on contraception, *The Fruits of Philosophy*, the movement gained considerable popularity. The book which was selling about 1,000 copies a year now jumped to a total sale of 200,000 copies.

Another important advance was the support given to the

---

[87] Hale, Edwin, *The Medical, Surgical and Hygienic Treatment of Diseases of Women*, New York: Boerich and Tafel, 1878, p. 180.

[88] Philadelphia: Vir. 1897, pp. 130–132.

[89] Malthusian Leagues were established in Germany (1889), Bohemia (1901), Spain (1904), Brazil (1905), Belgium (1906), Cuba (1907), Switzerland (1908), Sweden (1911) and Italy (1913).

movement by the first woman doctor in Holland, Aletta Jacobs, who pioneered in a method which was the forerunner of modern birth control clinics. In these clinics she instructed midwives to teach methods of contraception in the homes.[90] With the establishment of the various leagues, came the sponsorship of international congresses.[91] There was also a world conference at Geneva in 1927 and an international clinic in 1930. All of these gatherings were effective in the dispensing of information particularly with the distribution of printed materials.

In the United States Margaret Sanger began a work (1913) which resulted in the formulation of the National Birth Control League which led to the establishment of the American Birth Control League.[92] She also travelled to Japan (1921) and India (1936) distributing up-to-date information on birth control. Simultaneous with these organized efforts of propagandization there were several new types of mechanical devices being manufactured. By 1935, there were some 200 types. On another educational level, during the late 1800's there were discussions on the subject in the medical journals. Also instruction in contraceptive devices was being offered in various medical schools.

The reaction of church leaders and other humanitarians on the American scene to the rise of birth control organizations and the increase in the distribution of their propaganda is a fascinating chapter in American history. Among the groups disseminating the message of "purity" were the American Purity Alliance which sponsored the annual National Purity Congress; The New England Society for the Suppression of Vice (in 1884 the name was changed to New England Watch and Ward Society); Woman's Chris-

---

90 Himes, *Medical History*, p. 309.

91 These were held in Paris (1900), Leige (1905), Hague (1910), Dresden (1911), London (1922) and New York (1925).

92 Sulloway, Alvah W., *Birth Control and Catholic Doctrine*, Boston: 1959, pp. 18 ff.

tian Temperance Union; Young Woman's Christian Association; Young Men's Christian Association; Evangelical Alliance and the League for the Protection of the Family.[93] Another influence that slowed down the advancement of the control of human reproduction in the United States was the effort of Anthony Comstock. He carried on an effective crusade resulting in the adoption of a federal statute entitled "An Act for the Suppression of Trade in and Circulation of Obscene Literature and Articles of Immoral Use." Although this statute was effective at first in challenging the legality of birth control information, the court judgments which followed in 1930, 1936, 1939, and 1958, all of which challenged the phrase, "immoral use," served to rule out birth control as falling within the intended meaning of this phrase.[94]

Important to the progress of the total problem are the advancements by medical science. Although quasi-medical beliefs such as the idea that the use of contraceptives results in the contraction of horrible diseases and dissipates intellectual powers were widely accepted, books like Foote's *Medical Common Sense* and Hallick's *The Marriage Guide* [95] did much to popularize information gained through empirical research.

An indication that the advocates of birth control were meeting with success was the decline in the birth rate, particularly the Anglo-Saxon stock. Cries of "racial suicide", "race sterility" and "racial decay" were common along the eastern seaboard. Especially in New England,

---

[93] Dike, Amule, *A Review of Fifteen Years*—A report of the corresponding secretary to the Annual Meetings of the National Divorce Reform League, Montpelier, Vt.: Watchman and State Journal, 1896.

[94] Sulloway suggests that Comstock drew no distinction between contraceptives and obscenity. Apparently he derived his information from lurid sources and his Puritanical mind. Sulloway, *op. cit.*, p. 14.

[95] Foote, Edward Bliss, New York: Murray Hill, 1860. For Hallick, see footnote 85. See Yates' thesis, pp. 13–104, for a full review of the medical history during this period.

where the 1870 census report showed a decline, were the Protestants alarmed. It was argued that the American stock which was best equipped to have children by reasons of wealth, education, culture and health was failing substantially in its obligation. Protestants also saw the day fast approaching when the Roman Catholics with their large families would become a major threat to the Protestant extension of the Kingdom of God. Anti-Catholicism was a wide-spread phenomenon.[96]

Yet, in spite of these distressing signs, Protestants appeared to be satisfied that it was man's prerogative under God to control human reproduction. All that was lacking now was legislation allowing the sale of contraceptive instruments. This came in 1936 with the United States Court of Appeals [97] approving the importing of certain contraceptive devices for use by physicians or medical agencies.

Something of the total effect of the general trend of public thinking was expressed in 1930 by the Protestant Episcopal Church when the Lambeth Conference adopted a resolution allowing contraceptives wherever morally sound reasons substantiated such action.[98] To the Protestants this action may have been a mere acknowledgment of what was being practiced generally. However, it would be difficult to assess the significance of this resolution on the thinking of the Roman Catholic Church. In keeping with this ecclesiastical decision, considerable evidence pointed to the fact

---

[96] Ellis, John, *Deterioration of the Puritan Stock and Its Causes*, New York: Strong, 1884., Ross, E. A., *Annals, American Academy of Political and Social Science*, XVIII, July, 1901, Rauschenbusch, Walter, *Christianity and the Social Crisis*, New York: MacMillan, 1907, and Rauschenbusch, W., *Christianizing the Social Order*, Boston: Pilgrim, 1912.

[97] U.S. vs. One Package, Dec. 30, 1936, See Groves, Ernest R., *Marriage*, 2nd. ed. revised, New York: Holt, 1947.

[98] In 1920 the Lambeth Conference disallowed the use of contraceptives; in 1930 the Conference conceded in limited circumstances that contraceptives may be morally legitimate and in 1958 it gave unanimous approval to the use of contraceptives (see St. John-Stevas, pp. 72 ff.).

that birth control was widely practiced by Christians and non-Christians alike. In view of the accepted thesis that most of the rationale given for any decision in this moral struggle usually followed the fact of the practice itself, nothing short of a wide liberalization of the rulings on the control of human life seems possible.

EARLY TWENTIETH CENTURY ROMAN CATHOLIC THOUGHT

One of the principal advocates of revealing the so-called fallacies involved in birth control was the Roman Catholic, John A. Ryan (1865–1945).[99] In his work "Family Limitations" recorded in the *Ecclesiastical Review*,[100] he tends that the American Catholics know all about birth control and certainly practice it even to the use of contraceptives; however, he was also convinced that if these Catholics knew that it was wrong, they would desist. He called for the Church to speak out with clarity and authority. But the Church was not all of one mind. In fact, in some instances, the very foundations underlying the attack on Sulloway contends:

> The more one studies Catholic literature on birth control the more apparent it becomes that the Church has made a philosophical mistake of major proportions in contending that the natural law forbids the use of contraceptives. . . . Historically, the mistake arises out of two misconceptions, a needlessly dogmatic construction of the Onan incident and an interpretation of natural law which is neither necessary nor provable.[101]

On December 31, 1930, Pope Pius XI issued his *Casti Connubii* which amounted to the strongest statement issued

---

[99] He was a priest who served in France, Austria and the United States. He was a strong Thomist and he had a deep concern for the needs of modern society.
[100] 54, 1916, pp. 684–96.
[101] Sulloway, *op. cit.*, p. 157.

since the bull of Sixtus V-*Effraenatam*. He claimed that the goods of marriage were summarized according to the Augustinian formula—offspring, fidelity, and sacrament. An offspring was the primary good and those who deprived marriage of its natural power of procreative life actually violate the laws of God and nature. This is a reasonably strong statement. However, with the coming of Vatican II, even statements such as the above lose their impact as criticism is leveled at no less a power than the papal authority itself. At Vatican II the declaration was made that the infallibility extended "only as far as the deposit of divine revelation extends." [102] The question at point is: what does revelation say with clarity on the control of human reproduction?

One of the areas of concession granted not only by the Roman Catholic Church but by most Christians was that of the sterile period. This period as a means for non-generation intercourse was considered not only with theological and practical interest, but also with medical concern. This has been going on since approximately 1850. Some of the writings which brought this particular discussion to the fore were Leo Latz's *The Rhythm of Sterility and Fertility In Women* and Valere Coucke and James J. Walsh's *The Sterile Period in Family Life*. In 1880 the pentitentiary responded with a mediating emphasis. However, on October 29, 1951, Pope Pius XII, while speaking to the Italian Catholic Society of Midwives, stated that the rhythm method was open to all Christian couples, and not only as an alternative to be practiced cautiously by some offending onanists.[103] This was the most complete statement since *Casti Connubii*. One month later, Pius XII gave general approval of the regulation of birth. Here at last is a rather sharp line drawn between sexual intercourse and procreation.

---

[102] *Acta Apoltolicae Sedis*, 22:560.
[103] A. A. S. 43:845–46.

Again, however, it must be remembered that openness does not amount to concession.[104]

According to an American theologian, Gerald Kelly, writing on medical morality, once the Pope conceded that the principal of "the good of the whole" was to be interpreted as what is good for the person, it may be argued that certain organs may be destroyed in order to preserve the whole person or personality. This principle would not only allow for organ transplants, but married persons could have intercourse without the intended procreation if it could be substantiated that the health of the wife or the child as persons is at stake. This would hold even if sterilization is viewed as a form of destruction or mutilization.

THE PILL

Another factor which produced a most intriguing discussion not only among Christians but among all civilized people was the coming to market of the first contraceptive pill—hesperidin.[105] This pill which was first merchandised in the early 1950's was followed by another pill in 1953—progesterone, which was more effective than hesperidin. Progesterone regulated the menstrual cycle, which in turn allowed for the practice of the rhythm method with greater confidence.

All of this further stimulated the discussion to include mental health as a prime factor. Increasingly it was be-

---

[104] The Roman Catholic Church has utilized many forms of power to keep in check the forces advocating the propagation of birth control information. On the use of boycotts in the areas of social welfare and hospitals, see Sulloway, *Birth Control and Catholic Doctrine*, pp. 49ff. Were our study to have been theological rather than historical the subject of Church and state would be of major significance. Norman St. John-Stevas says pointedly, "In contemporary pluralist society many of the tensions and misunderstanding between Catholics, Protestants and Liberals may be traced back to radically conflicting views of the functions of the state." (*Life, Death and the Law*, Bloomington, 1961, pp. 24, 25).

[105] Hesperidin is an anti-enzyme which affects the hyaluronidose present in the semen.

coming a pathological study. Commenting on the pill, Franz Böckle says that with the information supplied by D. John Rock [106] and the gynecologist J. Ferin, Janssens is convinced that the use of antiovulation pills does not violate the structure of the act. To use the pill or the infertile period is the same. The sterilization in the rhythm method amounts to the same as using the pill. The suppression of ovulation does not destroy this reproductive power.[107]

Just when it appeared that the Roman Catholic Church might make a concession to the advocates of the use of some contraceptives, John Heenan, Archbishop of Westminster, replied to an article written by Thomas D. Roberts, former Archbishop of Bombay, in which he seriously questioned the legitimacy of the openness of some Catholic minds on this subject. Heenan said:

> It has been suggested that the Church could approve the practice of contraception. But the Church, while free to revise her own positive laws, has no power of any kind to alter the laws of God . . . contraception . . . is not an open question, for it is against the law of God.[108]

Heenan's statement, though supported by tradition, fell still-born on the ears of the people who heard Pope Paul VI (June 23, 1964) announce that the Church was again giving serious consideration to the subject of man's control of human reproduction.

HUMAN INSEMINATION

Although there are instances of a kind of insemination reported as having taken place in the distant past,[109] as the

---

[106] Rock, D. John, *The Time Has Come*, New York, 1963.

[107] *Birth Control*, pp. 114, 115.

[108] Heenan, John, *The Universe*, May 7, 1964 and reprinted in *The Pill and Birth Regulation*, ed., Pyle, pp. 95–99. See also, George A. Kelly, *Birth Control and Catholics*, New York, 1963, p. 100.

[109] See *Hebrew Medical Journal*, 2:164 (1942), "Artificial Insemination in the Talmud."

term is now used, it depicts a technique used first with humans less than two hundred years ago.[110] There are two kinds of artificial insemination. When the semen employed is from the husband (*homologous*) it is identified by (A.I.H.) and when the semen from a third person is used (heterologous), the identity is (A.I.D.). When these two are combined, that is, a mixture of the husband's and the donor's semen, the identity is (A.I.H.D.).

The extent of the practice of any of the three types is difficult to ascertain. The legality of the first appears to be in order; however, the use of the donor's semen might involve the problem of adultery.

The most obvious problem for some Christians has to do with A.I.D. and A.I.H.D. Among Protestants there appear to be few, if any, difficulties with A.I.H. However, this is not the case with the Roman Catholics. Still contending that the natural use of the several organs is intrinsically related to procreation, they maintain that the conjugal act must be experienced. Therefore, if a means can be devised whereby the necessary removal and insertion of semen conjoin with the act of intercourse, the discussion would have grounds for further consideration.

It appears that the message of Pius XII, "The Pope Speaks" (1957) in which he allowed only "assisted" insemination, still stands. Yet even this allowance would not have been possible in the 1940's. The full results of Vatican II are still unknown.

A FEW TEMPORARY CONCLUSIONS

In summary then, since approximately 1880 the situation in the entire civilized world has seen man taking upon himself a more responsible position. As man has increased in his understanding of himself and the world in which he is living, he has attempted to make appropriate adjustments.

---

[110] See St. John-Stevas, *op. cit.*, pp. 116ff.

The planned family has been accepted as a general rule; there has been something of an openness in the rethinking of the nature and the function of marriage; the explosion of populations in many lands is a reality; the status of women has been improved; the educational level of various persons has been expanded; the communication of semi-technical information now reaches countless millions of people in many lands. Also, knowledge in the organic sciences as well as psychological insights have grown radically and has been communicated widely. It can be seen from all of this that moral theology has not been produced in a vacuum nor on a horizontal line. Medical technicians, psychologists, theologians, as well as scholars from other disciplines both from within as well as outside the Church have contributed in the attempt to formulate a meaningful morality.

With the new spirit of freedom in almost every area of man's experience came the changing standards in the specific area of the prohibition of contraceptives with many Christian groups.[111]

Scholars of note who have taken a position against an absolute prohibition of contraception include Karl Barth, Emil Brunner, Jacques Ellul, Reinhold Niebuhr and Helmut Thielecke.

Although there was no mention of contraceptives as such,

---

[111] Those that have experienced a significant change within the last 40 years include the following:

1931	Congregational Christian General Council
1936	General Convention of the United Church of Canada
1939	Methodist Conference of Great Britain
1943	British Council of Churches
1944	A special Commission of the Church of Scotland
1951	The bishops of the Church of Sweden (Lutheran)
1952	The General Synod of the Netherlands Reformed Church
1954	Augustana Evangelical Lutheran Church
1956	General Conference of the Methodist Church in the U.S.A.
1956	The United Lutheran Church in the U.S.A.
1956	The National Council of the Reformed Churches of France
1956	The Church of Finland (Lutheran)
1958	The International Convention of the Disciples of Christ
1959	The World Council of Churches

Schema 13 in the Vatican II Council in 1964 calls for a renewal of effort by anthropologists, psychologists, sociologists, and Christian couples to collaborate with the theologians so that some practical solutions may be forthcoming. The Schema went on to say that each married couple should decide responsibly concerning the number of children they ought to have. One of the more recent prominent scholars also challenging the Roman Catholic stand against contraceptives is Thomas E. Roberts.[112] After relinquishing his post as Archbishop, and feeling free of censorship, he claimed that he knew of no rational argument which would rule out contraception.[113] There are several other important books which have appeared in recent years, among them are those written by a husband-wife team. In some cases, at least, these couples have not practiced something contrary to the authoritative utterances of their Church, thus freeing themselves from the criticism of self-justification.[114]

SOME CONTEMPORARY EVALUATIONS

Pope Paul VI gave expression of the thought of the Church at the present time when on June 23, 1964, he said:

> The problem is extremely complex and delicate. The Church recognizes in it multiple aspects, multiple competencies, among which certainly the first is that of the spouses, their liberty, their conscience, their duty. But the Church has also to affirm her own competency, which is that of the laws of God. The Church has to proclaim such laws of God in the light of scientific, social, and psychological truths which, in recent time, have received new and most ample studies and docu-

---

[112] An English Jesuit, who was the former Archbishop of Bombay.

[113] Roberts, Thomas E., *Contraception and Holiness*, New York, 1964.

[114] See *What Modern Catholics Think About Birth Control*, ed. W. Birmingham, New York, 1964. For a brief interpretation of a Protestant see John W. Montgomery's article, "How to Decide the Birth Control Question," Appendix 5.

mentation. It will be necessary to pay attention to this development of the question both in its theoretical and practical aspects. And this is precisely what the Church is doing.[115]

In the face of all the disciplines of learning, including the progress of biological and psychological data, Christians have attempted to meet the attacks and the modifications with personal concern. Intercourse exclusively for procreation, the prohibition of intercourse during menstruation, the idea that intercourse has only one natural position, and that pregnancy forbids additional intercourse have all disappeared as basic Christian opinions. In view of these alterations, is it not to be expected that contraception, certain instances of abortion and artificial insemination (A.I.H.) may also receive a more responsible analysis, looking upon them not as absolutes but as values? This appears to be the trend, with increasing attention given to the value of the whole person as expressed in the totality of life. Ouwerkerk, speaking within the mentality of Vatican II urges an evaluation of this type of thinking. He says:

> The emphatic and intransigent rejection of contraception by the *magisterium* makes one suppose that the Church sees connections between this norm and religious reality, i.e., the salvation aspect of marriage. But the moral uncertainty of this point grows day by day, and thus it becomes more and more difficult for Catholics to live by this norm.[116]

In the same direction but more philosophical and therefore primary to moral actions as well as being related to theological structures and even hermeneutical principles is the far-reaching statement of Franz Böckle:

> In the first part E. Schillebeeckx [117] deals with the principles underlying the question of whether the

---

[115]A. A. S. 56:588.

[116] *Ibid.*, p. 20.

[117] Shillebeeckx, E., *Jaarboek Der Katholieke Theologen*, 1961, Hilversum, 1963, pp. 5–51.

norms of morality can change. One should start from the fact that all human knowledge is a matter of perspective, i.e., it is a view of the truth from a particular point so that every insight can grow and become more complete. One and the same significant factor can be illuminated from various directions so that there are different ways of understanding it and these different views can complement each other. We must, therefore, draw a clear distinction between the truth itself and the truth insofar as man possesses it. Truth in itself (ultimately God) does not change; even our affirmation of the truth does not really change. What does change is the perspective along which we approach the truth. The more we are conscious of this perspective character of our knowledge, the less danger there is of falling into relativism because the more perspectives we have the closer we come to absolute truth. . . . The theology of the last twenty years has made the real, though not adequate, distinction between the moral norms for married life as a whole and the individual act of consummation. The real *actus humanus* of marriage is expressed in the basic decision to enter the married state, so that the individual act of intercourse is but an *actus humanus* insofar as it shares in this overall decision. . . . Those distinctions have not yet been embodied in ecclesiastical documents.[118]

THE ENCYCLICAL LETTER OF POPE PAUL VI

With all due respect to those who feared a liberalization of the guidelines on birth control as held by the Roman Catholic Church, a knowledge of the recent history of the struggle seemed to dictate the conclusion that the next papal utterance was destined to allow a control beyond that offered by use of the rhythm method. So when it was announced that Pope Paul VI would read his Encyclical Letter on the 25th of July (1968), feast of St. James the Apostle, nervous enthusiasm ran high. But as the Encyclical (*Humanae Vitae*) was read from St. Peter's in Rome, what was hoped to have been a day of liberation became for countless

---

[118] *Ibid.*, "Birth Control—A Survey of German, French, and Dutch Literature on the Question of Birth Control," pp. 122, 124.

thousands of clergy and laity a day of bewilderment, sorrow and even anger.

Although there was an acknowledged awareness of new aspects of the problem, after stressing the necessity of adhering to the doctrines of the Church, including "natural law," Pope Paul said,

> . . . the Church, calling men back to the observance of the norms of the natural law, as interpreted by their constant doctrine, teaches that each and every marriage act (*quilibet matrimonii usus*) must remain open to the transmission of life.[119]

The extent of the influence sociological, medical and psychological studies have had upon Pope Paul's thinking is clarified when he says,

> If, then, there are serious motives to space out births, which derive from the physical or psychological conditions of husband and wife, or from external conditions, the Church teaches that it is then licit to take into account the natural rhythms immanent in the generative functions, for the use of marriage in the infecund periods only, and in this way to regulate birth without ending the moral principles which have been recalled earlier.[120]

Not only has this Encyclical Letter stirred up a fervid protest among the Roman Catholics, but in that the letter was directed to public authorities, men of science and medicine, Christian husbands and wives, as well as priests and bishops, protest was heard from all quarters of the civilized world.

One of the serious by-products of this confrontation is the attack being made within the Roman Catholic Church on the Pope's "authority" to speak with binding force in the area of morals. As stated by Dr. J. J. Palen,

---

[119] *Boston Sunday Herald Traveler*, Aug. 4, 1968.
[120] *Ibid.*

The question is not, as the press suggests, whether or not to practice birth control; the great majority of American Catholics have already decided to solve that issue in the bedroom rather than in the confessional. The deeper question is whether concerned Catholics can much longer justify to themselves membership in an institutional church officially committed to policies they by conscience oppose.[121]

At the writing of this chapter, the outcome is problematical.

CONCLUSION

According to our survey of the problem, Protestants, from the inception of the Reformation, had accepted a definition of marriage sufficiently broad as to include the use of contraceptives in the control of human reproduction. Whereas the papal decrees of the Roman Catholic Church so limited the definition of marriage to include basically, and all but exclusively, the idea that procreation constitutes the purpose of marriage, thus setting the stage for the current controversy. So acute is this confrontation that the guidelines within the Roman Catholic Church may not be the only changes that are forthcoming, but the lines which exist between Roman Catholics and Protestants also may undergo radical change.

A problem so close to the center of human existence has the potential of revolutionizing man in his basic social relationships. So many priests and laity alike within the Roman Catholic Communion have so committed themselves to a liberal interpretation of birth control that there appears to be no exit, Encyclical or no.

---

[121] Palen, John J., "Catholicism, Contraception and Conscience," in *The Christian Century*, Vol. LXXXV, No. 37 (September 11, 1968).

**FURTHER
TOOLS FOR
RESEARCH**

POSITIONS AND STATEMENTS OF PROTESTANT BODIES ON CONTRACEPTION, STERILIZATION AND ABORTION

SUMMARY

The statements which follow from the Massachusetts Council of Churches and the American Baptist Convention deal only with abortion and represent the more liberal segment of Protestant thought on the subject. They are reprinted by courtesy of these organizations. Relatively few Protestant groups have issued official pronouncements on the subjects treated in this volume, perhaps because opinions are so diverse. The lack of specific discussions addressed to the subject only underscores the need for studies such as this one.

While not an official denominational position on the subject, two excellent booklets have been prepared by the Lutheran Church in America. These are: *Ethics of Conception and Contraception* and *Problem of Abortion*. They may be obtained at 50 cents each from the Board of Social Ministry, Lutheran Church in America, 231 Madison Avenue, New York, N.Y. 10016.

Views of the Episcopal churches on these issues may be reviewed in the Lambeth Conference Reports, obtainable from Seabury Press, New York. Statements of the United Presbyterian Church in the United States of America on conception, abortion, sterilization and artificial insemination may be obtained by requesting the booklet, *Responsible Marriage and Parenthood:* Resolutions adopted by the 174th General Assembly of the United Presbyterian Church in the U.S.A. in May, 1962. Requests should be addressed to: Office of the General Assembly, Witherspoon Building, Philadelphia, 19107.

POSITIONS AND STATEMENTS OF PROTESTANT BODIES ON CONTRACEPTION, STERILIZATION AND ABORTION

MASSACHUSETTS COUNCIL OF CHURCHES, 14 BEACON STREET, BOSTON 02108

Abortion

A Policy Statement adopted by the Assembly, November 30, 1967.

The problem of abortion—the induced termination of fetal life prior to viability—has become increasingly visible to the public as attempts are made in the various states to liberalize existing laws on abortion. The Massachusetts Council of Churches recognizes the existence of sincere differences of opinion on this subject, but believes that the laws of society on abortion must be adjusted to provide relief from unnecessary human suffering. Therefore, we advocate revisions in the Massachusetts abortion law, which is highly ambiguous but apparently permits abortion only to save the life of the mother.

In accord with the Judeo-Christian tradition, our position is founded on respect for the worth of persons and a commitment to maximize human well-being within the context of the community. We firmly acknowledge the prospective parents' moral responsibility to the future child, the binding duty to provide the best possible conditions for a creative life. However, the parents' responsibility to potential life can be invalidated by certain tragic circumstances, when the responsibility cannot be fulfilled adequately or at all. We claim that an important distinction exists between actual and potential human life, and that duties to promote the welfare of actual life may outweigh duties to potential life in particular situations, thereby making abortion morally permissible in these cases.

Among the reasons for favoring changes in the law are the following: 1) Illegal abortions are numerous and dangerous. Many desperate women are resorting to underworld "quacks" or abortifacients, with the consequent dangers of injuries or fatalities. Although the legal remedies we advocate will certainly not eliminate illegal abortions, they will at least prevent many illegal abortions that occur for morally justifiable reasons. 2) The birth of a child may be a virtual disaster in the situations of many women. Pregnancy resulting from rape or incest may cause the child to be a heavy psychological burden to the mother and/or father. The contraction of diseases, such as rubella or cancer, before or during pregnancy may result in physical deformities or mental deficiencies in the child, or endanger the life or health of the mother if the pregnancy is brought to term. In some cases, the stigma of scandal or other fears may lead the potential mother to attempt suicide or, more likely, become emotionally incapacitated to live normally.

Giving due consideration to such mitigating circumstances, the Massachusetts Council of Churches favors the legalization of abortion in cases in which the loss in human values by bearing the child is greater than the loss by aborting the fetus. The Model Penal Code of the American Law Institute seems to cover the major situations in which this criterion is applicable. Specifically, the Code proposes the legalization of abortion when the woman's physical or mental health is impaired or endangered, when the child might be born with serious physical or mental defects, or when pregnancy results from felonious intercourse such as rape or incest. Recognizing that abortion is a procedure which terminates potential life and requires the constraints of law, the Council believes that the General Court of Massachusetts should enact legislation which incorporates the above proposals of the Model Penal Code. Additionally, such legislation should provide that legal abortions must be approved by qualified physicians, be performed only in accredited hospitals, be preceded and followed by counseling of the patient, and be performed only with her explicit consent.

THE AMERICAN BAPTIST CONVENTION, VALLEY FORGE, PENNSYLVANIA 19481
A POLICY STATEMENT ADOPTED ON JUNE 2, 1968.
Abortion

Because Christ calls us to affirm the freedom of persons and the sanctity of life, we recognize that abortion should be a matter of responsible personal decision. To this end we as American Baptists urge that legislation be enacted to provide:

1) That the termination of a pregnancy prior to the end of the 12th week (first trimester) be at the request of the individual(s) concerned and be regarded as an elective medical procedure governed by the laws regulating medical practice and licensure.

2) After that period the termination of a pregnancy shall be performed only by a duly licensed physician at the request of the individual(s) concerned, in a regularly li-

censed hospital, for one of the following reasons as suggested by the Model Penal Code of the American Law Institute:

a) When documented evidence exists that this is a danger to the physical or mental health of the woman;

b) When there is documented evidence that the conceptus has a physical or mental defect;

c) When there is documented evidence that the pregnancy was the result of rape, incest or other felonious acts.

Further we encourage our churches to provide sympathetic and realistic counseling on family planning and abortion.

We commend study, research and development of understanding on the part of the populace led by the people of our churches toward an enlightened view of this provocative problem.

Appendix 2

HUMANAE VITAE
A PAPAL ENCYCLICAL
JULY 1968

ENCYCLICAL ON THE REGULATION OF BIRTH

Following is a translation of the encyclical letter of Pope Paul VI, issued July 29 at the Vatican, on the regulation of birth.

Encyclical letter of His Holiness Pope Paul VI on the regulation of birth.

To the venerable Patriarchs, Archbishops and Bishops and other local ordinaries in peace and communion with the Apostolic See, to priests, the faithful and to all men of good will.

Venerable brothers and beloved sons:

The Transmission of Life

1. The most serious duty of transmitting human life, for which married persons are the free and responsible collabo-

rators of God the Creator, has always been a source of great joys to them, even if sometimes accompanied by not a few difficulties and by distress.

At all times the fulfillment of this duty has posed grave problems to the conscience of married persons, but, with the recent evolution of society, changes have taken place that give rise to new questions which the Church could not ignore, having to do with a matter which so closely touches upon the life and happiness of men.

NEW ASPECTS OF THE PROBLEM AND COMPETENCY OF THE MAGISTERIUM

New Formulation of the Problem

2. The changes which have taken place are in fact noteworthy and of varied kinds. In the first place, there is the rapid demographic development. Fear is shown by many that world population is growing more rapidly than the available resources, with growing distress to many families and developing countries, so that the temptation for authorities to counter this danger with radical measures is great. Moreover, working and lodging conditions, as well as increased exigencies both in the economic field and in that of education, often make the proper education of an elevated number of children difficult today. A change is also seen both in the manner of considering the person of woman and her place in society, and in the value to be attributed to conjugal love in marriage, and also in the appreciation to be made of the meaning of conjugal acts in relation to that love.

Finally and above all, man has made stupendous progress in the domination and rational organization of the forces of nature, such that he tends to extend this domination to his own total being: to the body, to psychical life, to social life and even to the laws which regulate the transmission of life.

3. This new state of things gives rise to new questions.

Granted the conditions of life today, and granted the meaning which conjugal relations have with respect to the harmony between husband and wife and to their mutual fidelity, would not a revision of the ethical norms, in force up to now, seem to be advisable, especially when it is considered that they cannot be observed without sacrifices, sometimes heroic sacrifices?

And again: by extending to this field the application of the so-called "principle of totality," could it not be admitted that the intention of a less abundant but more rationalized fecundity might transform a materially sterilizing intervention into a licit and wise control of birth? Could it not be admitted, that is, that the finality of procreation pertains to the ensemble of conjugal life, rather than to its single acts? It is also asked whether, in view of the increased sense of responsibility of modern man, the moment has not come for him to entrust to his reason and his will, rather than to the biological rhythms of his organism, the task of regulating birth.

Competency of the Magisterium

4. Such questions required from the teaching authority of the Church a new and deeper reflection upon the principles of the moral teaching on marriage: a teaching founded on the natural law, illuminated and enriched by divine revelation.

No believer will wish to deny that the teaching authority of the Church is competent to interpret even the natural moral law. It is, in fact, indisputable, as our predecessors have many times declared,[1] that Jesus Christ, when com-

---

[1] Cf. Pius IX, encyclical Qui Pluribus, Nov. 9, 1846; in PII IX P. M. Acta, I, pp. 9–10; St. Pius X, encyc. Singulari Quadam Sept. 24, 1912; in AAS IV (1912), p. 685; Pius XI, encyc. Casti Connubii, Dec. 31, 1930; in AAS XXII (1930), pp. 579–581; Pius XII, allocution Magnificate Dominum to the episcopate of the Catholic world, Nov. 2, 1954; in AAS XLVI (1954), pp. 671–672; John XXIII, encyc. Mater et Magistra, May 15, 1961; in AAS LIII (1961), p. 457.

municating to Peter and to the Apostles His divine authority and sending them to teach all nations His commandments,[2] constituted them as guardians and authentic interpreters of all the moral law, not only, that is, of the law of the Gospel, but also of the natural law, which is also an expression of the will of God, the faithful fulfilment of which is equally necessary for salvation.[3]

Conformably to this mission of hers, the Church has always provided—and even more amply in recent times—a coherent teaching concerning both the nature of marriage and the correct use of conjugal rights and the duties of husband and wife.[4]

Special Studies

5. The consciousness of that same mission induced us to confirm and enlarge the study commission which our predecessor Pope John XXIII of happy memory had instituted in March, 1963. That commission which included, besides several experts in the various pertinent disciplines also married couples, had as its scope the gathering of opinions on the new questions regarding conjugal life, and in particular on the regulation of births, and of furnishing opportune elements of information so that the magisterium could give an

---

[2] Cf. Matt. 28, 18–19.

[3] Cf. Matt. 7, 21.

[4] Cf. Catechismus Romanus Concilii Tridentini, part II, ch. VIII; Leo XIII, encyc. Arcanum, Feb. 19, 1880; in Acta Leonis XIII, II (1881), pp. 26–29; Pius XI, encyc. Divini Illius Magistri, Dec. 31, 1929, in AAS XXII (1930), pp. 58–61; encyc. Casti Connubii, in AAS XXII (1930), pp. 545–546; Pius XII, alloc. to the Italian medico-biological union of St. Luke, Nov. 12, 1944, in Discorsi e Radio-messaggi, VI, pp. 191–192; to the Italian Catholic union of midwives Oct. 29, 1951, in AAS XLIII (1951), pp. 857–859; to the seventh Congress of the International Society of Haematology, Sept. 12, 1958, in AAS L (1958), pp. 734–735; John XXIII, encyc. Mater et Magistra, in AAS LIII (1961), pp. 446–447; Codex Iuris Canonici, Canon 1067; Can. 1968, S 1, Can. 1066 S 1–2; Second Vatican Council, Pastoral constitution Gaudium et Spes, nos. 47–52.

adequate reply to the expectation not only of the faithful, but also of world opinion.[5]

The work of these experts, as well as the successive judgments and counsels spontaneously forwarded by or expressly requested from a good number of our brothers in the episcopate, have permitted us to measure more exactly all the aspects of this complex matter. Hence with all our heart we express to each of them our lively gratitude.

Reply of the Magisterium

6. The conclusions at which the commission arrived could not, nevertheless, be considered by us as definitive, nor dispense us from a personal examination of this serious question; and this also because, within the commission itself, no full concordance of judgments concerning the moral norms to be proposed had been reached, and above all because certain criteria of solutions had emerged which departed from the moral teaching on marriage proposed with constant firmness by the teaching authority of the Church.

Therefore, having attentively sifted the documentation laid before us, after mature reflection and assiduous prayers, we now intend, by virtue of the mandate entrusted to us by Christ, to give our reply to these grave questions.

DOCTRINAL PRINCIPLES

A Total Vision of Man

7. The problem of birth, like every other problem regarding human life, is to be considered, beyond partial perspectives—whether of the biological or psychological, demographic or sociological orders—in the light of an in-

---

[5] Cf. Paul VI, allocution to the Sacred College, June 23, 1964, in AAS LVI (1964), p. 588; to the Commission for Study of Problems of Population, Family and Birth March 27, 1965, in AAS LVII (1965), p. 388, to the National Congress of the Italian Society of Obstetrics and Gynaecology, Oct. 29, 1966, in AAS LVIII (1966), p. 1168.

tegral vision of man and of his vocation, not only his natural and earthly, but also his supernatural and eternal vocation. And since, in the attempt to justify artificial methods of birth control, many have appealed to the demands both of conjugal love and of "responsible parenthood" it is good to state very precisely the true concept of these two great realities of married life, referring principally to what was recently set forth in this regard, and in a highly authoritative form, by the Second Vatican Council in its pastoral constitution Gaudium et Spes.

Conjugal Love

8. Conjugal love reveals its true nature and nobility when it is considered in its supreme origin, God, who is love,[6] "the Father, from whom every family in heaven and on earth is named".[7]

Marriage is not, then, the effect of chance or the product of evolution of unconscious natural forces; it is the wise institution of the Creator to realize in mankind His design of love. By means of the reciprocal personal gift of self, proper and exclusive to them, husband and wife tend towards the communion of their beings in view of mutual personal perfection, to collaborate with God in the generation and education of new lives.

For baptized persons, moreover, marriage invests the dignity of a sacramental sign of grace, inasmuch as it represents the union of Christ and of the Church.

Its Characteristics

9. Under this light, there clearly appear the characteristic marks and demands of conjugal love, and it is of supreme importance to have an exact idea of these.

This love is first of all fully human, that is to say, of the

---

[6] Cf. I John, 4, 8.
[7] Cf. Eph., 3, 15.

senses and of the spirit at the same time. It is not, then a simple transport of instinct and sentiment, but also, and principally, an act of the free will, intended to endure and to grow by means of the joys and sorrows of daily life, in such a way that husband and wife become one only heart and one only soul, and together attain their human perfection.

Then, this love is total, that is to say, it is a very special form of personal friendship, in which husband and wife generously share everything, without undue reservations or selfish calculations. Whoever truly loves his marriage partner loves not only for what he receives, but for the partner's self, rejoicing that he can enrich his partner with the gift of himself.

Again, this love is faithful and exclusive until death. Thus in fact do bride and groom conceive it to be on the day when they freely and in full awareness assume the duty of the marriage bond. A fidelity, this, which can sometimes be difficult, but is always possible, always noble and meritorious, as no one can deny. The example of so many married persons down through the centuries shows, not only that fidelity is according to the nature of marriage, but also that it is a source of profound and lasting happiness and finally, this love is fecund for it is not exhausted by the communion between husband and wife, but is destined to continue, raising up new lives. "Marriage and conjugal love are by their nature ordained toward the begetting and educating of children. Children are really the supreme gift of marriage and contribute very substantially to the welfare of their parents".[8]

Responsible Parenthood

10. Hence conjugal love requires in husband and wife an awareness of their mission of "responsible parenthood,"

---

[8] Cf. II Vat. Council, Pastoral const. Gaudium et Spes, No. 50.

which today is rightly much insisted upon, and which also must be exactly understood. Consequently it is to be considered under different aspects which are legitimate and connected with one another.

In relation to the biological processes, responsible parenthood means the knowledge and respect of their functions; human intellect discovers in the power of giving life biological laws which are part of the human person.[9]

In relation to the tendencies of instinct or passion, responsible parenthood means that necessary dominion which reason and will must exercise over them.

In relation to physical, economic, psychological and social conditions, responsible parenthood is exercised, either by the deliberate and generous decision to raise a numerous family, or by the decision, made for grave motives and with due respect for the moral law, to avoid for the time being, or even for an indeterminate period, a new birth.

Responsible parenthood also and above all implies a more profound relationship to the objective moral order established by God, of which a right conscience is the faithful interpreter. The responsible exercise of parenthood implies, therefore, that husband and wife recognize fully their own duties towards God, towards themselves, towards the family and towards society, in a correct hierarchy of values.

In the task of transmitting life, therefore, they are not free to proceed completely at will, as if they could determine in a wholly autonomous way the honest path to follow; but they must conform their activity to the creative intention of God, expressed in the very nature of marriage and of its acts, and manifested by the constant teaching of the Church.[10]

Respect for the Nature and Purpose of the Marriage Act

11. These acts, by which husband and wife are united in

---

[9] Cf. St. Thomas, Summa Theologica, I–II, q. 94, art. 2.
[10] Cf. Pastoral Const. Gaudium et Spes, nos. 50, 51.

chaste intimacy, and by means of which human life is transmitted, are, as the council recalled, "noble and worthy" [11],
and they do not cease to be lawful if, for causes independent
of the will of husband and wife, they are foreseen to be
infecund, since they always remain ordained towards expressing and consolidating their union. In fact, as experience bears witness, not every conjugal act is followed by a
new life. God has wisely disposed natural laws and rhythms
of fecundity which, of themselves, cause a separation in the
succession of births. Nonetheless the Church, calling men
back to the observance of the norms of the natural law, as
interpreted by their constant doctrine, teaches that each
and every marriage act (quilibet matrimonii usus) must
remain open to the transmission of life.[12]

Two Inseparable Aspects: Union and Procreation

12. That teaching, often set forth by the magisterium,
is founded upon the inseparable connection, willed by God
and unable to be broken by man on his own initiative, between the two meanings of the conjugal act: the unitive
meaning and the procreative meaning. Indeed, by its intimate structure, the conjugal act, while most closely uniting
husband and wife, capacitates them for the generation of
new lives, according to laws inscribed in the very being of
man and of woman. By safeguarding both these essential
aspects, the unitive and the procreative, the conjugal act
preserves in its fullness the sense of true mutual love and
its ordination towards man's most high calling to parenthood. We believe that the men of our day are particularly
capable of seizing the deeply reasonable and human character of this fundamental principle.

Faithfulness to God's Design

13. It is in fact justly observed that a conjugal act im-

---

[11] Ibid.. no. 49.
[12] Cf. Pius XI, encyc. Casti Connubii, in AAS XXII (1930), p.
560; Pius XII, in AAS XLIII (1951), p. 843.

posed upon one's partner without regard for his or her condition and lawful desires is not a true act of love, and therefore denies an exigency of right moral order in the relationships between husband and wife. Hence, one who reflects well must also recognize that a reciprocal act of love, which jeopardizes the responsibility to transmit life which God the Creator, according to particular laws, inserted therein, is in contradiction with the design constitutive of marriage, and with the will of the Author of life. To use this divine gift destroying, even if only partially, its meaning and its purpose is to contradict the nature both of man and of woman and of their most intimate relationship, and therefore it is to contradict also the plan of God and His will. On the other hand, to make use of the gift of conjugal love while respecting the laws of the generative process means to acknowledge oneself not to be the arbiter of the sources of human life, but rather the minister of the design established by the Creator. In fact, just as man does not have unlimited dominion over his body in general, so also, with particular reason, he has no such dominion over his generative faculties as such, because of their intrinsic ordination towards raising up life, of which God is the principle. "Human life is sacred," Pope John XXIII recalled; "from its very inception it reveals the creating hand of God." [13]

Illicit Ways of Regulating Birth

14. In conformity with these landmarks in the human and Christian vision of marriage, we must once again declare that the direct interruption of the generative process already begun, and, above all, directly willed and procured abortion, even if for therapeutic reasons, are to be absolutely excluded as licit means of regulating birth [14].

---

[13] Cf. John XXIII, encyc. Mater et Magistra, in AAS LIII (1961), p. 447.

[14] Cf. Catechismus Romanus Concilii Tridentini, part. II, Ch. VIII; Pius XI, encyc. Casti Connubii, in AAS XXII (1930), pp.

Equally to be excluded, as the teaching authority of the Church has frequently declared, is direct sterilization, whether perpetual or temporary, whether of the man or of the woman.[15] Similarly excluded is every action which, either in anticipation of the conjugal act, or in its accomplishment, or in the development of its natural consequences, proposes, whether as an end or as a means, to render procreation impossible.[16]

To justify conjugal acts made intentionally infecund, one cannot invoke as valid reasons the lesser evil, or the fact that such acts would constitute a whole together with the fecund acts already performed or to follow later, and hence would share in one and the same moral goodness. In truth, if it is sometimes licit to tolerate a lesser evil in order to avoid a greater evil or to promote a greater good [17] it is not licit, even for the gravest reasons, to do evil so that good may follow therefrom [18] that is, to make into the object of a positive act of the will something which is intrinsically disorder, and hence unworthy of the human person, even when the intention is to safeguard or promote individual, family or social well-being. Consequently it is an error to think that a conjugal act which is deliberately made infecund and so is intrinsically dishonest could be made honest and right by the ensemble of a fecund conjugal life.

562–564; Pius XII, discorsi e Radiomessaggi, VI (1944), pp. 191–192; AAS XLIII (1951), pp. 842–843; pp. 857–859; John XXIII, encyc. Pacem in Terris, Apr. 11, 1963, in AAS LV (1963), pp. 259–260; Gaudium et Spes, no. 51.

[15] Cf. Pius XI, encyc. Casti Connubii, in AAS XXII (1930) p. 565; decree of the Holy Office, Feb. 22, 1940, in AAS L (1958), pp. 734–735.

[16] Cf. Catechismus Romanus Concilii Tridentini, part. II, Ch. VIII; Pius XI, encyc. Casti Connubii, in AAS XXII (1930), pp. 559–561; Pius XII, AAS XLIII (1951), p. 843; AAS L. (1958), pp. 734–735; John XXIII, encyc. Mater et Magistra, in AAS LIII (1961) p. 447.

[17] Cf. Pius XII, alloc. to the National Congress of the Union of Catholic Jurists, Dec. 6, 1953, in AAS XLV (1953), pp. 798–799.

[18] Cf. Rom. 3, 8.

Licitness of Therapeutic Means

15. The Church, on the contrary, does not at all consider illicit the use of those therapeutic means truly necessary to cure diseases of the organism, even if an impediment to procreation, which may be foreseen, should result therefrom, provided such impediment is not, for whatever motive, directly willed [19].

Licitness of Recourse to Infecund Periods

16. To this teaching of the Church on conjugal morals, the objection is made today, as we observed earlier (no. 3), that it is the prerogative of the human intellect to dominate the energies offered by irrational nature and to orientate them towards an end conformable to the good of man. Now, some may ask: in the present case, is it not reasonable in many circumstances to have recourse to artificial birth control if, thereby, we secure the harmony and peace of the family, and better conditions for the education of the children already born? To this question it is necessary to reply with clarity: the Church is the first to praise and recommend the intervention of intelligence in a function which so closely associates the rational creature with his Creator; but she affirms that this must be done with respect for the order established by God.

If, then, there are serious motives to space out births, which derive from the physical or psychological conditions of husband and wife, or from external conditions, the Church teaches that it is then licit to take into account the natural rhythms immanent in the generative functions, for the use of marriage in the infecund periods only, and in this way to regulate birth without offending the moral principles which have been recalled earlier [20].

---

[19] Cf. Pius XII, alloc. to Congress of the Italian Association of Urology, Oct. 8, 1953, in AAS XLV (1953), pp. 674–675; AAS L (1958) pp. 734–735.

[20] Cf. Pius XII, AAS XLIII (1951), p. 846.

The Church is coherent with herself when she considers recourse to the infecund periods to be licit, while at the same time condemning, as being always illicit, the use of means directly contrary to fecundation, even if such use is inspired by reasons which may appear honest and serious. In reality, there are essential differences between the two cases; in the former, the married couple make legitimate use of a natural disposition; in the latter, they impede the development of natural processes. It is true that, in the one and the other case, the married couple are concordant in the positive will of avoiding children for plausible reasons, seeking the certainty that offspring will not arrive; but it is also true that only in the former case are they able to renounce the use of marriage in the fecund periods when, for just motives, procreation is not desirable, while making use of it during infecund periods to manifest their affection and to safeguard their mutual fidelity. By so doing, they give proof of a truly and integrally honest love.

Grave Consequences of Methods of Artificial Birth Control

17. Upright men can even better convince themselves of the solid grounds on which the teaching of the Church in this field is based, if they care to reflect upon the consequences of methods of artificial birth control. Let them consider, first of all, how wide and easy a road would thus be opened up towards conjugal infidelity and the general lowering of morality. Not much experience is needed in order to know human weakness, and to understand that men —especially the young, who are so vulnerable on this point— have need of encouragement to be faithful to the moral law, so that they must not be offered some easy means of eluding its observance. It is also to be feared that the man, growing used to the employment of anti-conceptive practices, may finally lose respect for the woman and, no longer caring for her physical and psychological equilibrium, may come to the

point of considering her as a mere instrument of selfish enjoyment, and no longer as his respected and beloved companion.

Let it be considered also that a dangerous weapon would thus be placed in the hands of those public authorities who take no heed of moral exigencies. Who could blame a government for applying to the solution of the problems of the community those means acknowledged to be licit for married couples in the solution of a family problem? Who will stop rulers from favoring, from even imposing upon their peoples, if they were to consider it necessary, the method of contraception which they judge to be most efficacious? In such a way men, wishing to avoid individual, family, or social difficulties encountered in the observance of the divine law, would reach the point of placing at the mercy of the intervention of public authorities the most personal and most reserved sector of conjugal intimacy.

Consequently, if the mission of generating life is not to be exposed to the arbitrary will of men, one must necessarily recognize unsurmountable limits to the possibility of man's domination over his own body and its functions; limits which no man, whether a private individual or one invested with authority, may licitly surpass. And such limits cannot be determined otherwise than by the respect due to the integrity of the human organism and its functions, according to the principles recalled earlier, and also according to the correct understanding of the "principle of totality" illustrated by our predecessor Pope Pius XII [21].

The Church Guarantor of True Human Values

18. It can be foreseen that this teaching will perhaps not be easily received by all: Too numerous are those voices— amplified by the modern means of propaganda—which are

---

[21] Cf. AAS XLV (1953), pp. 674–675; AAS XLVIII (1956), pp. 461–462.

contrary to the voice of the Church. To tell the truth, the Church is not surprised to be made, like her divine founder, a "sign of contradiction" [22], yet she does not because of this cease to proclaim with humble firmness the entire moral law, both natural and evangelical. Of such laws the Church was not the author, nor consequently can she be their arbiter; she is only their depositary and their interpreter, without ever being able to declare to be licit that which is not so by reason of its intimate and unchangeable opposition to the true good of man.

In defending conjugal morals in their integral wholeness, the Church knows that she contributes towards the establishment of a truly human civilization; she engages man not to abdicate from his own responsibility in order to rely on technical means; by that very fact she defends the dignity of man and wife. Faithful to both the teaching and the example of the Saviour, she shows herself to be the sincere and disinterested friend of men, whom she wishes to help, even during their earthly sojourn, "to share as sons in the life of the living God, the Father of all men" [23].

PASTORAL DIRECTIVES

The Church Mater et Magistra

19. Our words would not be an adequate expression of the thought and solicitude of the Church, mother and teacher of all peoples, if, after having recalled men to the observance and respect of the divine law regarding matrimony, we did not strengthen them in the path of honest regulation of birth, even amid the difficult conditions which today afflict families and peoples. The Church, in fact, cannot have a different conduct towards men than that of the Redeemer: She knows their weaknesses, has compas-

---

[22] Cf. Luke 2, 34.
[23] Cf. Paul VI, encyc. Populorum Progression, March 26, 1967, No. 21.

sion on the crowd, receives sinners; but she cannot renounce the teaching of the law which is, in reality, that law proper to a human life restored to its original truth and conducted by the spirit of God.[24]

Possibility of Observing the Divine Law

20. The teaching of the Church on the regulation of birth, which promulgates the divine law, will easily appear to many to be difficult or even impossible of actuation. And indeed, like all great beneficent realities, it demands serious engagement and much effort, individual, family and social effort. More than that, it would not be practicable without the help of God, who upholds and strengthens the good will of men. Yet, to anyone who reflects well, it cannot but be clear that such efforts ennoble man and are beneficial to the human community.

Mastery of Self

21. The honest practice of regulation of birth demands first of all that husband and wife acquire and possess solid convictions concerning the true values of life and of the family, and that they tend towards securing perfect self-mastery. To dominate instinct by means of one's reason and free will undoubtedly requires ascetical practices, so that the affective manifestations of conjugal life may observe the correct order, in particular with regard to the observance of periodic continence. Yet this discipline which is proper to the purity of married couples, far from harming conjugal love, rather confers on it a higher human value. It demands continual effort yet, thanks to its beneficent influence, husband and wife fully develop their personalities, being enriched with spiritual values. Such discipline bestows upon family life fruits of serenity and peace, and facilitates the solution of other problems; it favors attention for one's

---

[24] Cf. Rom. 8.

partner, helps both parties to drive out selfishness, the enemy of true love; and deepens their sense of responsibility. By its means, parents acquire the capacity of having a deeper and more efficacious influence in the education of their offspring; little children and youths grow up with a just appraisal of human values, and in the serene and harmonious development of their spiritual and sensitive faculties.

Creating an Atmosphere Favorable to Chastity

22. On this occasion, we wish to draw the attention of educators, and of all who perform duties of responsibility in regard to the common good of human society, to the need of creating an atmosphere favorable to education in chastity, that is, to the triumph of healthy liberty over license by means of respect for the moral order.

Everything in the modern media of social communications which leads to sense excitation and unbridled customs, as well as every form of pornography and licentious performances, must arouse the frank and unanimous reaction of all those who are solicitous for the progress of civilization and the defense of the common good of the human spirit. Vainly would one seek to justify such depravation with the pretext of artistic or scientific exigencies [25], or to deduce an argument from the freedom allowed in this sector by the public authorities.

Appeal to Public Authorities

23. To Rulers, who are those principally responsible for the common good, and who can do so much to safeguard moral customs, we say: Do not allow the morality of your peoples to be degraded; do not permit that by legal means practices contrary to the natural and divine law be intro-

---

[25] Cf. II Vatican Council, decree Inter Mirifica On the Media of Social Communication, nos. 6–7.

duced into that fundamental cell, the family. Quite other is the way in which public authorities can and must contribute to the solution of the demographic problem: namely, the way of a provident policy for the family, of a wise education of peoples in respect of moral law and the liberty of citizens.

We are well aware of the serious difficulties experienced by public authorities in this regard, especially in the developing countries. To their legitimate preoccupations we devoted our encyclical letter Popularum Progressio. But with our predecessor Pope John XXIII, we repeat: no solution to these difficulties is acceptable "which does violence to man's essential dignity" and is based only on an utterly materialistic conception of man himself and of his life. The only possible solution to the question is one which envisages the social and economic progress both of individuals and of the whole of human society, and which respects and promotes true human values [26]. Neither can one, without grave injustice, consider divine providence to be responsible for what depends, instead, on a lack of wisdom in government, on an insufficient sense of social justice, on selfish monopolization, or again on blame-worthy indolence in confronting the efforts and the sacrifices necessary to ensure the raising of living standards of a people and of all its sons [27].

May all responsible public authorities—as some are already doing so laudably—generously revive their efforts. And may mutual aid between all the members of the great human family never cease to grow: This is an almost limitless field which thus opens up to the activity of the great international organizations.

To Men of Science

24. We wish now to express our encouragement to men

---

[26] Cf. encyc. Mater et Magistra, in AAS LIII (1961), p. 447.
[27] Cf. encyc. Populorum Progressio, nos. 48–55.

of science, who "can considerably advance the welfare of marriage and the family, along with peace of conscience, if by pooling their efforts they labor to explain more thoroughly the various conditions favoring a proper regulation of births" [28]. It is particularly desirable that, according to the wish already expressed by Pope Pius XII, medical science succeed in providing a sufficiently secure basis for a regulation of birth, founded on the observance of natural rhythms [29]. In this way, scientists and especially Catholic scientists will contribute to demonstrate in actual fact that, as the Church teaches, "a true contradiction cannot exist between the divine laws pertaining to the transmission of life and those pertaining to the fostering of authentic conjugal love" [30].

To Christian Husbands and Wives

25. And now our words more directly address our own children, particularly those whom God calls to serve Him in marriage. The Church, while teaching imprescriptible demands of the divine law, announces the tidings of salvation, and by means of the sacraments opens up the paths of grace, which makes man a new creature, capable of corresponding with love and true freedom to the design of his Creator and Saviour, and of finding the yoke of Christ to be sweet [31].

Christian married couples, then, docile to her voice, must remember that their Christian vocation, which began at baptism, is further specified and reinforced by the sacrament of matrimony. By it husband and wife are strengthened and as it were consecrated for the faithful accomplishment of their proper duties, for the carrying out of their proper vocation even to perfection, and the Christian wit-

---

[28] Cf. Pastoral Const. Gaudium et Spes, no. 52.
[29] Cf. AAS XLIII (1951), p. 859.
[30] Cf. Pastoral Const. Gaudium et Spes, no. 51.
[31] Cf. Matt. 11, 30.

ness which is proper to them before the whole world [32]. To them the Lord entrusts the task of making visible to men the holiness and sweetness of the law which unites the mutual love of husband and wife with their cooperation with the love of God the author of human life.

We do not at all intend to hide the sometimes serious difficulties inherent in the life of Christian married persons; for them as for everyone else, "the gate is narrow and the way is hard, that leads to life" [33]. But the hope of that life must illuminate their way, as with courage they strive to live with wisdom, justice and piety in this present time [34], knowing that the figure of this world passes away [35].

Let married couples, then, face up to the efforts needed, supported by the faith and hope which "do not disappoint . . . because God's love has been poured into our hearts through the Holy Spirit, who has been given to us" [36]. Let them implore divine assistance by persevering prayer; above all, let them draw from the source of grace and charity in the Eucharist. And if sin should still keep its hold over them, let them not be discouraged, but rather have recourse with humble perseverance to the mercy of God, which is poured forth in the sacrament of Penance. In this way they will be enabled to achieve the fullness of conjugal life described by the Apostle: "husbands, love your wives, as Christ loved the Church . . . husbands should love their wives as their own bodies. He who loves his wife loves himself. For no man ever hates his own flesh, but nourishes and cherishes it, as Christ does the Church . . . this is a great mystery, and I mean in reference to Christ and the

---

[32] Cf. Pastoral Const. Gaudium et Spes, no. 48; II Vatican Council, Dogmatic Const. Lumen Gentium, no. 35.

[33] Matt. 7, 14; cf. Heb. 11, 12.

[34] Cf. Tit. 2, 12.

[35] Cf. I Cor. 7, 31.

[36] Cf. Rom. 5, 5.

Church. However, let each one of you love his wife as himself, and let the wife see that she respects her husband" [37].

Apostolate in Homes

26. Among the fruits which ripen forth from a generous effort of fidelity to the divine law, one of the most precious is that married couples themselves not infrequently feel the desire to communicate their experience to others. Thus there comes to be included in the vast pattern of the vocation of the laity a new and most noteworthy form of the apostolate of like to like; it is married couples themselves who become apostles and guides to other married couples. This is assuredly, among so many forms of apostolate, one of those which seem most opportune today [38].

To Doctors and Medical Personnel

27. We hold those physicians and medical personnel in the highest esteem who, in the exercise of their profession, value above every human interest the superior demands of their Christian vocation. Let them persevere, therefore, in promoting on every occasion the discovery of solutions inspired by faith and right reason, let them strive to arouse this conviction and this respect in their associates. Let them also consider as their proper professional duty the task of acquiring all the knowledge needed in this delicate sector, so as to be able to give to those married persons who consult them wise counsel and healthy direction, such as they have a right to expect.

To Priests

28. Beloved priest sons, by vocation you are the counselors and spiritual guides of individual persons and of fam-

[37] Eph. 5, 25, 28–29, 32–33.
[38] Cf. Dogmatic Const. Lumen Gentium, nos. 35 and 41; Pastoral Const. Gaudium et Spes, nos. 48–49; II Vatican Council, Decree Apostolicam Actuositatem, no. 11.

ilies. We now turn to you with confidence. Your first task—especially in the case of those who teach moral theology—is to expound the Church's teaching on marriage without ambiguity. Be the first to give, in the exercise of your ministry, the example of loyal internal and external obedience to the teaching authority of the Church. That obedience, as you know well, obliges not only because of the reasons adduced, but rather because of the light of the Holy Spirit, which is given in a particular way to the pastors of the Church in order that they may illustrate the truth [39]. You know, too, that it is of the utmost importance, for peace of consciences and for the unity of the Christian people, that in the field of morals as well as in that of dogma, all should attend to the magisterium of the Church, and all should speak the same language. Hence, with all our heart we renew to you the heartfelt plea of the great Apostle Paul: "I appeal to you, brethren, by the name of Our Lord Jesus Christ, that all of you agree and that there be no dissensions among you, but that you be united in the same mind and the same judgment" [40].

29. To diminish in no way the saving teaching of Christ constitutes an eminent form of charity for souls. But this must ever be accompanied by patience and goodness, such as the Lord himself gave example of in dealing with men. Having come not to condemn but to save [41], he was indeed intransigent with evil, but merciful towards individuals.

In their difficulties, may married couples always find, in the words and in the heart of a priest, the echo of the voice and the love of the Redeemer. And then speak with confidence, beloved sons, fully convinced that the spirit of God, while He assists the magisterium in proposing doctrine, illumines internally the hearts of the faithful inviting them

---

[39] Cf. Dogmatic Const. Lumen Gentium, no. 25.
[40] Cf. I Cor. 1, 10.
[41] Cf. John 3, 17.

to give their assent. Teach married couples the indispensable way of prayer; prepare them to have recourse often and with faith to the sacraments of the Eucharist and of Penance, without ever allowing themselves to be discouraged by their own weakness.

To Bishops

30. Beloved and venerable brothers in the episcopate, with whom we most intimately share the solicitude of the spiritual good of the people of God, at the conclusion of this encyclical our reverent and affectionate thoughts turn to you. To all of you we extend an urgent invitation. At the head of the priests, your collaborators, and of your faithful, work ardently and incessantly for the safeguarding and the holiness of marriage, so that it may always be lived in its entire human and Christian fullness. Consider this mission as one of your most urgent responsibilities at the present time.

As you know, it implies concerted pastoral action in all the fields of human activity, economic, cultural and social; for, in fact, only a simultaneous improvement in these various sectors will make it possible to render the life of parents and of children within their families not only tolerable, but easier and more joyous, to render the living together in human society more fraternal and peaceful, in faithfulness to God's design for the world.

Final Appeal

31. Venerable brothers, most beloved sons, and all men of good will, great indeed is the work of education, of progress and of love to which we call you, upon the foundation of the Church's teaching, of which the successor of Peter is, together with his brothers in the episcopate, the depositary and interpreter. Truly a great work, as we are deeply convinced, both for the world and for the Church, since man

cannot find true happiness—towards which he aspires with all his being—other than in respect of the laws written by God in his very nature, laws which he must observe with intelligence and love. Upon this work, and upon all of you, and especially upon married couples, we invoke the abundant graces of the God of holiness and mercy, and in pledge thereof we impart to you all our apostolic blessing.

Given at Rome, from St. Peter's, this 25th day of July, feast of St. James the Apostle, in the year 1968, the sixth of our pontificate.

PAULUS PP.VI.

Appendix 3

BIBLIOGRAPHY

LEWIS P. BIRD, S.T.M. *Mr. Bird is presently the Eastern Regional Director of the Christian Medical Society. He was appointed to this position in 1964; prior to this he served in the pastorate for five years. His undergraduate degree was earned at Nyack College, he received his Bachelor of Divinity degree from Gordon Divinity School, and subsequently he was granted a Master's in Sacred Theology by the Lutheran School of Theology at Chicago. His master's thesis was on the subject: "The Genesis and Early Development of Church Moral Discipline in the Pauline Literature." His responsibilities during the years he has served the Christian Medical Society have included the study and exposition of medical ethical problems from the Christian perspective.*

BIBLIOGRAPHY

Compiled by Lewis P. Bird

Since this symposium was multidisciplinary in nature, an effort has been made to organize the literature according to disciplines wherever appropriate. Hence the journal articles cited in this bibliography follow the bibliographical form of their respective field. The research scholar seeking to explore the inter-disciplinary literature should consult the following journal and periodical indices:

MEDICINE

> *Index Medicus*

THEOLOGY

> *Biblica*
> *Guide to Religious Periodicals*
> *Index to Religious Periodical Literature*

*Internationale Zeitschriftenschau fuer Bibelwissenschaft
und Grenzgebiete
New Testament Abstracts*

LAW

*American Law Reports
Index of Legal Periodicals
West's Decennial Digest*

SOCIOLOGY

*Social Sciences & Humanities Index
Sociological Abstracts*

I. MEDICAL ETHICS

1. General Studies

Darthmouth Convocation. *The Great Issues of Conscience in Modern Medicine.* Hanover, N.H., n.p., 1960.

Davidson, Maurice, ed. *Medical Ethics.* London: Lloyd-Luke, Ltd., 1957.

Dawson, G. G. *Healing: Pagan and Christian.* New York: Macmillan, 1935.

Dubos, R. "Individual Morality and Statistical Morality" in Colloquium: *Annals of Internal Medicine.* 67, Supplement 7, 1967.

Glass, B. *Science and Ethical Values.* Chapel Hill: University of North Carolina Press, 1965.

Huxley, Julian. *The Humanist Frame.* London: Allen & Unwin, 1961.

Leake C. D. "Technical Triumphs and Moral Muddles" in Colloquium: *Annals of Internal Medicine.* 67, Supplement 7:43, 1967.

Lister, J. "Medicine, Morals and Money." *New England Journal of Medicine.* 276:971, 1967.

Meserve, Harry C., ed. *The Place of Value Systems in Medical Education.* New York: Academy of Religion and Mental Health, 1961.

Ormrod, Sir Roger. "Medical Ethics." *British Medical Journal.* 2:7, 1968.

Proger, Samuel, ed. *The Medicated Society.* New York: The Macmillan Co., 1968.

Sperry, William L. *The Ethical Basis of Medical Practice.* New York: P. B. Hoeber, Inc., 1950.

Webb, J. C. "The Mythology of Asclepius." *The University of Southern California Medical Bulletin.* VIII, (Oct.), 1955.

Wolstenholme, G. E. W. and O'Connor, M., eds. *Ethics in Medical Progress.* London: J. & A. Churchill, 1966.

2. World's Religions

Barton, Richard T. *Religious Doctrine and Medical Practice.* Springfield, Ill.: Charles C. Thomas, 1958.

3. Jewish Studies

Bernstein, A. and Bernstein, H. C. "Medicine in the Talmud." *California Medicine.* 74:267, (April) 1951.

Friendenwald, H. *Jews and Medicine.* Baltimore: Johns Hopkins Press, 1944.

Gordon, M. B. "Medicine Among the Ancient Hebrews." *Isis.* (Dec.) 1941.

Jakobovits, Immanuel. *Jewish Medical Ethics.* New York: Bloch Publishing Co., 1959.

Jiggets, J. I. *Religion, Diet and Health of Jews.* New York: Bloch Publishing Co., 1949.

Mason, W. A. "The Monotheistic Concept and the Evolution of Medical Thought." *Phylon.* No. 3, 1951.

Pool, D. and Chavel, C. B. *The Jewish Dietary Laws.* New York: The Union of Orthodox Jewish Congregations of America, 1946.

4. Roman Catholic Studies

Bonnar, A. *The Catholic Doctor.* London: Burns, Oates and Washbourne, 1948.

Burke, E. F. *Acute Cases of Moral Medicine.* New York: The Macmillan Co., 1922.

Connell, F. J. *Morals in Politics and Professions.* Westminster, Md.: The Newman Press, 1946.

Davis, Henry. *Moral and Pastoral Theology.* II. New York: Sheed & Ward, 1943.

Ficarra, B. J. *Newer Ethical Problems in Medicine and Surgery.* Westminster, Md.: The Newman Press, 1951.

Finney, P. A. *Moral Problems in Medical Practice.* St. Louis: B. Herder Book Co., 1922.

Flood, Dom Peter. *New Problems in Medical Ethics.* 4 vols. Westminster, Md.: The Newman Press. 1963ff.

Good, F. L. and Kelly, O. F. *Marriage, Morals, and Medical Ethics.* New York: P. J. Kennedy & Sons, 1951.

Healy, Edwin F. *Medical Ethics.* Chicago: Loyola University Press, 1956.

Kelly, Gerald. *Medico-Moral Problems.* St. Louis: The Catholic Hospital Association, 1958.

Klarman, A. *The Crux of Pastoral Medicine.* New York: 1905.

Larochelle, Stanislas. *Handbook of Medical Ethics for Nurses, Physicians and Priests.* Westminster, Md.: The Newman Press, 1943.

Marshall, John. *Medicine and Morals.* New York: Hawthorn Books, 1960.

McFadden, Charles J. *Medical Ethics.* Philadelphia: F. A. Davis Co., 1962.

O'Brien, Patrick. *Moral Problems in Hospital Practice.* St. Louis: B. Herder Book Co., 1956.

O'Donnell, T. J. *Morals in Medicine.* Westminster, Md.: The Newman Press, 1956.

Smith, G. D. *The Teaching of the Catholic Church.* London: Burns, Oates and Washbourne, 1948.

St. John-Stevas, Norman. *Life and Death and the Law.* London: Eyre & Spottiswoode, 1961.

Walsh, James J. *Religion and Health.* Boston: Little, Brown & Co., 1920.

5. Protestant Studies

Barth, Karl. *Church Dogmatics.* III, 4. "The Doctrine of Creation." Trans. A. T. Mackay, et. al. Edinburgh: T. & T. Clark, 1961.

Bird, Lewis P. *The Ten Commandments in Modern Medicine.* Oak Park, Ill.: Christian Medical Society, 1965.

Connell, A. M. and Lindeboom, G. A., eds. *The Christian Physician in the Advance of the Science and Practice of Medicine.* (Proceedings of The Second International Congress of Christian Physicians, Oxford, July 11–15, 1966.) Oak Park, Ill.: Christian Medical Society, 1966.

Edmunds, Vincent and Scorer, C. Gordon, eds. *Ethical Responsibility in Medicine.* Baltimore: The Williams and Wilkins Co., 1968.

————, eds. *Medical Ethics: A Christian View.* London: The Tyndale Press, 1966.

Fletcher, Joseph. *Morals and Medicine.* Boston: Beacon Press, 1960.

Hiltner, Seward. "Religion and Health." *American Scholar.* July, 1946.

Heim, Karl. *Christian Faith and Natural Science.* New York: Harper, 1957.

Jacoby, G. W. *Physician, Pastor and Patient.* New York, 1936.

Jenkins, Daniel T. *The Doctor's Profession.* London: SCM Press, 1949.

Julian, F. B. "Influence of Religion on the Progress of Medicine." *Hibbert Journal.* April, 1953.

Klotz, John W., ed. *Proceedings of the Colloquium on Medical Ethics.* St. Louis: Concordia Publishing Co., 1962.

Lambeth Conference Reports. London: 1912, 1920, 1930, 1958.

Lindeboom, G. A., ed. *The Service of the Christian Doctor in a Modern Society.* (Proceedings of The First International Congress of Christian Physicians, Amsterdam, July 15–18, 1963). Oak Park, Ill.: Christian Medical Society, 1963.

Man, Medicine and Theology. New York: Board of Social Ministry, Lutheran Church in America, 1967.

McNeill, John T. *A History of the Cure of Souls.* New York: Harper, 1951.

Schlemmer, Andre. *Faith and Medicine.* London: The Tyndale Press, 1957.

Weatherhead, Leslie D. *Psychology, Religion and Healing.* New York: Abingdon Press, 1955.

Westberg, Granger E. *Minister and Doctor Meet.* New York: Harper & Row, 1961.

White, Dale, ed. *Dialogue in Medicine and Theology.* Nashville: Abingdon Press, 1968.

II. CHRISTIAN ETHICS

1. Basic Ethics

Altaner, Berthold. *Patrology.* Trans. H. C. Graef. New York: Herder and Herder, 1960.

Barclay, R. A. *The Law Givers.* New York: Abingdon Press, 1964.

Bennett, John C., et al. *Storm Over Ethics.* Philadelphia: The United Church Press, 1967.

Böckle, Franz, ed. *Moral Problems and Christian Personalism.* Concilium, V. New York: Paulist Press, 1965.

Bonhoeffer, Dietrich. *Ethics.* Trans. N. H. Smith. New York: The Macmillan Co., 1962.

Brunner, Emil. *The Divine Imperative.* Trans. Olive Wyon. Philadelphia: The Westminster Press, 1947.

Cave, Sydney. *The Christian Way.* New York: Philosophical Library, Inc., 1949.

Coleman-Norton. *Roman State and Christian Church: A Collection of Legal Documents to A.D. 535.* London: S.P.C.K., 1961.

Cox, Harvey, ed. *The Situation Ethics Debate.* Philadelphia: The Westminster Press, 1968.

Fitch, Robert E. "The Protestant Sickness." *Religion In Life.* XXXV, 498, 1966.

Fletcher, Joseph. *Moral Responsibility.* Philadelphia: The Westminster Press, 1967.

———. *Situation Ethics: The New Morality.* Philadelphia: The Westminster Press, 1966.

Forell, George W. *Ethics of Decision.* Philadelphia: The Muhlenberg Press, 1955.

Haring, Bernard. *The Law of Christ.* Westminster, Md.: The Newman Press, 1961.

Henry, Carl F. H. *Aspects of Christian Social Ethics.* Grand Rapids: Wm. B. Eerdmans Publishing Co., 1964.

———. *Christian Personal Ethics.* Grand Rapids: Wm. B. Eerdmans Publishing Co., 1957.

Knox. J. *The Ethic of Jesus in the Teaching of the Church.* London: Epworth, 1962.

Lehmann, Paul L. *Ethics in a Christian Contest.* New York: Harper & Row, 1963.

Lillie, W. *Studies in New Testament Ethics.* London: Oliver & Boyd, 1961.

Lunn, Arnold and Lean, Garth. *The New Morality*. London: Blandford Press, 1964.

Macquarrie, John, ed. *A Dictionary of Christian Ethics*. London: SCM Press, 1967.

Manson, T. W. *Ethics and the Gospel*. London: SCM Press, 1960.

Marshall, L. H. *The Challenge of New Testament Ethics*. New York: St. Martin's Press, 1960.

Murray, John. *Principles of Conduct*. Grand Rapids: Wm. B. Eerdmans Publishing Co., 1957.

Niebuhr, Reinhold. *An Interpretation of Christian Ethics*. New York: Meridian Books, 1956.

———. *Moral Man and Immoral Society*. New York: Charles Scribner's Sons, 1932.

Pierce, C. A. *Conscience in the New Testament*. London: SCM Press, 1955.

Ramsey, Paul. *Basic Christian Ethics*. New York: Charles Scribner's Sons, 1950.

———. *Deeds and Rules in Christian Ethics*. New York: Charles Scribner's Sons, 1967.

———. *Who Speaks for the Church?* New York: Abingdon Press, 1967.

Rhymes, Douglas. *No New Morality*. Indianapolis: Bobbs-Merrill Co., Inc., 1964.

Robinson, John A. T. *Christian Morals Today*. Philadelphia: The Westminster Press, 1964.

———. *Honest to God*. Philadelphia: The Westminster Press, 1963.

Salm, C. Luke. *Readings in Biblical Morality*. Englewood Cliffs, N.J.: Prentice-Hall, Inc., 1966.

Sellers, James "Mr. Ramsey and the New Morality." *Religion In Life*. XXXVII, 282, 1968.

Thielecke. Helmut. *Theological Ethics: Foundations*. William H. Lazareth, ed. Philadelphia: Fortress Press, 1966.

Vidler, A. R., ed. *Soundings: Essays Concerning Christian Understanding*. Cambridge: Cambridge University Press, 1962.

Waddams, Herbert. *A New Introduction to Moral Theology*. New York: The Seabury Press, 1965.

Walters, Orville S. "Theology and Changing Concepts of the Unconscious." *Religion In Life*. XXXVII, 112, 1968.

Wilder, A. *Eschatology and Ethics in the Teaching of Jesus*. London: SCM Press, 1954.

2. Sexual Ethics

Babbage, Stuart Barton. *Christianity and Sex*. Chicago: Inter-Varsity Press, 1963.

———. *Sex and Sanity*. Philadelphia: The Westminster Press, 1965.

Bailey, D. Sherwin. *Sexual Ethics: A Christian View*. New York: The Macmillan Co., 1963.

———. *Sexual Relations in Christian Thought.* New York: Harper, 1959.

Bertocci, Peter A. *The Human Venture in Sex, Love, and Marriage.* New York: Association Press, 1949.

Cabot, Richard O. *Christianity and Sex.* New York: The Macmillan Co., 1939.

Cole, William G. *Sex and Love in the Bible.* New York: Association Press, 1959.

Cox, Harvey. "Evangelical Ethics and the Ideal of Chastity" in *Witness to a Generation.* Indianapolis: Bobbs-Merrill, 1966.

Demant, V. A. *Christian Sex Ethics.* New York: Harper & Row, 1964.

Feucht, Oscar E., ed. *Sex and the Church: A Sociological, Historical, and Theological Investigation of Sex Attitudes.* St. Louis: Concordia Publishing House, 1961.

Hiltner, Seward. *Sex Ethics and the Kinsey Reports.* New York: Association Press, 1953.

Holmes, Urban T., III, ed. *A Christian Understanding of Human Sexuality.* Second Edition. Baton Rouge: Diocese of Louisiana, 1968.

Lewis, C. S. *The Four Loves.* New York: Harcourt, Brace & World, Inc., 1960.

MacKinnon, D. M., et al. *God, Sex and War.* Philadelphia: The Westminster Press, 1963.

Pittenger, W. N. *The Christian View of Sexual Behavior: A Reaction to the Kinsey Report.* New York: The Seabury Press, 1954.

Scorer, C. Gordon. *The Bible and Sex Ethics Today.* London: Tyndale Press, 1966.

Thielecke, Helmut. *The Ethics of Sex.* Trans. John W. Doberstein. New York: Harper & Row, 1964.

III. MARRIAGE

1. Medical Sources

Beigel, Hugo G., ed. *Advances in Sex Research.* New York: Hoeber-Harper, 1963.

Farnsworth, Dana L. *Psychiatry, Education, and the Young Adult.* Springfield, Ill.: Charles C. Thomas, Publisher, 1966.

Fishbein, Morris and Kennedy, Ruby, J. R., eds. *Modern Marriage and Family Living.* New York: Oxford University Press, 1957.

Ginott, Haim G. *Between Parent and Child.* New York: The Macmillan Co., 1965.

Golden, Joshua S. "Management of Sexual Problems by the Physician." *The Journal of the American College of Obstetricians and Gynecologists.* XXIII/3.

Klemer, Richard H., ed. *Counseling in Marital and Sexual Problems: A Physician's Handbook.* Baltimore: The Williams and Wilkins Co., 1965.

Lewin, S. A. and Gilmore, John. *Sex Without Fear*. Revised Edition. New York: Medical Research Press, 1961.

Masters, William H. and Johnson, Virginia E. *Human Sexual Response*. Boston: Little, Brown & Co., 1967.

Nash, Ethel M., et al. *Marriage Counseling in Medical Practice*. Chapel Hill: The University of North Carolina Press, 1964.

Oliven, John F. *Sexual Hygiene and Pathology*. Second Edition. Philadelphia: J. B. Lippincott Co., 1965.

Trainer, Joseph B. *Physiologic Foundations for Marriage Counseling*. St. Louis: C. V. Mosby Co., 1965.

Van de Velde, Th. H. *Ideal Marriage*. Trans. Stella Browne. New York: Random House, 1957.

2. Theological Sources

Bailey, D. S. *The Man-Woman Relation in Christian Thought*. London: Longmans, Green & Co., 1959.

————. *The Mystery of Love and Marriage*. New York: Harper & Bros., 1952.

Bainton, Roland H. *What Christianity Says About Sex, Love, and Marriage*. New York: Association Press, 1957.

Biezanek, Anne. *All Things New*. New York: Harper, 1964.

Capper, W. Melville and Williams, H. Morgan. *Toward Christian Marriage*. Chicago: Inter-Varsity Press, 1958.

Colacci, Mario. *Christian Marriage Today*. Revised Edition. Minneapolis: Augsburg Publishing House, 1965.

Cole, William G. *Sex in Christianity and Psychoanalysis*. New York: Oxford University Press, 1955.

Emerson, James G. Jr. *Divorce, The Church, and Remarriage*. Philadelphia: The Westminster Press, 1961.

Epstein, Louis. *Marriage Laws in the Bible and the Talmud*. Cambridge: Harvard University Press, 1942.

————. *Sex Laws and Customs in Judaism*. New York: Bloch Publishing Co., 1948.

Fairchild, Roy W. *Christians In Families*. Richmond: Covenant Life Curriculum Press, 1964.

Geldenhuys, J. Norval. *The Intimate Life*. Grand Rapids: Wm. B. Eerdmans Publishing Co., 1957.

Gordon, Albert I. *Intermarriage: Interfaith, Interracial, Interethnic*. Boston: Beacon Press, Inc., 1964.

Hansen, Paul G., et al. *Engagement and Marriage: A Sociological, Historical and Theological Investigation by the Family Life Committee of the Lutheran Church—Missouri Synod*. St. Louis: Concordia Publishing Co., 1959.

Joyce, G. H. *Christian Marriage: An Historical and Doctrinal Study*. Second Edition. London: Sheed and Ward, 1948.

Mace, David R. *Hebrew Marriage: A Sociological Study*. London: The Epworth Press, 1953.

————. *Whom God Hath Joined*. Philadelphia: Westminster Press, 1953.

Mehl, Roger. *Society and Love.* Trans. James H. Farley. Philadelphia: The Westminster Press, 1964.

Mielziner, M. *The Jewish Law of Marriage and Divorce in Ancient and Modern Times.* Cincinnati: The Bloch Publishing Co., 1884.

Murray, John. *Divorce.* Philadelphia, 1953.

Neufeld, E. *Ancient Hebrew Marriage Laws.* New York: Longmans, Green & Co., 1944.

Pike, James A. *If You Marry Outside Your Faith.* Revised Edition. New York: Harper & Row, Publishers, 1954.

Piper, Otto A. *The Biblical View of Sex and Marriage.* New York: Charles Scribner's Sons, 1960.

Schopp, Ludwig, ed. dir. *The Fathers of the Church.* New York: CIMA, 1947, 57 vols.

van Selms, A. *Marriage and Family Life in Ugaritic Literature.* London: Luzac & Co., 1954.

Sheppard, L. C. *Chastity.* Westminster, Md.: The Newman Press, 1963.

Small, Dwight H. *Design for Christian Marriage.* New York: Fleming H. Revell Co., 1959.

Smith, W. Robertson. *Kinship and Marriage in Early Arabia.* London: C. J. Clay & Son, 1885.

Tarn, W. W. *Hellenistic Civilization.* London: Edward Arnold, 1947, 334 pages.

Troeltsch, Ernst, *The Social Teachings of the Christian Churches,* 2 Vols. London: George Allen and Unwin. New York: Macmillan, 1931.

United Presbyterian Church in the USA, The. *Responsible Marriage and Parenthood.* Report adopted by the 174th General Assembly. May, 1962. Philadelphia: Westminster Press, 1962.

Wynn, J. C., ed. *Sex, Family, and Society in Theological Focus.* New York: Associated Press, 1966.

Yates, Herschel Wilson, Jr., *American Protestantism and Birth Control: An Examination of Shifts Within A Major Religious Value Orientation.* An unpublished Harvard thesis, 1968.

3. Sociological Sources

Anderson, Wayne J. *Design for Family Living.* Minneapolis: T. S. Denison & Co., Inc., 1964.

Bell, Norman W. and Vogel, Ezra F., eds. *A Modern Introduction to the Family.* New York: Free Press of Glencoe, Inc., 1960.

Bossard James H. and Boll, Eleanor S. *One Marriage, Two Faiths.* New York: The Ronald Press Co., 1957.

Bowman, H. A. *Marriage for Moderns.* Fourth Edition. New York: McGraw-Hill, 1960.

Burgess, Ernest W. and Wallin, Paul. *Courtship, Engagement and Marriage.* Philadelphia: J. B. Lippincott Co., 1953.

Crawley, Lawrence Q., et al. *Reproduction, Sex, and Preparation for Marriage.* Englewood Cliffs, N.J.: Prentice-Hall, Inc., 1964.

Ditzion, Sidney H. *Marriage, Morals and Sex in America*. New York: Bookman, 1953.
Eckert, Ralph G. *Sex Attitudes in the Home*. New York: Popular Library, 1963.
James, E. O. *Marriage and Society*. London: Hutchinson, 1952.
LeMasters, E. E. *Modern Courtship and Marriage*. New York: The Macmillan Co., 1957.
Sussman, Marvin B. *Sourcebook in Marriage and the Family*. Second Edition. Boston: Houghton Mifflin Co., 1963.
Williams, Gordon. "Some Aspects of Roman Marriage Ceremonies and Ideals." *Journal of Roman Studies*. 48, 1958.

4. Legal Sources

Pilpel, Harriet F. and Zavin, Theodora. *Your Marriage and the Law*. New York: Holt, Rinehart & Winston, Inc., 1952.

IV. CONTRACEPTION

1. Medical Sources

AMA Committee on Human Reproduction. "The Control of Fertility." *Journal of the American Medical Association*. 194:467, 1965.
Ayd, Frank J., Jr. "Contraceptives for Teenagers?" *Medical Science*. (Sept.) 1967.
Best, Winfield and Taffe, Frederick S. *Simple Methods of Contraception: An Assessment of their Medical, Moral and Social Implications*. New York: Planned Parenthood Federation of America, 1958.
Calderone, Mary S., ed. *Manual of Contraceptive Practice*. Baltimore: The Williams & Wilkins Co., 1964.
———. "The Case for Chastity." *Sex in America*. New York: Bantam Books, 1964.
Group for the Advancement of Psychiatry. *Sex and the College Student*. New York: GAP, 1965.
Guttmacher, Alan J. *Babies by Choice or by Chance?* New York: Doubleday & Co., Inc., 1959.
——— and Gould, Joan. "New Facts About Birth Control." *Public Affairs Pamphlet*, No. 136B.
Halleck, S. L. "Sexual Problems of College Students." *Medical Aspects of Human Sexuality*. II/5:14, (May) 1968.
Himes, Norman E. *Medical History of Contraception*. Baltimore: William Wood, 1936.
Levin, Max. "The Physician and the Sexual Revolution." *New England Journal of Medicine*. 273:1366, (Dec.) 1965.
———. *Vassar and the Non-Virgins*. Baltimore: The Williams & Wilkins Co., 1966.
Lippes, J. "Observations after Four Years of Experience with the Intra-Uterine Plastic Loop at the Buffalo Planned Parenthood Centre." *Journal of Sex Research*. 3:323, 1967.

Menninger, Karl. "Psychiatric Aspects of Contraception." *Bulletin of the Menninger Clinic.* VII:1 (Jan.) 1943.

Moore, Edward R. *The Case Against Birth Control.* New York: Century Co., 1931.

Pierce, A. Grace. "Fertility Control—Temporary or Permanent." *Current Medical Digest.* 34 (Mar.) 1967.

Rock, D. John. *Medical and Biological Aspects of Contraception.* Boston: J. P. Lippincott Co., 1943.

————. *The Time Has Come: A Catholic Doctor's Proposals to End the Battle Over Birth Control.* London: Longman's, Green and Co., 1963.

Rozin, Samuel, et al. "Studies of the Mode of Action of Intrauterine Contraceptive Devices." *Obstetrics & Gynecology.* 30:855, 1967.

Sanders, Mervyn S. "What Are the Psychological Effects of Premarital Intercourse?" *Medical Aspects of Human Sexuality.* (April), 1968.

Sanger, Margaret and Stone, H. M., eds. *The Practice of Contraception.* Baltimore: The Williams & Wilkins Co., 1931.

Scott, Roger B. "Critical Illnesses and Deaths Associated with Intrauterine Devices." *Obstetrics & Gynecology.* 31:322, 1968.

Shainess, Natalie. "The Problem of Sex Today." *American Journal of Psychiatry.* 124:8, 1968.

Southerland, Halledy. *Birth Control.* London: Harding and Mare Ltd., n.d.

Vincent, Clark. *Unmarried Mothers.* New York: The Free Press, 1961.

Wilson, J. Robert. "Intrauterine Contraceptive Devices." *Pacific Medical & Surgical Journal.* 73:44, 1965.

2. Theological Sources

Astour, Michael C. "Tamar the Hierodule" in the *Journal of Biblical Literature.* 85 (1966).

Birmingham, W., ed. *What Modern Catholics Think About Birth Control.* New York, n.p., 1964.

Braaten, Carl E. *The Ethics of Conception and Contraception.* New York: Board of Social Ministry, Lutheran Church in America, 1967.

Bromley, Dorothy D. *Catholics and Birth Control.* New York: Devin-Adair Co., 1965.

Doniger, Simon, ed. *Sex and Religion Today.* New York: Association Press, 1953.

Duvall, Evelyn M. *Why Wait Til Marriage?* New York: Association Press, 1965.

———— and Duvall, Sylvanus M., eds. *Sex Ways in Fact and Faith.* New York: Association Press, 1961.

Feldman, David M. *Birth Control in Jewish Law.* New York: New York University Press, 1968.

Heron, Alastair, ed. *Towards a Quaker View of Sex.* London: Friends Home Service Committee, 1963.

Kelley, George A. *Birth Control and Catholics*. New York: Doubleday, 1963.

——. *The Catholic Family Handbook*. New York: Random House, 1959.

Monsma, John C., ed. *Religion and Birth Control*. New York: Doubleday & Co., Inc., 1963.

Montgomery, John Warwick. "How to Decide the Birth-Control Question" in *Christianity Today*. X, 11 (March 4, 1966).

Noonan, John T., Jr. *Contraception: A History of Its Treatment by the Catholic Theologians and Canonists*. Cambridge: Harvard University Press, 1966.

Pope Paul VI. *Humanae Vitae*. Rome, 1968.

Pope Pius XI. *Casti Connubii*. Rome, 1930.

Pyle, Leo, ed. *The Pill and Birth Regulation*. Baltimore: Helicon Press, 1964.

Rehwinkel, Alfred M. *Planned Parenthood*. St. Louis: Concordia Publishing House, 1959.

Roberts, Thomas D., et al. *Contraception and Holiness*. New York: Herder & Herder, 1964.

Sulloway, Alvah W. *Birth Control and Catholic Doctrine*. Boston: Beacon Press, 1959.

Weatherhead, Leslie. *The Mastery of Sex Through Psychology and Religion*. New York: The Macmillan Co., 1932.

3. Sociological Sources

Brown, Helen Gurley. *Sex and the Single Girl*. New York: Bernard Geis, 1962.

David, Katherine B. *Factors in the Sex Life of Twenty-Two Hundred Women*. New York: Harper & Bros., 1929.

Dennett, Mary W. *Birth Control Laws: Shall We Keep Them, Change Them, or Abolish Them?* New York: Grafton Press, 1926.

Ehrmann, Winston W. *Premarital Dating Behavior*. New York: Holt, Rinehart & Winston, Inc., 1954.

Greene, Gael. *Sex and the College Girl*. New York: Dell, 1964.

Himmelhoch, J. and Fava, S. F. *Sexual Behavior in American Society: An Appraisal of the First Two Kinsey Reports*. New York: W. W. Norton & Co., 1955.

Kinsey, A. C., Pomeroy, W. B., and Martin, C. E. *Sexual Behavior in the Human Male*. Philadelphia: W. B. Saunders Co., 1948.

Kinsey, A. C., Pomeroy, W. B., Martin, C. E., and Gebhard, P. H. *Sexual Behavior in the Human Female*. Philadelphia: W. B. Saunders Co., 1953.

Kirkendall, Lester A. *Premarital Intercourse and Interpersonal Relationships*. New York: Julian Press, 1961.

Kronhausen, Phyllis and Eberhard. *Sex Histories of American College Men*. New York: Ballantine Books, 1960.

Reiss, Ira L. *Premarital Sexual Standards in America*. New York: The Free Press of Glencoe, 1960.

Roberts, Robert W., ed. *The Unwed Mother*. New York: Harper & Row, 1966.
Sanger, Margaret. *My Fight for Birth Control*. New York: Farrar & Rinehart, Inc., 1931.
Sorokin, Pitirim A. *The American Sex Revolution*. Boston: P. Sargent, 1956.
Trilling, Lionel. "The Kinsey Report" in *The Liberal Imagination*. New York: The Viking Press, Inc., 1950.
Wall Street Journal, Editorial. "Illegitimacy: 'Sin' or Social Problem?" (March 14, 1968).

V. ABORTION
1. Medical Sources

Adams, M. and Neel, J. "Children of Incest." *Pediatrics*. 40/1:61, 1967.
Aren, Per. "On Legal Abortion in Sweden." *Acta Obstetricia et Gynecologica Scandinavica*. XXXVII, Supplement 1:62, 1958.
Baird, Dugald. "Sterilization & Therapeutic Abortion in Aberdeen." *British Journal of Psychiatry*. 113:705, 1967.
Barno, A. "Criminal Abortion Deaths, Illegitimate Pregnancy Deaths, and Suicides in Pregnancy." *American Journal of Obstetrics & Gynecology*. 98:356, 1967.
Bolter, S. "The Psychiatrist's Role in Therapeutic Abortion: The Unwitting Accomplice." *American Journal of Psychiatry*. 119:312, 1962.
British Medical Association Committee on Therapeutic Abortion. "Indications for Termination of Pregnancy." *British Medical Journal*. (Jan.), 1968.
Burch, T. K. "Induced Abortion in Japan under Eugenic Protection Law of 1948." *Eugenic Quarterly*. II, 1955.
Calderone, Mary S., ed. *Abortion in the U.S.A.* New York: Hoeber-Harper, 1958.
Carlson, E. A. "The Ever Increasing Importance of Genetics to Medicine & Man." *Queen's Medical Review* (Kingston, Ont.). 1960–61 Annual.
Cogan, N. M. "A Medical Social Worker Looks at the New Abortion Law." *British Medical Journal*. 2:235, 1968.
Colpills, R. V. "Trends in Therapeutic Abortion." *American Journal of Obstetrics & Gynecology*. 68:988, 1954.
Cooke, Robert E., ed. *The Terrible Choice: The Abortion Dilemma*. New York: Grosset & Dunlap Bantam Books, 1968.
Crawley, Ralph M. and Laidlaw, R. W. "Psychiatric Opinion Regarding Abortion: Preliminary Report of a Survey." *American Journal of Psychiatry*. 124:148, 1967.
Daube, D. "The Sanctity of Life." In Symposium, *The Cost of Life*. Proceedings of the Royal Society of Medicine. 60:1235, 1967.
Dunwoody, I. "Abortion on Social Grounds." *The Lancet*. 1:857, 1968.

Ekblad, M. "Induced Abortion on Psychiatric Grounds." *Acta Psychiatric et Neurol.* Scandinav. Trans. D. Burton. Supp. 99.

————. "The Relation of the Legal-Abortion Clientele to the Illegal-Abortion Clientele and the Risk of Suicide." *Acta Psychiatric et Neurol.* Scandinavia, Suppl. 1955.

Fodor. "Emotional Trauma Resulting from Illegitimate Birth." *Archives of Neurology and Psychiatry.* 54:381, 1945.

Gampell, R. J. "Legal Status of Therapeutic Abortion and Sterilization in the United States." *Clinical Obstetrics & Gynecology.* 7:22, 1964.

Gebhard, Paul H., et al. *Pregnancy, Birth and Abortion.* New York: Harper & Row, 1958.

Gold, E. M., Erhardt, C. L., Jacobziner, H., and Nelson, F. G. "Therapeutic Abortions in New York City: A Twenty Year Review." *American Journal of Pharmacology.* 55:964, 1965.

Goodhart, C. B. "Abortion Regulations." *British Medical Journal.* 2:298, 1968.

Guttmacher, Alan F. and Rovinsky, J. J. *Medical, Surgical and Gynecological Complications During Pregnancy.* Baltimore: Williams and Wilkins, 1961.

Hall, R. E. "Therapeutic Abortion, Sterilization, and Contraception." *American Journal of Obstetrics & Gynecology.* 91:518, 1965.

Hardin, G. "Abortion or Compulsory Pregnancy?" *Journal of Marriage & the Family.* 30/2:250, 1968.

————. "Blueprints, DNA, and Abortion: A Scientific and Ethical Analysis." *Medical Opinion and Review.* III:74, (Feb.) 1967.

Heffernan, R. J. and Lynch, W. A. "What Is the Status of Therapeutic Abortion in Modern Obstetrics?" *American Journal of Obstetrics & Gynecology.* 66, 1953.

Hemphill, R. E. "The Abortion Bill." *The Lancet.* 1:324, 1967.

Howells, J. G. "Legalising Abortion." *The Lancet.* 1:728, 1967.

Huldt, Lars. "Outcome of Pregnancy when Legal Abortion is Readily Available." *The Lancet.* 1:467, 1968.

Javert, C. T. *Spontaneous and Habitual Abortion.* New York: McGraw-Hill, 1957.

Kretzschmar, R. and Norris, B. "Psychiatric Implications of Therapeutic Abortion." *American Journal of Obstetrics & Gynecology.* 98:368, 1967.

Lederberg, J. "A Geneticist Looks at Contraception and Abortion." *Annals of Internal Medicine.* 67. Supplement 7, 1967.

McKusick, Victor A. "Genetics in the Practice of Medicine." *Annals of The Royal College of Physicians and Surgeons of Canada.* July, 1968.

Medical Defence Union. "The Abortion Act, 1967." *British Medical Journal.* 1:761, 1968.

Moore, J. G. and Randall, J. H. "Trends in Therapeutic Abortion." *American Journal of Obstetrics & Gynecology.* 63:28, 1952.

Niswander, K. R., et al. "Changing Attitudes Toward Therapeutic

Abortion." *Journal of the American Medical Association.* 196: 1143, 1966.

Niswander, K. R., et al. "Therapeutic Abortion: Indications and Technics." *Obstetrics & Gynecology.* 28:124, 1966.

Pommerenke, W. T. "Abortion in Japan." *Obstetrics and Gynecology Survey.* X, 1955.

Rogler, L. H. and Hollingshead, A. B. *Trapped: Families & Schizophrenia.* New York: Wiley, 1965.

Rosen, H., ed. *Therapeutic Abortion: Medical, Psychiatric, Legal, Anthropological and Religious Considerations.* New York: Julian Press, 1954.

Rosenberg, A. J. and Silver, E. "Suicide-Psychiatrist & Therapeutic Abortion." *California Medicine.* 102:408. 1965.

Rovinsky, J. J. and Gusberg, S. B. "Current Trends in Therapeutic Termination of Pregnancy." *American Journal of Obstetrics & Gynecology.* 98:11, 1967.

Russell, K. P. and Moore, J. G. "Maternal Medical Indications for Therapeutic Abortion." *Clinical Obstetrics & Gynecology.* 7:43, 1964.

Savel, L. E. "Adjudication of Therapeutic Abortion and Sterilization." *Clinical Obstetrics & Gynecology.* 7:14, 1964.

Sim, M. "Abortion and the Psychiatrist." *British Medical Journal.* July 20, 1963.

Simon, A. "Psychiatric Indications for Therapeutic Abortion and Sterilization." *Clinical Obstetrics & Gynecology.* 7:67, 1964.

Spivak, M. M. "Therapeutic Abortion." *American Journal of Obstetrics & Gynecology.* 97:316, 1967.

Stern, S. G. "The Issue of Legalized Abortion." *Canadian Medical Association Journal.* 88:899, 1963.

Studdiford, W. E. "The Common Medical Indications for Therapeutic Abortion." *Bulletin of the New York Academy of Medicine.* 26, 1950.

Taussig, D. "A Study of the German Outbreak of Phocomelia: The Thalidomide Syndrome." *Journal of the American Medical Association.* 181:1106, 1962.

Taylor, H. C., ed. *The Abortion Problem.* Baltimore: Williams & Wilkins, 1944.

"Therapeutic Abortion." Editorial, *Canadian Medical Association Journal.* 98:513, 1968.

TIME Essay. "The Desperate Dilemma of Abortion." *Time.* Vol. 90, No. 15. Oct. 13, 1967.

Trueta. "Care of Thalidomide Babies." *The Lancet.* 1:1162, 1962–3.

Wearing, M. P., et al. "A Medical and Sociologic Study of the Unwed Mother." *American Journal of Obstetrics & Gynecology.* 97:792, 1967.

2. Theological Sources

Carles, Jules. *La Fecondation.* Fifth Edition. Paris: Presses Universitaires de France, 1967.

Chauchard, Paul. *Le Respect de la Vie.* Paris: Beauchesne, 1963.

Granfield, David. *The Abortion Decision*. New York: Doubleday, 1969.

Hardesty, Nancy. "Should Anyone Who Wants an Abortion Have One?" *Eternity*. XVIII, No. 6 (June, 1967).

Hellegers, A., Neuhaus, R., Pleasants, J. and Wassmer, T. "Abortion Beyond Assumptions." *Commonweal*. LXXXVI, No. 15 (June 30, 1967).

Noonan, John T., Hellegers, A., and Richardson, H. *Abortion*. Cambridge: Harvard University Press, 1968.

St. John-Stevas, Norman. *The Right to Life*. New York: Holt, Rinehart, and Winston, 1964.

Van Peursen, C. A. *Body, Soul, Spirit: A Survey of the Body-Mind Problem*. Trans H. H. Hoskins. London: Oxford University Press, 1966.

Wentz, Frederick K. and Witmer, Robert H. *The Problem of Abortion*. New York: Board of Social Ministry, Lutheran Church in America, 1967.

3. Sociological Sources

Aptekar, H. *Infanticide, Abortion and Contraception in Savage Society*. New York: Godwin, 1931.

Browne, F. W. S. "The Right of Abortion" in *Journal of Sex Education*. V, 1952.

Davis, K. "Illegitimacy and the Social Structure" in the *American Journal of Sociology*. 45, 1939.

Devereux, G. *A Study of Abortion in Primitive Societies*. New York: Julian Press, 1955.

Family Planning Conference. *Abortion in Britain*. London: Pitman, 1966.

Ridgeway. "One Million Abortions." *The New Republic*. Feb. 9, 1963.

Time. "Progress Report on Liberalized Abortion." *Time*. Vol. 92, No. 20. (November. 15, 1968).

Watson, C. "Birth Control and Abortion in France Since 1939" in *Population Studies*. V, 1952.

Young, L. *Out of Wedlock: A Study of the Problems of the Unmarried Mother and Her Child*. New York: McGraw-Hill, 1954.

4. Legal Sources

Comment. *The Legal Status of Therapeutic Abortion*. 27. University of Pittsburgh Law Review. 669 (1966).

Culiner. *Trauma to the Unborn Child*. 5. Trauma. No. 1 (June, 1963).

Del Tufo. *Recovery for Prenatal Torts*. 15. Rutgers Law Review. 61 (1960).

Federal Constitutional Limitations on the Enforcement and Administration of State Abortion Statutes, 46 No. Car. Law Review 730.

Freund. *Civil Rights and the Limits of Law.* 14. Buffalo Law Review. 199 (Winter, 1964).

George. *Current Abortion Laws: Proposals and Movements for Reform.* 17. Western Reserve Law Review. 371 (1965).

Gordon. *The Unborn Plaintiff.* 63. Michigan Law Review. 579 (Feb., 1965).

Grannella. *The Difficult Quest for a Truly Humane Abortion Law.* 13. Villanova Law Review. 257 (Winter, 1968).

Parry, L. A. *Criminal Abortion.* London: J. Bale & Danielssohn, *peutic Abortion and the Law; Some New Approaches.* 27. Ohio St. Law Review. 647 (1966).

Leavy & Charles. *California's New Therapeutic Abortion Act: An Analysis and Guide to Medical and Legal Procedure.* 15. U.C.L.A. Law Review. 1 (1967).

Leavy & Kummer. *Criminal Abortion, A Failure of Law.* 50. Am. Bar Assn. Journal 52 (1964).

Legislation. *Abortion Legislation: The Need for Reform.* 20. Vanderbilt Law Review. 1313 (Nov., 1967).

Legislation. *Colorado's New Abortion Law.* 40. University of Colorado Law Review. 297 (Winter, 1968).

Lintgen. *Impact of Medical Knowledge on the Law Relating to Prenatal Injuries.* 110. University of Pennsylvania Law Review. 554 (1962).

Niswander. *Medical Abortion Practices in the United States.* 17. Western Reserve Law Review. 403 (1965).

Note. *Compensation for the Harmful Effects of Illegitimacy.* 66. Columbia Law Review. 127 (Jan., 1966).

Note. *Prenatal Injuries and Wrongful Death.* 18. Vanderbilt Law Review. 847 (1965).

Note. *Torts: Prenatal Injuries—Viability and Live Birth.* 21. Oklahoma Law Review. 114 (1968).

Packer & Gampbell. *Therapeutic Abortion.* 11. Stanford Law Review. 417 (1959).

Parry, L. A. *Criminal Abortion.* London: J. Bale & Danielssohn, 1932.

Personal Injury—Actions, Defenses, Damages. New York: Matthew Bender & Co., n.d.

Quay. *Justifiable Abortion, Medical and Legal Foundation,* 49 Georgetown Law Review. 395 (1961).

Rongy, A. J. *Abortion: Legal or Illegal?* New York: Vanguard Press, 1933.

Schwartz. Abortion and 19th Century Laws. *Trial.* 41 (June/July, 1967).

Shaw, Russell. *Abortion on Trial.* Dayton: P. S. Pfaum, 1968.

Smith, David, ed. *Abortion and the Law.* Cleveland: Western Reserve University Press, 1967.

Storer, H. R. and Heard, F. F. *Criminal Abortion.* Boston: Little, Brown, and Co., 1968.

Trout. *Therapeutic Abortion Laws Need Therapy.* 37. Temple Law Quarterly. 172 (1964).

Williams, G. *The Sanctity of Life and the Criminal Law*. New York: Knopf, 1957.
Winfield. *The Unborn Child*. 4. University of Toronto Law Journal. 278 (1942).

VI. STERILIZATION*

1. Medical Sources

Birnbaum, Morton. "Eugenic Sterilization." *Journal of the American Medical Association*. 175:951, (March) 1961.
Child, C. G. *Sterility and Conception*. New York: Appleton, 1931.
Davis, F. P. *Impotency, Sterility, and Artificial Impregnation*. Second Edition. St. Louis: Mosby, 1923.
Davis, M. E. "Recent Trends in the Study of Infertility." *The Annals of the New York Academy of Science*. 54 (1952).
Duncan, J. M. *Fecundity, Fertility, Sterility and Allied Topics*. Second Edition. Edinburgh: Black, 1871.
Farris, E. J. *Human Ovulation and Fertility*. Philadelphia: Lippincott, 1956.
Ferber, A. S., Teitze, C. and Lewit, S. *Psychosomatic Medicine*. 29:354, 1967.
Garrison, P. L. and Gamble, C. J. "Sexual Effects of Vasectomy." *Journal of the American Medical Association*. 144:293, 1950.
Guttmacher, Alan J. "Artificial Insemination and the Physician." *Ob-Gyn Observer*. I/2, (Jan.–Feb.) 1962.
Rodgers, D. A., Ziegler, F. J. and Levy, N. *Psychosomatic Medicine*. 29:367, 1967.
Schellen, A. *Artificial Insemination in the Human*. New York: American Elsevier Publishing Co., Inc., 1968.
Thompson, B. and Baird, Sir Dugald. "Follow-up of 186 Sterilized Women." *The Lancet*. 1:1023, 1968.
Williams, J. Whitridge. "Indications for Therapeutic Sterilization in Obstetrics." *Journal of the American Medical Association*. XCI/17:1237, (Oct.) 1928.
Ziegler, F. J., Rodgers, D. A. and Kriegsman, S. A. *Psychosomatic Medicine*. 28:50, 1966.

2. Theological Sources

Anon. "Artificial Insemination in the Talmud." *Hebrew Medical Journal*. 2, 1942.
Hinton, J. P. and Calcutt, J. E. *Sterilization: A Christian Approach*. London, 1935.
Jakobovits, Immanuel. "Artificial Insemination, Birth-Control and Abortion." *Hebrew Medical Journal*. 26, 1953.

---

* Note a number of articles on sterilization which have already been cited in the above bibliographies on contraception and abortion.

VII. POPULATION CONTROL

1. Medical Sources

Freedman, Ronald., Whelpton, Pascal K., and Campbell, Arthur A. *Family Planning, Sterility, and Population Growth.* New York: McGraw-Hill, 1959.

Lewis-Faning, E. "Report on an Enquiry into Family Limitation and Its Influence on Human Fertility during the Past Fifty Years." *Papers of the Royal Commission on Population.* Vol. I. London: His Majesty's Stationery Office, 1949.

Meier, Richard L. *Modern Science and the Human Fertility Problem.* New York: John Wiley & Sons, 1959.

Merrill, Malcolm H. "Expanding Populace in a Contracting World." *Journal of the American Medical Association.* 197/8: 632, (Aug.) 1966.

Planned Parenthood: Its Contribution to Family, Community and Nation. New York: Planned Parenthood Federation of America, 1944.

Whelpton, Pascal K., Campbell, Arthur A. and Patterson, John E. *Fertility and Family Planning in the United States.* Princeton: Princeton University Press, 1966.

2. Theological Sources

Barrett, Donald N., ed. *The Problem of Population.* South Bend: The University of Notre Dame Press, 1963.
Vol. I Moral and Theological Considerations
Vol. II Practical Catholic Applications
Vol. III Educational Considerations

Burkhart, Roy A. *Ministerial Counselling and Planned Parenthood.* New York: Planned Parenthood Federation of America, n.d.

Coser, Ruth L., ed. *The Family: Its Structure and Functions.* New York: St. Martin's Press, 1964.

de Chardin, Pierre Teilhard. *L'Energie Humaine.* Paris, 1962.
———. *Le Milieu Divin.* London, 1960.

Fagley, Richard M. *The Population Explosion and Christian Responsibility.* New York: Oxford University Press, 1960.

Mansfield College Report (April, 1959). "Report of the Study Group on Responsible Parenthood and the Population Problem." *The Ecumenical Review.* XII, Oct., 1959.

Ramsey, Paul. "Moral and Religious Implications of Genetic Control." *Genetics and the Future of Man.* A Discussion at the Nobel Conference. Minnesota, 1965.

Warren, M. A. C., et al. *The Family in Contemporary Society.* London: S.P.C.K., 1958.

World Council of Churches. *Statements on Parenthood and the Population Problem.* Geneva, 1960.

3. Sociological Sources

Boulding, Kenneth E. "The Prospects of Economic Abundance" in *The Control of Environment*. Amsterdam, 1967.

Carr-Saunders, A. M. *The Population Problem*. Oxford: Clarendon Press, 1922.

———. *World Population: Past Growth and Present Trends*. London: Oxford University Press, 1936.

Chandrasekhar, S. *Population and Planned Parenthood in India*. London: Allen and Unwin, 1955.

Davis, Kingsley. *Human Society*. New York: Macmillan, 1949.

Eldridge, Hope T. *Population Policies: A Survey of Recent Developments*. Washington, D. C.: International Union for the Scientific Study of Population, 1954.

Francis, Roy G., ed. *The Population Ahead*. Minneapolis: University of Minnesota Press, 1958.

Glass, David V., ed. *Introduction to Malthus*. New York: John Wiley & Sons, 1953.

Greep, Roy O., ed., *Human Fertility and Population Problems*. New York: Schenkman, 1963.

Hatt, Paul K., ed. *World Population and Future Resources*. New York: American Book Co., 1952.

Hauser, Philip M. and Duncan, Otis D. *The Study of Population*. Chicago: The University of Chicago Press, 1959.

Hertzler, J. O. *The Crisis in World Population*. Lincoln: University of Nebraska Press, 1956.

Hill, R., Stycos, J. M., and Back, K. W. *The Family and Population Control*. Chapel Hill: University of North Carolina Press, 1959.

Kalven, Harry, Jr. "The Problems of Privacy in the Year 2000." *Daedalus*. Summer, 1967.

de Lestapis, Stanislas. *La Limitation des Naissances*. Paris: SPES, 1959.

Malthus, Thomas Robert. *An Essay on the Principle of Population*. London, 1826.

Mead, Margaret. "The Life Cycle and Its Variations." *Daedalus*. Summer, 1967.

Moore, Hugh. *The Population Bomb*. New York: The Hugh Moore Fund, n.d.

Osborn, Fairfield. *The Limits of the Earth*. Boston: Little, Brown & Co., 1953.

Place, Frances. *Illustrations and Proofs of the Principles of Population*. Boston: Houghton Mifflin Co., 1930.

Population Division, U.N. Department of Social Affairs. *The Determinants and Consequences of Population Trends*. New York: United Nations Press, 1953.

———. *The Future Growth of World Population*. New York: United Nations Press, 1958.

Quarton, Gardner C. "Deliberate Efforts to Control Human Behavior and Modify Personality." *Daedalus*. Summer, 1967.

Sax, Karl. *Standing Room Only?* Boston: Beacon Press, 1955.

Stamp, L. Dudley. *Land for Tomorrow: The Underdeveloped World*. Bloomington, Ind.: The University of Indiana Press, 1952.

Takeshita, John Y. "Population Control in Japan: A Miracle or Secular Trend?" *Marriage and Family Living*. XXV/1:46, (Feb.) 1963.

Thomlinson Ralph. *Population Dynamics*. New York: Random House, 1965.

Thompson, W. S. *Population and Progress in the Far East*. Chicago: University of Chicago Press, 1959.

Tien, H. Yuan. "Induced Abortion and Population Control in Mainland China." *Marriage and Family Living*. XXV/1:41, (Feb.) 1963.

SELECTED RESPONSES TO PAPERS OF SYMPOSIUM

INTRODUCTION

The six essays which follow were prepared by Discussants at the Symposium in response to other papers. They formed part of the basis for the discussions at Portsmouth. With the exception of Professor Bouma, who also wrote Chapter 17, brief biographies of the authors appear with their essays. These papers were selected from two dozen responses presented at the Symposium because they:

1) Contain information not given elsewhere in this book.
2) Present important alternative views on aspects of the subject.
3) Suggest possible applications of guidelines for decision.
4) Illustrate the complex nature of population control and its attendant problems.

SELECTED RESPONSES TO
PAPERS OF SYMPOSIUM

INTRODUCTION

ABORTION IN A
CHANGING SOCIAL CONTEXT

by Donald H. Bouma

When the 1st International Conference on Abortion was held in the fall of 1967 in Washington, D.C., under sponsorship of the Harvard Divinity School and the Joseph P. Kennedy, Jr. Foundation, there was a recognition of several significant things.

First, no longer was the term "abortion" a nasty word never to be mentioned in polite company or in the mass media. We had finally reached the point of maturity in this country where the problem could be discussed openly and with an attempt at objective detachment. Whereas only a short time before, a TV program which had hardly more than mentioned the word was sharply criticized, so many mass circulated popular magazines now carried articles on the subject that it was impossible to approach a newsstand without being confronted by the word.

Second, the conference recognized the interdisciplinary nature of the problem. Specialists in medicine, ethics, law, and the social sciences were invited to make contributions to the discussion.

Third, there was an increased awareness that the problem of abortion is emotion-laden, surrounded by myth and misunderstanding, and caught on the horns of various ethical positions of wide-ranging degrees of specification and delineation. Further, even professionals finely tuned to understanding different points of view and the ideological frame back of them found it impossible to reach any kind of concensus.

It is banal to observe that while academicians debate in conferences the medical, ethical, legal and sociological aspects of this controversial issue, abortion is a matter of presently-urgent personal and social concern. The lives of real people are marred, altered, ruined by unwanted pregnancies. Illegal and unprofessional abortions feed a pool of damaged mental health, sterility, broken bodies, and death. And countless thousands of young are denied the fundamental right of being born a wanted child.

Meanwhile it is increasingly a matter of social concern as a number of state legislatures face demands for liberalizing abortion laws. Many states have already done so. This past year abortion bills were introduced in 16 of the 29 states which have not recently adopted more liberal abortion laws and which did have legislative sessions.

Colorado was one of the first states to adopt liberalized abortion laws similar to those recommended in the Model Penal Code of the American Law Institute. The 1967 Colorado law permits abortion if all three members of a special hospital board judge that continued pregnancy is likely to result in death of the mother or the serious impairment of her physical or mental health, or would likely result in the birth of a child suffering a grave and permanent physical or mental defect. In addition, abortion is permitted within the first 16 weeks of pregnancy resulting from rape or incest, including statutory rape of a girl younger than 16.

In the first six months of the new law, 120 legal abortions were reported to the Colorado Health Department with patient ages ranging from 12 to 48. Nine of the patients were the victims of rape, two were suicide risks, 50 abortions were approved for other psychiatric reasons, and in 22 cases approval was given because of physical danger to the woman or child. The report listed 37 abortions simply as "therapeutic."

During the first two months of the new California abortion law 254 women received legal abortions. There were 214 abortions done to preserve the woman's mental health, 15 were done to preserve her physical health, 18 were in cases of pregnancy resulting from rape, and seven in incest cases.

Demands for an even greater liberalization of abortion laws are growing. In New York, Governor Rockefeller's Abortion Law Review Commission recommended several additional grounds for abortion, beyond those typically found in the liberalized laws. These include the physical or mental incapacity of the mother to care for the child, the pregnancy commenced while the female was unmarried and under 16, and where the female already has four living children. With the exception of the last one, these were endorsed by the Governor.

The report of the New York commission, composed of four Catholic and seven non-Catholic members, anticipating the criticism it did in fact receive, noted that the recommendations require no woman to seek an abortion and no physician, no hospital or staff member to participate in one.

Going still further, the American Civil Liberties Union, after 18 months of study by its due-process committee and its board of directors, proposed that legislatures abolish all laws imposing criminal penalties for abortions performed by licensed physicians, no matter what the reason. Insisting that abortion is a medical, not a legal matter, the ACLU asserted that a woman has a right to have an abortion—that is, a termination of pregnancy prior to the viability of the fetus—and that a licensed physician has a right to perform an abortion, without the threat of criminal sanctions.

The 1968 ACLU decision faults abortion laws on four grounds: 1. They deprive women of the liberty to decide whether and when their bodies are to be used for procreation; 2. They discriminate against women in the lower economic groups, since abortions are now freely available to the rich, but unobtainable by the poor; 3. They infringe upon the right to decide whether and when to have a child, as well as the marital right of privacy; 4. They impair the right of physicians to practice in accordance with their professional obligations in that they require doctors not to perform a necessary medical procedure.

Careful discussion of the problem of abortion is made difficult not only by the ignorance, but also the misinformation, that surrounds the subject. This is especially true of the popular notions about the danger of abortion and the failure to distinguish between one done professionally and an amateur one. The number of illegal abortions per year in the United States, as well as the deaths resulting from such operations, can only be estimated. However, it was recently reported that bungled, illegal abortions were now the leading cause of maternal deaths in Michigan.

We also know that childbirth, under the best circumstances, is four times as dangerous as a competently performed abortion. However, there is evidence that the public is not so well informed. A survey of New York state residents was recently conducted by Oliver Quayle and Company at the request of the Association for the Study of

Abortion, Inc. The survey was based on a representative cross-section of the state's residents. The respondents were asked if they considered abortions more or less dangerous than five other surgical operations, each of which is, in fact, more dangerous than a hospital abortion.

A clear majority felt an abortion to be more dangerous than a tonsillectomy or an appendectomy, and about one-third of them thought it more dangerous than gall bladder removal, or a caesarean section, or removing the uterus. This erroneous notion that abortion is more dangerous than it is in fact is probably one reason which explains the opposition to liberalizing the present laws in most of the states, which permit abortion only to save the life of the mother.

In spite of this over-emphasis of the dangers of professionally-performed abortions, there is considerable public support for liberalization of the abortion laws. In the study cited above the respondents were asked whether they would favor a legal change which would permit abortions to preserve the woman's health, in case of the possibility of fetal deformity, and in cases of pregnancy resulting from rape or incest.

Seventy-five per cent of the respondents were in favor of this change, 17 per cent were against, and eight per cent were undecided. Abortion reform was favored by 83 per cent of the Protestants, 72 per cent of the Catholics, and 98 per cent of the Jews.

Today most people in the United States are in favor of abortion law reform, but the support varies with the situation involved. There is little public support for the extreme positions of the American Civil Liberties Union, which would remove all legal restrictions on abortion, or that of the Roman Catholic church. In a long-awaited pronouncement on birth control, Pope Paul VI in late July of this year renewed the Catholic Church's ban on abortion "even for therapeutic reasons." In spite of this historic ban on all abortions there has been no effort by Catholic leaders to have this Church position translated into state law. Rather, there has been an acceptance of the "save the life of the mother" justification found in practically all state laws. All of which is to say that for most people it is not a matter of whether to approve of abortion, but rather a difference of opinion as to which circumstances should merit approval.

Two years ago the National Opinion Research Center did a careful study of what a national sample thought about abortion law reform under these varying circumstances. Approval for abortion was given in three situations: The health of the mother (71%); rape or incest (56%); strong chance of serious defect in the baby (55%). Abortion in three other situations was not approved: Low income and cannot afford child (21%); mother is unmarried (18%); mother is married but wants no more children (15%). No differences were found between Protestants and Catholics, but all percentages were lower for "frequent church attenders."

It is important to note that even if all of the 50 states were to liberalize abortion laws to permit operations to protect the physical and mental health of the mother, in cases of rape and incest, and where serious possibilities of fetal deformity exist, this would have little impact on the problem of illegal abortions. The vast majority of illegal abortions today are not for these three reasons, but rather because the birth of a child is not wanted. Only a complete elimination of legal restrictions on abortion would get at this large part of the problem.

While it is true that increased use of new contraceptive techniques will undoubtedly decrease the demand for abortion, this demand will never completely be eliminated. Hence, the need for serious discussion of the problem should have high priority.

However, the problem is considerably broader than this. If we were to assume that medical responsibility includes providing the healthiest kind of family situation for the healthiest possible child, the medical indications for abortion would cover a much wider range—and would necessarily be much more controversial.

OZZIE L. EDWARDS, B.A., M.A., M.S.W., Ph.D. *B.A., Wheaton College; M.A., California State College; M.S.W., U.C.L.A.; Ph.D., University of Wisconsin; Social worker, Los Angeles County; Social worker, California State Department of Mental Health. At present he is Assistant Professor, Department of Sociology, University of Illinois, at Chicago Circle.*

A CRITICAL LOOK AT POPULATION CONTROL PROGRAMS

by Ozzie L. Edwards

INTRODUCTION

The control of human reproduction involves some very complex, interrelated problems. Most proposals are based on population studies rather than on demographic analysis.[1] Such studies originated with Thomas Robert Malthus, who gave a gloomy prognosis but no remedy.

The first edition of Malthus' essay, published in 1798, was given the title, "An Essay on the Principle of Population as It Affects The Future Improvement of Society,

---

[1] Philip M. Hauser and Otis Dudley Duncan, "The Nature of Demography," in *The Study of Population*. Edited by Philip M. Hauser and Otis Dudley Duncan. Chicago: The University of Chicago Press, 1959. "Population studies embrace the investigation of relationships between spatio-temporal variations in population and other bodies of subject matter." "Demographic anaylsis involves the study of components of population variation and change, which may be identified as natality, mortality, territorial movement, and social mobility (change of status)." pp 31,33.

with Remarks on the Speculations of Mr. Godwin, M. Condorcet, and Other Writers." The sixth edition of this essay, published in 1826, was entitled "An Essay on the Principle of Population, or a View of Its Past and Present Effects on Human Happiness, with an Inquiry into Our Prospects Respecting the Future Removal or Mitigation of the Evils which It Occasions." Malthus expressed a concern for the manner in which population growth serves as a barrier to human happiness. He set forth the propositions that "1) Population is necessarily limited by the means of subsistence" and "2) Population invariably increases where the means of subsistence increase, unless prevented by some very powerful and obvious checks." [2] If we agree with these two propositions, we are forced also to agree that no matter how resourceful man may be, it is possible to envision a point at which need will exceed resources. Not all demographers agree with Malthus' second premise. Still fewer economists agree that we have as yet reached the day when world resources have been exhausted, or for that matter, seriously threatened. In fact, the "weight control pill" is also quite popular in our time.

To be sure, there is maldistribution of existing resources. This was not a matter of serious concern for Malthus. He was convinced that "The structure of society, in its great features, will probably always remain unchanged" [3] and that the "fixed laws of our nature" made it absolutely impossible "that the pressure of want can ever be completely removed from the lower classes." [4] There are several excellent critiques of Malthusian theory. [5]

---

[2] Thomas Robert Malthus, *An Essay on the Principle of Population*, London, 1826. p 14.

[3] *Ibid.*, p. 543.

[4] *Ibid.*

[5] Kingsley Davis, *Human Society*. New York: Macmillan, 1949 and David V. Glass (ed.) *Introduction to Malthus* New York: John Wiley & Sons, 1953. These represent two of the more complete discussions of Malthus.

FERTILITY AND SOCIAL PROBLEMS

There is a positive correlation between fertility and certain social problems. Numbered among these problems are perinatal, neonatal, and infant death rates; illegitimacy; crime; dependency and poverty; tuberculosis, syphilis, gonorrhea and other types of physical illness; mental retardation; and even the "battered child syndrome". Are we free to conclude that fertility "causes" these social problems or that reduction in fertility will mitigate or eliminate these problems? It is at least of interest to note that Malthus said, "I should always particularly reprobate any artificial and unnatural modes of checking population, both on account of their immorality and their tendency to remove necessary stimulus to industry." [6] It was his opinion that fewer children would lead to indolence, poverty, and dependency. Which position are we to take? Perhaps the most appropriate position is one of skepticism with regard to oversimplified explanations of complex problems.

For example, from the point of view of demographic analysis, one recognizes the fact that a high birth rate may be "caused" by a high death rate. If few persons live beyond the child bearing years, those living will be bearing children. A reduction of the death rate results in an increase in the denominator of the fraction used to compute birth rates, giving a smaller rate. This problem is dealt with in part by computing "age specific" birth rates. This is not to say that populations in which we find a concentration of social problems do not also have higher birth rates. It simply alerts us to the complexity of the problem before us.

It should also be noted that when we speak of variation in the fertility of social categories, we are in most instances referring to a very limited range in the number of children. In 1960, women in the lowest income category had an aver-

---

[6] Malthus, Essay, *op. cit.*, p. 572.

age of 2.8 children as compared to 2.5 children for women in the highest income category.[7] At the same time we might note that this represents a difference of twelve percent. If the latter figure (2.5) were as low as 1.8 children per woman, the absolute difference would be only one child but the relative difference would be 55.5 percent. Our concern for the "higher" fertility of the lower class population must be viewed in proper perspective.

ALTERNATIVE VIEWS OF POPULATION GROWTH

There are several alternative approaches to the problems at hand. First, there is an alternative view of population growth. Malthus was perhaps the most popular demographic theorist but there are others. More recent theorists have observed a "demographic transition" in a number of countries of northwest Europe and are being led to believe that there may have been at least an element of truth in the theories of population growth set forth by Pearl and Reed.[8]

In its essence, transition theory states that whereas at one point in time stable population size was maintained by a high level of fertility and a high level of mortality, a second point will be reached at which stability will be maintained through low fertility and low mortality. At the upper and lower ends of such a model, fertility varies directly with socioeconomic status (high-high or low-low), but because of the temporal sequence of classes in the pattern decline, inverse differentials (high-low or low-high) are observed during the transition. There are a number of pieces of supporting evidence for such a theory. Not the least of these is the

---

[7] U.S. Bureau of Census, *U.S. Census of Population: 1960* Subject Reports. "Women by number of Children Ever Born". Final Report PC (2)—3A (Washington D.C.: U.S. Government Printing Office, 1964).

[8] Ralph Thomlinson, *Population Dynamics*. New York: Random House, 1965 pp 12–25. Also see Norman B. Ryder, "Fertility" in Hauser and Duncan, *The Study of Population*, pp. 409–413, and Peter W. Frank, "Ecology and Demography" in the same volume.

decreasing predictive value of socioeconomic status in the fertility studies conducted between 1941 and 1966.[9]

The transition from high to low fertility in northwest Europe occurred prior to the development of the more efficient methods of contraception. However, in no case did it develop prior to or apart from industrialization, modernization, and improvement of social conditions. This suggests the possibility that it is not the development and dissemination of knowledge concerning contraceptive techniques but a change in certain social conditions and the associated mentality which leads to a reduction of fertility.

This leads to a second alternative which we might consider, namely, an alternative approach to the task of spreading information concerning contraception. There is a need to provide such information to an element of the population which is seeking by ineffective means to control its fertility. Apart from certain ideological arguments being dealt with at this Symposium, this represents an act of benevolence on the part of those who possess the information. However, at least implicit in our thinking is the assumption that effort should be directed toward providing such information for an element of the population which at present has little or no concern about the control of fertility. It is in the light of this assumption that we now speak.

Norms and values tend to appear in sets or clusters, not in isolation. Members of such sets tend to provide mutual support. For this reason, the change of a single member of a set can prove difficult apart from change in the complete cluster of norms and values. Cohen recognizes this in his discussion of delinquency.[10] He finds that the working class

[9] A bibliography of such studies may be found in Pascal K. Whelpton, Arthur A. Campbell, and John E. Patterson, *Fertility and Family Planning*. Princeton: Princeton University Press, 1966 (In particular see pp. 7–8).

[10] Albert Cohen, *Delinquent Boys: The Culture of the Gang*. Glencoe: The Free Press, 1955.

youth, after being exposed to middle-class goals and having avenues of achieving these goals systematically closed, develops a mentality which rejects middle-class goals en masse. Bringing this individual back into the larger social system requires a change in his rejection mentality, not in a single item of behavior. Similar approaches have been found to be of value to community organizers in their efforts to be innovative. It may be that contraception represents an idea which does not mesh with a certain value-set or that contraception is a part of a cluster of values which has for other reasons been rejected. The task then becomes one of more than simply providing necessary information. It involves the eradication of barriers which prevent acceptance of such information.

Finally, we might consider an alternative route to the goals of "improvement of society" and "human happiness". We must recognize the fact that the greatest obstacle to human happiness in our time is not fertility but attitudes and practices which exclude certain men from those things which bring happiness. Many of those caught up in the vast net of social problems have a smaller number of children than do those who casually observe from the safe distance of the suburbs. Can we honestly tell a family of six which pays as much rent as a family of five for less than eighty percent of the housing that their problem is the number of children in the family?

If we offer controlled fertility as a way to happiness and a solution to social problems, we are to be chastened and criticized. In so doing, we offer that which costs us nothing. Furthermore, we propagate the false notion that blame lies at the foot of the victim. Social problems are not the consequence of higher fertility. While the latter may indeed compound the problem, it is as much a symptom as are other social ills.

If on the other hand we are concerned about liberating

men from fears and misconceptions which prevent controlled fertility, ours is a worthy task. It can then be viewed
in proper perspective, dealt with, and we can go on to other
tasks.

ABORTION LAW REFORM

At what point has an individual the right and the responsibility to stand up and speak out for what he believes? We
live in a society which is, at least to some degree, ordered
by laws. These laws are a consequence of (someone's) personal beliefs. The well-meaning but silent Christian has all
too often been a liability in the struggle for that which is
right and good. The issue of modified abortion laws ought to
be settled in terms of what we are convinced is right and not
because of lack of information, lack of conviction, or lack of
willingness to stand for our convictions. This is not to argue
against liberalization of abortion laws but to argue in favor
of the Christian assuming a position of more informed,
more vigorous participation in matters of larger social concern.

The question is, what is our purpose in liberalization of
the laws regarding abortion? If the purpose is one of reducing the number of children among a certain element of the
population (in particular, reference is made to the poor in
urban ghettoes), are we employing the proper means? Is it
likely that given liberal abortion laws, the method of fertility control will be employed by this segment of the population. Or is this one of several methods of fertility control
practiced by those concerned about the control of fertility
and rejected by those to whom fertility control is a matter
which is of little concern or an idea which is totally rejected? It appears that the poor, uneducated urbanites are
more likely to resort to sterilization in the event that they
become concerned about fertility control. If our purpose is
to ease ourselves of this burdensome element of the popu-

lation, efforts expended in the area of sterilization might prove more effective than those directed toward liberalization of abortion laws.

ABORTION AND STERILIZATION AS ALTERNATIVES

A further question concerns the relative incidence of abortion and sterilization in various cultures. Apparently it is possible to identify cultures having each of four approaches to fertility control. In Japan there is widespread practice of both abortion and sterilization. In France abortion appears to exceed sterilization. In Puerto Rico sterilization seems to be dominant. In China both abortion and sterilization are rejected. If we consider contraception, it is at least conceivable that each of the eight possible permutations of practice of these three methods of fertility control (contraception, sterilization, abortion) might be discovered. One is inclined to wonder as to the nature of underlying factors. Undoubtedly such factors must be taken into consideration if the goal of controlled fertility is to be achieved.

There is at least one additional piece of information which ought to be considered in this discussion. It is of more than incidental interest to note the temporal variation in rates of legal abortion where liberal abortion laws exist. For example, in New York City the number of legal abortions per 1,000 live births declined from 5.1 in 1943 to 2.0 in 1957.[11] Prior to liberalization of abortion laws in Sweden, there were approximately 5 legal abortions per 1,000 live births each year. After the liberalization of these laws, the rate soared to a high of 57 legal abortions per 1,000 live births in 1951. After that point, the rate declined regularly

---

[11] Christopher Tietze, "Some Facts About Legal Abortion," in Roy O. Greep, *Human Fertility and Population Problems*. Schenkman, 1963 p. 223.

and steadily to 29 legal abortions per 1,000 live births in 1959. The same trend was characteristic of Denmark where the rate increased from 7 in 1939 to 70 in 1955 and then declined to 48 in 1959.[12]

In Japan there were 3.0 legal abortions per 1,000 live births in 1949.[13] The abortion rate increased to 13.1 in 1955 after abortion was made available without restriction by the Eugenic Protection Law of 1948. Between 1955 and 1961 the abortion rate declined steadily to a rate of 11.0. While the abortion rate was following this curvilinear pattern, the live birth rate showed a steady decline from 33.2 to 16.9 with no particular correlation between the two rates.

Such data raises a number of questions concerning the relationships between abortion, sterilization, contraception, and the control of fertility. Although the abortion rates in each of the above countries remain quite high, the pattern of immediate increase followed by subsequent decline casts some doubt on the "need" for at least some of the abortions. Whatever the case, we stand in the advantageous postion of being able to profit from past experience and certainly ought to do so.

---

[12] *Ibid., p.* 225.
[13] *Ibid.*

SARA CREWS FINLEY, B.S., M.D. *B.S. University of Alabama; M.D. Medical College of Alabama; Assistant Professor of Pediatrics—Laboratory of Medical Genetics; Research & Publications: Cytogenetics, congenital malformations, human growth and development, genetic counseling.*

GENETICS, ABORTION AND STERILIZATION

by Sara Crews Finley

Few people argue with the principle of sacrificing a fetus if necessary to preserve the life or the health of the mother. However, until the recent demand for more liberal abortion laws in the United States, there has been no legal consideration for the fetal indications for abortion. Even today, only four of our states have laws permitting abortion for a fetal indication.

There are several commonly recognized considerations including maternal rubella, known teratogenic drug exposure, and certain hereditary conditions. From the medical geneticist's viewpoint, I would like to emphasize the genetic aspects of this problem. With newer techniques and concepts in genetics, the list of genetic diseases continues to grow and ranges from those associated with a single biochemical anomaly to those with multiple structural malformations often including mental retardation. There are approximately 250 disorders in the human which are transmitted in an autosomal dominant pattern which means that an affected individual has a 50–50 chance of having any of his or her offspring so affected. Many of these disorders are mild and would never be considered in a discussion of this type. Others, however, such as achondroplastic dwarfism, Marfan's disease, and Huntington's Chorea seriously interfere with an individual's well-being and normal role in the family and in society. They present a problem in genetic counseling because many times the affected parent realizes more than anyone else the burden of the disease and is adamant against having offspring which may well be similarly affected. In these situations in which the family history indicates that there is a dominant mode of transmission, genetic counseling is significant and will continue to become more so. Ideally, contraception or, if preferred, sterilization should prevent the birth of more affected children in these families. However, on a practical basis, we recognize that unplanned pregnancies do occur; and the question of therapeutic abortion becomes the main issue in some of these cases.

Many other genetic diseases which affect both the quality and quantity of life are transmitted in an autosomal recessive pattern. If a couple has a child with one of these disorders such as cystic fibrosis, PKU, galactosemia, or sickle cell anemia, there is a 1 in 4 chance of a subsequent child being affected. While few would argue with the fact that the impact of two or more children with debilitating, life-shortening diseases is more than many couples can manage, are we justified in recommending an abortion to terminate a pregnancy which has 3 chances in 4 of producing a normal child and 1 chance in 4 of having the recessive disease in question? Some of the sex-linked diseases such as Duchenne's muscular dystrophy pose a similar problem. The chromosome aberrations of which mongolism is the prime example not infrequently raise the question as to the feasibility of therapeutic abortion. Some types of chromosomal aberrations are now identifiable in which one parent is a carrier and has a risk of 1 in 3 of having another grossly abnormal child.

Singularly, the various genetic diseases do not constitute a major problem with regard to the question of induced abortion. Collectively, however, they are a significant factor in considering the fetal indications for abortion. As increased knowledge of biochemical genetics and cytogenetics permits better identification of carriers, genetic counseling will become more important.

Today, however, those of us concerned with fetal indicacations for abortion face basically these two questions:

(1) What is a "high risk" for fetal abnormality— is it 1 in 2, 1 in 4, 1 in 10, or what is it?

(2) How severe must the abnormality in question be— is a debilitating, crippling disease such as muscular dystrophy in a brilliant child an indication or must the disease result in gross structural deformities and/or mental retardation?

As our scientific background for genetic counseling broadens, we may expect contraception, sterilization, artificial insemination or newer techniques such as ova transplants to aid more and more in the prevention of genetic diseases. In the meantime, however, the question of the role of abortion in these families is a major practical consideration.

WAYNE H. FINLEY, B.S., M.D., M.S., Ph.D. *B.S. Jacksonville (Ala.) State College; M.D. Medical College of Alabama; M.S. University of Alabama Medical Center; Ph.D. University of Alabama Medical Center; Associate Professor, Department of Pediatrics; Director, Laboratory of Medical Genetics, University of Alabama Medical Center, Birmingham, Alabama; Research & Publications: Cytogenetics, malformations, biochemistry.*

GENETIC REASONS FOR LIMITING CONCEPTION

by Wayne H. Finley

Few believe that the human race has an obligation to bring about the birth of as many children as possible. Instead, a child ideally should be born into a home where he or she was conceived in an atmosphere of love, where his or her arrival is contemplated and planned for and where provisions are made for his or her infancy and childhood. This concept is the foundation of the grandeur of the family unit.

Contraception is the leading birth control measure in our society and there are both chemical and mechanical means which are important to an individual couple or to a comprehensive health program which aims at improving the quality of life. Various methods including both those with a temporary objective and those with a permanent objective have been used for centuries to limit family size and to lengthen the interval between children. The success of some methods has resulted in their widespread use to safeguard the physical or mental health of parents and children and to control fertility in some geographical regions.

Medical indications for contraception would be expected to include those usually outlined for therapeutic abortion and sterilization plus others not warranting such drastic measures. When we are discussing the medical indications, we cannot ignore the social, economic, and personal aspects. We must consider not only the voluntary regulation of birth in an affluent society such as ours but also consider it as a part of a preventive medicine program for underdeveloped countries.

The private physician who has the family health care responsibility is alerted for indications for birth control in order to promote general well-being of the family. The public health physicians responsible for large-scale planning, while using the same indications, also must include extreme poverty, inadequate housing and other factors. In some settings contraception of a temporary nature may be the only means available. With perfection of several rather reliable methods and the promise of other developments and refinements in medications and devices, contraception will be the key to population control.

In genetic counseling we are concerned with (1) diagnostic procedures to obtain information which would be of value in determining the likelihood of a family having a child affected with a severe genetic disease and (2) guiding the family to the decision in family planning which is best for them once the odds for having an affected child are established.

Medically, we would expect to indicate the need of contraception to those families who have an increased risk of having children with undesirable genetic disease, those who are unable to adjust mentally to a pregnancy and a birth, those who are unable physically to care for a child, and those mothers who are unable physically to carry a fetus to term.

While voluntary contraception incites little opposition in our society today among Protestants, involuntary contraception or sterilization is more controversial. In the near future, responsible members of society may have to make decisions regarding permanent contraception or sterilization of segments of the population who are reproducing so rapidly that they are depleting themselves and their offspring of a healthy, useful life. Others who may have decisions, hopefully responsible decisions, made for them include individuals who are incompetent to provide a suitable environment for an infant. A fertile mongoloid woman who has a 1 in 2 chance of having a mongoloid baby if pregnancy occurs represents such a situation. These facets of reproduction control must be considered. We should ask ourselves if involuntary contraception should be demanded of certain individuals or groups, and if so, we should look carefully at the possible criteria.

New developments in the regulation of conception can be expected to cause a reappraisal of objectives from time to time.

KENNETH KANTZER, A.B., M.A., B.D., S.T.M., Ph.D.
A.B. Ashland College; M.A. Ohio State University; B.D., S.T.M., Faith Theological Seminary; Ph.D., Harvard; Dean, Trinity Evangelical Divinity School; Professor of Bible and Systematic Theology.

THE ORIGIN OF THE SOUL AS RELATED TO THE ABORTION QUESTION

by Kenneth Kantzer

On the issue of the origin of the human soul Biblical scholars are generally divided between traducianism and creationism. Traducians argue that man inherits his soul just as much as his body. Creationists, on the contrary, maintain that the human soul is not derived from parents but is created individually and placed into conjunction with the body at some point between conception and birth.

According to creationists, therefore, the significance of abortion depends upon whether the abortion takes place before or after the implantation of the human spirit. Abortion before this occurs is a very serious matter but technically speaking it is not murder.

The following arguments are frequently adduced to support a creationist view of the orgin of the soul.

1. Genesis 2:7: The creation of the soul by God is taken as an act different from the act of the creation of the physical aspects of man, and, by contrast with the *mediate* creation of human flesh, is an immediate act of creation.
2. Numbers 16:22: God is spoken of as God of the spirits of men in a way so as to contrast with his relation to flesh.
3. Eccles. 12:7: At death the spirit of man, by contrast with his flesh which decays, returns to God who gave it.
4. Zech. 12:1: This passage explicitly states that God "formed the spirit of man within him."
5. Isaiah 42:5: God gives to man his spirit.
6. Isaiah 57:16: God speaks of the "souls which I have made."
7. Heb. 12:9: God, as the Father of our spirit, is contrasted with man as the father of our flesh.

Unfortunately, even if these arguments are accepted as conclusive, the problem of abortion is not solved unless there is clear evidence as to the time in fetal development when the spirit of man is created. Most recent scholars tend to identify this time as the moment of conception. No clear evidence is available one way or the other, however. Certainly the Bible does not provide specific teaching on this point.

A careful assessment of the Biblical grounds offered in support of the creationist view brings the entire theory into serious doubt. We conclude that the creationist view offers us no helpful solution to the ethical problem of abortion.

The traducian view, as ordinarily presented by those Biblical scholars who defend it, suggests a neat but rigid conclusion:

1. The fetus is constituted a human person at the moment

of conception by traducian inheritance of the soul from parents.

2. To kill a human individual is murder.

3. Therefore, abortion is murder.

As an alternative hypothesis I suggest the following: The human being originates at conception by a traducian process and constitutes a unitary being which is from the first potentially human and thus of immeasurable value, develops a distinguishable but intricately united and interdependent body and spirit, and eventually consummates, as a result of his relationship to God by means of the divine creative will, in a human being, who is a divinely-purposed-and-sustained, immortal soul with a body (i.e., body-form).

Relevant Data by which this hypothesis may be tested:

1. No Biblical passage speaks of man as fully human before birth or condemns abortion as murder. The absence of any specific condemnation of abortion (even in view of the fact that the practice was known in the ancient world and that such condemnations occurred in the writings of other ancient peoples) is *not* to be pressed, however, because the Bible commands man to be fruitful and multiply and uniformly sets such high value on the human life process and human reproduction as to make the negative unnecessary. Biblically speaking, abortion is not stated to be murder; but it is wrong because it represents the reversal of what is positively commanded by God.

2. The Exodus 21:22-24 passage explicitly distinguishes the killing of a fetus from murder on the ground that the fetus is not a human life. In the latter case, a human life is to be forfeited as penalty. This distinction becomes clearer when the passage is compared with Lev. 24:17. To destroy a (fully human) soul of Adam is murder. The grounds for considering such an act

murder rest in the fact that man possesses the image
of God (Gen. 9:6). A fetus, therefore, is not a true
"soul of Adam" or a truly human soul with the image
of God implanted on it.

3. In Scriptural language the existence of the soul as such
does not by any means constitute that being a human
person. Animals, too, possess a soul. Just as there are
many kinds of bodies, so are there many kinds of souls.

4. Traducianism, basically, seems to interpret faithfully
the important Biblical viewpoint: that the "stuff" out
of which man is made he receives from his parents:
Gen. 2:2: God created man and then ceased from his
creative work.
Gen. 2:21: The creation of Eve from Adam points to a
derivation of more than the mere physical—rather the
whole woman.
Gen. 46:26: Levi existed, "lived" and "acted" in the
loins of Abraham.
Isa. 44:24: "He who formed thee from the womb".
Psa. 139:13–15: "Thou hast covered me in my mother's womb. "Thine eyes did see my substance yet being
imperfect (unformed) in the womb."
Luke 1:40–44: The baby, John, leaped in his mother's
womb.
I Cor. 11:8: woman is "of" man.

Man secures his soul (or immaterial aspects of his being)
as well as his body (or physical inheritance) from his pro-
genitors: but man, body and soul, develops in the womb. The
philosophical argument that a soul cannot be propagated by
"division" is specious. This is to employ a model from the
science of physics to express a non-physical *derivation from*.
Perhaps sharing would be a better word to use, but in any
case an argument based on the analogy of the spiritual to
the physical is not convincing. For the same reason, the objection that the soul cannot grow and develop is invalid

as an argument against the idea of an inheritance of the human soul.

Traducianism, however, is not adequate, in itself, to account for man as he is viewed in Biblical perspective. The essence of man is not merely what he secures from father and mother, it includes also what God *wills* for him and how God freely chooses to relate Himself to man. To Aristotle's vegetative, animal, and rational, we must add "spiritual." Exactly *when* man becomes an immortal soul and truly human person related to God, in the final analysis, rests on the divine decree—God's freely willed activity and purpose with man.

5. An indirect substantiation of this understanding of the role of developing body-soul is found in the Biblical picture of heaven as populated by human beings who went through a test in life on this earth (physical universe?). The view that every fertilized egg is a full human individual, coupled with the known fact that at least one-third of all fertilized human eggs are naturally aborted, would require a heaven in which the vast majority of human inhabitants in heaven would be human beings who originated in miscarriages. Such a view simply does not fit the Biblical picture of the after life drawn for us in some detail in the relevant passages of Scripture.

6. While Biblical passages such as Psalm 139:13–15, Isaiah 44:24 and Luke 1:40 and 44 indicate a traducian origin of that which constitutes man, they do not prove that man existed as personal and fully human from conception any more than the Biblical statement that Levi paid tithes in the loins of his father Abraham proves that Levi had personal and fully human existence in the semen of Abraham. Such passages have quite different points to make, and their reference to the individual man serves to call attention to the origin

and explanation of man. They do not imply that a process was unnecessary before that which constituted the stuff from which man came would become fully and truly human and personal. This represents the inadequacy of the traditional traducian explanation for the origin of man.

7. Negatively, the idea that man becomes human through a process, including a will of God to express His purpose for man, is often rejected because, so it is alleged, we must then define man functionally and thus must forfeit any right to object to the murder of a man in his sleep or an insane man. Man, however, is *not* to be defined functionally. He is to be defined, rather, in terms of a being (including body and soul) who is the subject of God's sovereign action and purpose. Scripture may not tell us how to recognize the functions of a truly human and immortal soul for this is not important. Scripture does teach us that a human fetus is of immeasurable value because of its potential, in spite of the fact that it is not yet fully human; and Scripture demands, accordingly, that the human fetus be treated as of such immeasurable value by man. On the other hand, human offspring at birth are human souls of Adam and are to be treated so—i.e., to put one to death is murder (certain types of exceptions, such as warfare, capital punishment, and self-defence, being also enumerated).

Incidentally the development of the fertilized ovum outside the womb would not materially affect this judgment. The *culminating* decisive factor in *constituting* the human person is God's decision and purpose. The decisive factor in *guiding our attitude towards the fetus* is provided by Biblical instruction as to the value and sacredness of human life and as to the increasing value of the fetus, which is potential human life in process of becoming a human being. As such, from the Biblical point of view, its value is so large as to be immeasurable by us except in terms of the essential and infinite worth of humanity. This process culminates (by the development of the body *and* soul, and by the intent of God in a fully human being) to destroy whom would be manslaughter (or worse). Or to put the whole matter in its simplest and most unambiguous form, I must assert the following:

As I understand the scriptural revelation bearing directly and indirectly on this issue, it is ordinarily wrong to kill the life of the fetus, but it is not manslaughter. It is wrong because the fetus is potentially human and because of the sacredness of human life. It is not manslaughter because the fetus is not yet man. The exact moment or point in development at which a fetus becomes fully human we cannot determine for this lies in the freedom of God. On the other hand we do not need to know this. We do need to know how to treat the fetus. Scripture gives us this instruction by warning us that to take the life of a living infant is manslaughter (blameable killing if not murder). What Holy Scripture does *not* do is to give us a precise numbered value to be set on the human fetus at each stage from fertilized egg up through viability to birth and a neatly categorized numerical value on each alternative evil with which we may be faced so as to enable us in every case to make an exact calculation. Scripture does give us guidelines for acting by indicating that:

a. The life of the fetus is sacred and valuable from the first.
b. By implication, it indicates that this value increases.
c. Such value may not be destroyed except in case of necessity to preserve weighty human values.
d. The value increases in accordance with the investment in human life residing in the fetus until at the time of viability only another human life could balance the scale.
8. Even man's production of human life by artificial

stimulation of the ovum or by manufactured human semen or by a manufactured human egg or by cross fertilization of man and ape or man and mosquito, would have to be interpreted in accordance with these same basic principles though confessedly the applications of these principles could become very difficult. On Biblical grounds, however, it is impossible to give serious consideration to the origin of man solely out of what Scripture calls the "dust" of the earth plus an intent or purpose of God. Man, after all, is not just a very complex arrangement of physical atoms. He is this plus spirit.

CONCLUSION

The hypothesis that fits the Scriptural data best includes these factors:

1. Man is a unity of body and soul, each incomplete without the other.
2. Both are received by inheritance from the parents (the aspect of truth in traducianism).
3. There is development of both body and soul.
4. Man is not constituted an immortal fully human being apart from the willing and purpose of God for him as an "individual-before-God" (the aspect of truth in creationism).
5. From conception, the fetus is of immeasurable value because of its potential humanity; and, therefore, to destroy it is an evil which can only be willed by man in obedience to God as a lesser evil so that not to destroy it would be to destroy other immeasurable values which are yet known to be greater (i.e., not just the well-being as in the sense of greater pleasure but the greater humanity of man (as life, sanity, and perceptible personhood).

WILLIAM B. KIESEWETTER, B.S., M.D. *B.S. Davidson College, Phi Beta Kappa; M.D. University of Pennsylvania; Chief of Surgical Services, Children's Hospital of Pittsburgh; Professor of Pediatric Surgery, University of Pittsburgh, School of Medicine; Fellow, American College of Surgeons.*

CHRISTIAN ETHICS, THE PHYSICIAN AND ABORTION

by William B. Kiesewetter

It is the aim of this paper to deal with these topics within the Protestant Christian context. It is the purpose for this symposium. It is our only possible point of usefulness. Philosophical, non-Christian attitudes can be as intelligently discussed by others. It is essential, however, to guard against two extremes. Rigid, authoritarian evangelicals so often extract from the Word of God precepts which they then congeal into a legalism by which everybody is admonished to live. The other risk can best be summarized as "my thoughts (because I am a Christian) are certainly God's will".

I will limit my few remarks to three points as related to therapeutic abortion: (1) the personal ethics of the physician; (2) his relationship to the professional codes of his day; (3) his accommodation to the social pressures of the day. I will try to ask two questions under each: (1) Does the Protestant Christian have a clear-cut answer? (2) Is this answer singular and distinct from the answer one would get from the average physician who makes no pretense at including God in his thoughts?

Initially, we might seek a definition of "therapeutic abortion". Do we mean the termination of pregnancy for organic disease only? Or do we include within the scope of the term the mental health of the mother as well? Does our definition encompass the family's reaction to the possible addition from a social, psychiatric and economic standpoint? Organic disease is very seldom the single cause for therapeutic abortion, and, when the indications are there, none of us would have much trouble in arriving at a decision. Our considerations will have to go beyond that straightforward situation. The mental health of the mother and the family needs are always involved, except where the mother is unmarried, and so they must be included within the scope of our definition.

THE INDIVIDUAL PHYSICIAN'S PERSONAL ETHICS

In regard to the personal ethics of individual physicians, it boils down to the question of the proportion of absolutism and relativism we are going to permit in the ethical questions involved. An inviolate legalism has more often than not been the standard of the past. One must admit that we live in a relativistic age in which the boundary lines of good and bad, right and wrong are sometimes as fuzzy as the outlines of a river valley in the early morning mist. I honestly can't write a prescription, either for myself or for others, to include the proper percentage of strict principle and relative expediency. However, I do know that in order to have any practical impact on the day in which we live we must not abandon our principles, nor must we fail to have a Christ-like elasticity in applying them that will accommodate to a variety of situations. If we can settle the personal equation of whether abortion is always an evil or simply apply the indiscrimate rule of expediency to a situation, then we can come to a point of decision and action. I feel that the fundamental principle involved is that often used, but poorly understood term "Christian love". In so "loving", we are fulfilling our Lord's and the Apostles' commands. Admittedly, this is a hard word to define. Of this I am certain, it is not the vague mystique of John Robinson's "Honest to God", which left me feeling that it was a mirage of feeling that disappeared into unreality as one approached it. Nor is it the situational ethical quicksand of Fletcher; in his mind, it is no doubt specific, but to listen to him gives one the feeling that "anything goes", depending on the circumstances of the moment.

The whole discussion to this point may sound somewhat ephemeral and theoretical, but it is really bed rock for the Christian physician. If he does not apply his principles in the constraining love of the Master, he has no workable guidelines. Such personal concern for the individual patient will achieve the proper blend of the absolutism of divine principle and the relativism of human need. I equally firmly believe that a Christian has a distinctive ethic and motivation here. He is lovingly involved with his patient because he knows the love of God in his own heart. He is not acting out of simple expediency.

RELATIONSHIP TO PROFESSIONAL CODES

Having found an accommodation with the issue of individual ethics, the physician's relationship to professional codes and social pressures would seem to fall into place rather naturally, the personal ethic being the horse, the other two the cart.

The professional codes of the medical community should be a mirror of the concerns and concensus of medicine.

These codes have arisen over the years out of a variety of circumstances and experience. They should not be lightly cast aside as being outmoded. However, too often we hide behind the codes as justification for not thinking of them in relationship to the day in which we live. Perhaps they need some modification. If so, a review of such changes is indicated after a stated short period of trial.

As Christians, we must never find ourselves on the side of those who would indiscriminately do away with the standards which have served us reasonably well down through the years. We must be willing to stand up and be counted on a given issue where a Christian principle is at stake. We must be willing to think through the problems and concerns embodied in our professional codes on therapeutic abortion and influence them in the light of our Christian convictions. This must not be done rigidly and legalistically, but with truly enlightened and adaptable Christian guidelines.

A point that is infrequently thought of is that many of our medical ethical decisions are increasingly arrived at by men and methods that are devoid of simple idealism, much less Christian principle. Practicality, majority concensus, or expediency seem to be the factors that control the establishment of our accepted ethical behavior. The Christian physician does have something to say here; at the least, he can present the leaven of Christ-inspired idealism, if not the higher concerns of Christian involvement.

RELATIONSHIP TO SOCIETY'S PRESSURES

We cannot be in touch with current thinking on therapeutic abortion without realizing that society is moving towards liberalizing both our ethical and legal codes. This is not all bad nor are the pressures generated by solely self-seeking and expedient human beings. Seeking change stems from a practical desire. Since terminating pregnancy is much discussed and readily available, the possibility is no longer taboo. People are asking the question as to how to use it most wisely and effectively, yet with principle. There is a justifiable realism in the pressures of our society for overthrowing the secrecy and hypocrisy of the past wherein abortion, in any form, was too often "the privilege of the rich".

The Christian physician must not be unaware of what generates these pressures. We cannot simply ignore them or consider them all "bad". We must deal with the underlying cause in a way to help shape it in our own individual sphere of influence to God-directed ends. Doctors have the opportunity not to fall prey to the trite phraseology which came from the lips of a man at a point of high emotion: "I feel lifted up and my love for mankind is unlimited, but that fellow next door who throws his weeds in my garden vexes me no end." It is the "fellow next door" in our professional lives who makes up one of the ingredients of society, much as our attitudes towards applying Christian principles to the problem of abortion. We must deal with him and this problem if we are to see the changes that we desire in the broader context.

I would submit that the social issues of our day are solved by changed attitudes on the part of the individuals involved in the issues: changed individual lives in the truest Christian sense mean changed attitudes towards these issues. As Christian physicians, we can put our weight in the scale of social pressure on the side of godly right. We then may seek to get our neighbors to see the values through the eyes of a follower of Christ. In so changing the bricks of the house, we bring about a change in the configuration of the house itself.

CONCLUSIONS

Nowhere in our discussion of medical ethics as applied

to therapeutic abortion have I come across the solicitation of opinions from that group of people most vitally concerned —women. They often have keener sensitivity to the idealistic issues involved and the Christian overtones which should be applied to them. How can we be oblivious to the fact that, in this particular problem, they are the ones who have the most subjective understanding of what is involved? Perhaps, as a minimum suggestion, one should ask both Christian and non-Christian women to share in discussions of this sort and in the decisions derived from them.

Most of us would agree that we must get away from the hypocrisy we seem to be living under as doctors and Christians. We must have the facts, think them through, and arrive at a decision which may mean change. This involves being personally honest, prayerful, and as right before God as we know how to be. The codes and laws, as they undoubtedly will evolve in the near future, will probably be broad enough to fit almost any point of view. Our conclusions may not be those of a few decades back, nor even those pressed upon us today. We may, in Christian conscience, resort to a course of action which a doctor friend of mine pursued several years ago. A fellow-missionary had four children and a wife who found missionary life, her family and her physical strength not always completely in accord. This couple, faced with an unexpected and undesired pregnancy, sought his help in their dilemma. After prayerful consideration on the part of all concerned, my friend terminated the pregnancy. No social pressures were on him. No professional codes in the country where he was a missionary led him to or away from this decision. His personal, ethical principles and Christian concern for this individual woman and family led him to this course of action.

OLIVER J. STEINER, B.A., M.D. *B.A. Taylor University, Upland, Indiana; M.D. University of Buffalo, New York; Clinical Instructor in Obstetrics & Gynecology; Private practice of Obstetrics & Gynecology—Williamsville, New York*

ARTIFICIAL INSEMINATION: MORAL AND LEGAL IMPLICATIONS

by Oliver J. Steiner

Extreme legal caution must be exercised when a physician is confronted with a medical problem involving artificial insemination, (A.I.). Artificial insemination is defined as the introduction of sperm (semen) into the genital tract of the female by means other than coitus or sexual intercourse for the purpose of impregnation of the female.

Married couples who find it impossible to conceive through natural intercourse sometimes seek impregnation by artificial insemination. There are three types of artificial insemination:

1) Use of semen from the husband, commonly referred to as (A.I.H.)

2) Insemination with semen from a donor who is usually anonymous and with whom the recipient has no contact, (A.I.D.)

3) Insemination with semen from the husband and semen from a donor who is again usually anonymous, (C.A.I.)

The history of this means of impregnation in humans began in the mid-eighteenth century in Italy and England. John Hunter stated he advised a successful A.I.H. in 1793. Approximately one hundred years later Dehatu, J.M. Sims and Gerault published works on artificial fecundation.

The present estimated number of A.I.D.'s performed yearly in the United States varies from 1000 to 7000, indicating the secrecy and inaccuracy of reporting attendant to this procedure.

Reaction to artificial insemination has been very heated, for individuals and groups are either intensely for or against, with very little indication of a middle of the road attitude.

Those advocating A.I.D. and C.A.I. feel that this procedure is superior to adoption because the potential mother experiences pregnancy and birth. They reason that couples of "mixed marriages" cannot adopt, saying not enough babies are available for adoption, that the marriage is made more complete and happier, and that artificial insemination is sound eugenically. Many see no difference between having a blood transfusion or receiving an organ transplant and receiving semen from a donor.

Legal problems to many are apparent, but are not deemed insurmountable. It is not within the scope of this paper to deal with these in great detail, but questions which need to be answered will be posed in this paper to be considered by the reader.

Those in favor of A.I.D. have many reservations. They believe that social, moral and legal implications narrow the field of donors to the intellectually sound and emotionally mature. The procedure is expensive and inconvenient, but many feel that these are minor considerations. Many who oppose artificial insemination maintain that the procedure presents too many drawbacks, and since there are many doubts, they conclude that, "Whatsoever does not proceed from faith is sin." (Romans 14:23)

Some believe that the procedure is unnatural and immoral because it involves masturbation and is a usurpation of the rights of our Creator. They also state that the only means which is scriptural is sexual intercourse between marital partners, and that conception is not necessary for the fulfillment and completion of the husband and wife in each other. In donor insemination some argue that an unholy trinity is created which violates the teaching in Matthew 19:5–6 which states that, "Two shall become one . . . What God therefore has joined together, let no man put asunder." There is also the possibility that there is a violation of ethics which does not take into account the possible effects upon all involved if the anonymity of the donor, donor's wife and children is not maintained.

Danger of consanguinity remains an objection, although it is estimated that this would rarely occur. The danger of incestuous marriages is repeatedly noted in the literature, and it is possible to see how this could occur if a donor were repeatedly used in a small community.

Adultery, illegitimacy and bigamy are objections posed by many in questioning A.I.D. Roman Catholics say the procedures in A.I.H. and A.I.D. are unnatural. Most Protestants feel that A.I.H. is morally right, but that A.I.D. and C.A.I. are morally and legally indefensible.

This paper, as I mentioned before, is intended to be only a springboard for further discussions, so no conclusions will be drawn by the writer.

In closing let me pose several questions which should be answered, as outlined by W. T. Pommerenke in his paper entitled *Artificial Insemination: Genetic and Legal Implications:*

"1) Is the helping of a normal woman to achieve motherhood without her husband's participation, but with his consent, morally defensible?

2) Is the act of artificial insemination properly regarded as a medical procedure?

3) If artificial insemination is a medical procedure, should it be governed by laws applying to medical practices generally?

4) If artificial insemination connotes adultery, is the physician who transfers the semen a co-respondent or principal or, in fact, adulterer? Some have regarded him as such, although it would appear silly to so designate a woman physician. Adultery as usually understood, denotes an intimate physical relationship which hardly exists when semen is artificially injected by a third party.

5) If artificial insemination is an illegal act, is instructing the husband so that he may inject the donor's semen also illegal?

6) To what extent may the doctor be held accountable should the child be defective?

7) When he signs the birth certificate, does the physician perjure himself if he attributes paternity to the husband?

8) Does the husband have the right to divorce his wife on the basis of alleged adultery? Need he accept the child by condonation or adoption?

9) Is the child legitimate?

10) May the mother sue the proxy father for support of her child?

11) May the proxy father sue for the custody of this child?

12) If the biologic father later becomes known, may the child sue for the estate of the proxy father?"

HOW TO DECIDE
THE BIRTH CONTROL QUESTION

HOW TO DECIDE
THE BIRTH CONTROL QUESTION

by John Warwick Montgomery

The English Renaissance exegete and saintly "Oxford reformer" John Colet, a close friend of Erasmus and Thomas More, is supposed to have remarked: "Better that no one should marry." Whereupon someone asked, "But Dean Colet, then what would happen to the human race?" Taken aback, the Dean of St. Paul's pondered the question, then suddenly brightened and said, "Why then the end of the age and our Lord's coming could not tarry!" This tale may well be apocryphal, and certainly Colet eventually acquired a positive view of the marital state (Seebohm informs us that he advised More to marry and entrusted the control of St. Paul's school to married burghers); but the story typifies some of the confusions that have attended theological thinking on the subject of marriage and childbearing across the centuries. Christians have often manifested strange blind spots in dealing with the theology of marriage, and current discussion of birth control by both Roman Catholics and Protestants is the unwitting manifestation of a theological perplexity that extends far beyond specifics such as the "rhythm method" or "the pill."

Roman Catholics: Marriage as a Means

The attitude of the Roman church toward birth control is well known, though its rationale is seldom comprehended. Rome has never been happy with the principle of birth control. Limitations on childbearing in marriage are indeed permitted (preferably by sexual continence, but also today by the so-called natural rhythm method); however, such limitations are regarded as exceptions, applicable in cases of ill health, disease, acute poverty, serious temptation to sin, and so on. The use of "unnatural" (i.e., mechanical) birth-control devices stands condemned by papal decree; indeed, in 1930, the famous encyclical *Casti Connubii* declared that artificial contraception is "an unspeakable crime" and "shameful and intrinsically immoral." Widespread debate is presently going on in Roman Catholic circles over the legitimacy of the birth-control pill (see *The Pill and Birth Regulation: The Catholic Debate*, ed. by Leo Pyle; London: Darton, Longman and Todd, 1964), but Pope Paul has as yet given no indication that the pill will be classed with "natural" birth-control methods. The Pope's conservative statement of June, 1964, and his reported directive to the Ecumenical Council to re-endorse the affirmations on birth-control made by Popes Pius XI and XII suggest that Rome still looks with grave concern upon any techniques that would limit offspring in marriage (see CHRISTIANITY TODAY, Dec. 17, 1965, p. 34). (See *Humanae Vitae*, Appendix 2 in this volume.)

Critics of Rome have often gleefully pointed out the

strange inconsistency that holds up the celibate state as an ideal for the clergy and at the same time seems to do all within its power to encourage childbearing on the part of the married. This is not, however, a genuine inconsistency at all, as one can see if he understands the theological base of the Roman view of marriage. Celibacy is most definitely regarded as the ideal state of life, permitting undivided attention to things spiritual (cf. the "marriage" between nun and Christ symbolized by wedding ring and white vesture). Marriage is of value not as an end in itself but *as a means to an end*. What end? As the *Corpus Iuris Canonici* makes clear (1013, Par. 1), and as the Holy Office reasserted in 1944 (Denzinger, 2295), the primary purpose of marriage is the generation and raising of children; other aspects of the marriage relationship must be viewed as contributory to the procreative purpose. Even the progressive Vatican II Schema 13, which endeavors to set marriage in a more Christocentric framework, twice states that "matrimony and conjugal love are by their very nature ordained for the procreation and education of children." Rome is thus quite consistent in making every effort to discourage birth control, and in taking particularly strong measures against all attempts to limit birth by techniques in opposition to the "natural law" doctrine fundamental to all Thomistic theology.

The traditional Roman view of marriage and birth control has been a source of embarrassment to its advocates and a fruitful base for criticism by moderns who resent religious authority. It is pointed out that, pragmatically, fewer and fewer Roman Catholics accept the procreative "marriage as means" interpretation of their church. Thus in a 1956 survey of the marital relationships of English women, Chesser found that of his sample of Roman Catholics 47 per cent were practicing birth control; and in 1959 Freedman and his associates, in investigating the contraceptive practices of American wives, discovered that even among the Roman Catholics who were regular churchgoers, 26 per cent were using birth-control devices considered gravely sinful by the Church.

The application of "natural law" thinking to the birth-control issue seems especially bizarre, since it is difficult to see why man can legitimately control "natural" phenomena such as vegetation and animal population and yet cannot without sin control his own numbers in the face of severe population pressures. As one writer has put it, a fixed law of nature dictates that male Caucasians grow hair on their faces; but it is not sinful to use a razor—whether straight or electric! And why is the use of mechanical contraceptives more "unnatural" than the application of the rhythm method? The latter obviously creates an unnatural pressure on the married couple to restrain their desire during one phase of the menstrual cycle, whereas the use of contraceptives or birth-control pills permits intercourse when natural desire dictates. The rhythm method, according to Dr. John Rock of the Harvard Medical School, himself a Roman Catholic, "is to be considered an unnatural method, for it is during the fertile period that the whole psychosomatic psychology of the healthy, normal female is prepared and intended by her primate nature for coitus" (*Medical and Biological Aspects of Contraception,* Boston: Lippincott, 1943).

Secularists and Liberal Protestants: Marriage as an End

More important, however, than these specific objections to the Roman Catholic theology of birth control has been the rise of a very different philosophy of marriage in modern times. This is the view, nourished by the courtly love tradition of the medieval period and the romantic movement of the nineteenth century, that sees the union of man and woman not as a means to an end but as an end in itself. The twentieth-century ideological shift from essentialistic to existentialistic patterns of thought has greatly accentuated the new view of man-woman relationships; as the distinguished French medical scholar Chauchard puts it, "To speak of natural law is to produce an easy indifference. Modern man sees himself as free. . . . He refuses every constraint" (*Apprendre à aimer; régulation des naissances et morale sexuelle*, Paris: Fayard, 1963, p. 62). When combined with a thinly disguised contemporary humanism, the result is a sex ethic (not limited to marriage) that sees in the love relation per se the fulfillment of human aspirations and the manifestation of God-as-Agape. Thus we arrive at the so-called new morality of the Bishop of Woolwich and the permissive sex ethics of numerous moderns—philosophies that, in radical contract with Roman Catholicism, absolutize the love relation with hardly a second look at procreation.

The attitude toward birth control arising from such an existentialistic-humanistic context is easily predictable: Birth control is no longer a theological problem; "we are faced with a problem that must be solved at the purely biological level" (David J. McCallion, "Human Population Pressures and Birth Control," *Canadian Journal of Theology*, July, 1960). The ethics of birth control becomes situational and *ad hoc*. As a car sticker my wife saw yesterday expressed it: "Trouble Parking? Try Planned Parenthood." The overpopulation issue engulfs birth-control thinking, resulting in weird volumes such as retired Army Colonel Alexander J. Stuart's *Overpopulation—Twentieth Century Nemesis: A Condensed, Objective Study of Procreation—from the Amoeba to Modern Man* (New York, 1958). Even a respectable work like *The Population Explosion and Christian Responsibility* (1960) by Richard Fagley, an official spokesman for the World Council of Churches, focuses chief attention on the economic and technological aspects of population growth and sees the ecumenical movement, with its united witness to an overpopulated world, as "the way forward."

Though liberal Protestants and secularists have readily identified the erroneous reasoning in Roman Catholic birth-control doctrine, they have, strange to say, fallen into a more acute form of the same error. Roman Catholic "natural law" thinking is a variety of what G. E. Moore in his *Principia Ethica* called the "naturalistic fallacy": the assumption that the descriptive (what is) automatically gives rise to the normative (what ought to be). But the liberals commit this same blunder with far less "justification" (since they have neither absolute church nor inerrant Scripture to interpret nature for them). The overpopulation problem in itself does not establish the morality of birth control, any more than it would establish the morality of war as a means of reducing the population. And the situational ethic of *agape*-love, as I emphasized in a previous article in CHRISTIANITY TODAY ("The Law's Third Use: Sanctification," April 26, 1963), leaves man with no guideline for the content of ethical action. Love is a motive, not a structure, and one makes a severe logical "category mistake" to think that it can serve both functions. A reliable revelation of God's divine will is *sine qua non* for man's ethical decisions in the realm of marriage and birth control as in all other areas of life. In Holy Scripture, one has the key to interpret God's hand in nature and human life and the guideline for love's operations.

Biblical Christianity: Marriage as Analogy

And how does the Bible view the problem area we are confronting? To answer this question we must move beyond proof-texting to the focal center of scriptural teaching on marriage. This center is not to be found in the first two chapters of Genesis, so often cited in isolation, but in Ephesians 5:22–32, which quotes Genesis in the context of the New Covenant in Christ. Understood in the light of New Testament fulfillment, marriage cannot be regarded simply as a means ("Be fruitful, and multiply, and replenish the earth") or unqualifiedly as an end ("They shall be one flesh"). Rather, it is seen as an *analogy*—indeed, as the best human analogy—of the relationship between Christ and his Church. After having connected husband-and-wife with Christ-and-the-Church by no less than three *hōs*'s ("as") and two *kathōs*'s ("just as") in ten verses, Paul concludes with a summary statement on the marriage relation: "This is a great mystery: but I speak concerning Christ and the church." When and only when marriage is viewed as the "type" of which Christ-and-Church are "antitype" can we avoid the Hegelian-like dialectic extremes of the Roman and liberal Protestant views of marriage and birth control. Specifically:

1. As Christ's relation with the Church is a *total* love relation, not just a means to an end, so one must not view marriage simply as a procreative function. Where birth control can contribute to "subduing the earth" in order to achieve a better total human relationship, it is not to be condemned (cf. William E. Hulme, "A Theological Approach to Birth Control," *Pastoral Psychology,* April, 1960). By the same token, the psychosomatic wholeness implied in Christ's incarnation for man's salvation condemns the Manichaean and neo-Platonic depreciation of the flesh that colors so much of Roman Catholic celibacy teaching. No better counteractive exists to all such functional misunderstandings of marriage than the writings of Charles Williams, the late Christian poet and friend of C. S. Lewis (Shideler well titles her treatment of Williams's thought *The Theology of Love*).

2. Yet neither is the human love relationship an end in itself. "In the resurrection they neither marry nor are given in marriage"—why? Because "when that which is perfect is come, then that which is in part shall be done away"; in the full manifestation of the antitype the type is embraced and disappears. Thus the love relationship between male and female must never be absolutized. It is truly meaningful only insofar as it reflects the Christ relationship. Apart from this it becomes idolatrous, taking on demonic quality despite its lack of genuine ultimacy. The present state of American mores and morals is sufficient evidence of the appalling consequences that attend the isolation of sex from God's revealed will.

3. In light of the divine analogy of marriage, we can see the centrality of children to marital union. Christ did not give himself up to death as an isolated deed; he did it to "bring many sons unto glory" (Heb. 2:10). As the union of Christ and his Church does not exist for its own sake but to bring others to spiritual rebirth, so the marital union is properly fulfilled in natural birth. And since natural birth precedes spiritual birth, as creation precedes redemption (John 3:3–12), so the Christian home can be the greatest single agency for nurture in the twofold sense; thus did the Reformers view it (cf. Lazareth's *Luther on the Christian Home*). The burden of proof rests, then, on the couple who wish to restrict the size of their family; to the extent possible and desirable, all Christian couples should seek to "bring many sons unto glory." After all, as C. G. Darwin pointed out at the University of Chicago's Darwin centennial, those who restrict their birth rate will ultimately be engulfed by those who do not: *"Homo contracipiens* would become extinct and would be replaced by the variety *Homo progenetivus."* The Christian application of this principle is obvious.

4. Sexual relations outside marriage are unqualifiedly to be condemned, not for the naturalistic (and logically questionable!) reasons set forth by Bertocci ("Extramarital Sex and the Pill," *The Christian Century*, Feb. 26, 1964), but because they violate the high analogy of Christ-and-Church. Thus Israel's prostitution of God's grace through idolatry was symbolized by Hosea's wife, who lived as a woman of the street, and Paul expresses revulsion at the thought of those who are "members of Christ" becoming "one flesh" with harlots, thereby violating the temple of the Holy Spirit (I Cor. 6:13–20). The crux of Paul's argument against illicit sex is the analogy relation—that Christians "are bought with a price." So the use of birth-control devices outside of marriage is not to be tolerated. And the hypocrisy of gas-station dispensers "for prevention of disease" is to be made clear in no uncertain terms.

How practically are Christian marriage partners to decide the birth-control question? Within the framework of the analogy relation, they are to consider it personally and prayerfully in light of their own physical, emotional, financial, and spiritual situation, and in light of the population picture in their area of the world. (The answer will not be the same for Christians in India and those in Canada; for those led to lucrative vocations and those led to pioneer missionary work.) They will act responsibly, remembering that irresponsibility is equally possible at the Roman Catholic anti-birth-control and the secularistic pro-birth-control extremes. Viewing marriage as neither means nor end, but as the great analogy of Christ's work of salvation, the Christian will seek to do all he can to make his marriage evangelistic—generatively and regeneratively. He will consider with all seriousness such proposals as that recently made by the Rev. Eldon Durham, who, in the face of the severe and rapidly growing population problem in so many parts of the world, advocates that Christians "begin to constitute families by means of adopting the unwanted, the disinherited, the dispossessed and the rejected children" of the earth (*Time*, Dec. 3, 1965, p. 77). Though such a suggestion must not be used to justify non-childbearing in American marriages and irresponsibility or immorality on the part of couples living elsewhere in the world, is not the proposal genuinely analogous to the "grafting" of the Gentiles unto the tree of salvation (Rom. 11)? Surely the childless Christian couple is here offered a superlative privilege and opportunity.

But however he is led to fulfill his personal responsibility before the Lord of the Church, the Christian stands free from the shackles of legalism and from the chaos of libertarianism. "If the Son shall make you free," said Jesus, "you shall be free indeed." On the basis of this merciful freedom in Christ the Apostle beseeches us as a reasonable act of worship to present our bodies "a living sacrifice holy, acceptable unto God."

INDEX*

BIBLICAL INDEX

Genesis 1:27, 72, 95; 1:28, 21, 99, 101, 155, 248, f., 278; 2:7, 72, 552; 2:18, 101, 249; 2:16–17, 57; 2:24, 37, 101, 250; 3:8, 58; 3:17–19, 95; 4:1, 12; 9: 278; 9:1, 7, 21; 9:6, 59, 554; 16:2, 12; 17:19, 12; 22:18, 20; 29:31, 12; 30:22, 12; 38:8–10, 16, 17; 46:26, 554

Exodus 19:15, 15; 21: 278; 21:10, 15, 250; 21:22–24, 11, 60, 87, ff., 212, 323, 553; 28:3, 57

Leviticus 12:1–5, 15, 428; 15:16–18, 19; 15:19–28, 15; 18: 250; 18:19, 15; 18:21, 14; 20:2, 14; 20:10–21, 19; 20:18, 15; 24:17, 553; 24:18, 10

Numbers 6: 15

Deuteronomy 4:29, 73; 6:4, 22; 7:4, 13; 12:23, 24, 59; 13:3, 58; 23:1, 13; 24:5, 250; 26:16, 73; 28:15–18, 21

Ruth 4:13, 12

I Samuel 21:4–5, 15

I Kings 8:48, 73

II Kings 23:25, 73

Job 30:3, 57

Psalms 19:7, 10; 51:5, 61, 82, 212; 68:6, 20; 104: 56; 119: 129, 57; 119:167, 57; 127:3–5, 21; 139:13–18, 12, 212; 139:13–15, 60, f., 554

Proverbs 22:6, 253

Ecclesiastes 3:19, 57; 9:9, 20

Isaiah 1:17, 307; 44:24, 554

Jeremiah 31:27, 21

Ezekiel 16:5, 14

Micah 7:1, 73

Malachi 2:15, 22

Matthew 5: 429; 5:29, 38; 5:32, 33; 5:42, 424; 10:28, 73; 12:39, 33; 16:4, 33; 16:26, 73; 19: 279, 421, 429; 19:5, 250; 19:8, 9, 277, 298; 19:10, 37, f.; 19: 13–15, 82; 22:37, 58, 73, 82; 25:31–46, 85

Mark 7:21, 33, 239; 8:38, 33; 10: 421; 10:6, 250; 10:7, 34; 10:11, 33; 10:13–16, 82; 10:28, 39; 12:30, 98

Luke 1:40–44, 41, 61, 82, 87, 554; 9:60, 38; 18:15, 82; 20:35, 149

John 3:3–12, 584; 8:3, 33

Acts 4:32, 73

Romans 1: 36; 1:18, 95; 1:21, 95; 1:29, 33; 7:6, 7; 11: 586; 12:1, ff., 42; 13:8–10, 98; 14:1,ff., 43; 14:23, 296

I Corinthians 6:9, 33, 239; 6:13, 33; 6:13–20, 585; 7: 34, f., 39, 254; 7:2–6, 250, f.; 7:5, 16; 7:7, 421; 7:9, 255; 10:31, 254; 11:8, 554; 15:8, 40; 15:35–44, 75

* Compiled by Joseph D. Ludders, M.A., Western Regional Representative, Christian Medical Society

TOPICAL INDEX

NAMES AND TITLES